Photograph by Aerofilms and Aero Pictorial Ltd.

Coombe Hill, Ellesborough and the Vale of Aylesbury. The arable fields at the foot of the scarp are mainly on soils of the Wantage series.

AGRICULTURAL RESEARCH COUNCIL

Memoirs of the Soil Survey of Great Britain

England and Wales

The Soils and Land Use of the District around

AYLESBURY
and
HEMEL HEMPSTEAD

SHEET 238]

BY B. W. AVERY

LONDON

HER MAJESTY'S STATIONERY OFFICE

1964

PREFACE

THE detailed soil survey described in this memoir covers parts of the contrasting regions of the Chiltern Hills and the Vale of Aylesbury. Except for the works of agricultural writers of the 18th and 19th centuries, there is little published information on the soils of either region. A short account of the soils of Buckinghamshire by M. S. Temple, based on geological maps, was published in 1929 and, in detailed investigations of the vegetation on the Chilterns in 1934, A. S. Watt described soil profiles and their ecological relationships. Since its inception, many studies have been made of the soils of the Rothamsted Experimental Station at Harpenden, situated on the Chiltern Plateau just beyond the eastern boundary of the survey area. In view of the increasing size of towns and the consequent need to make the best use of land, the present survey should be valuable to those concerned with the many aspects of land use in these and similar terrains.

The survey was made between 1951 and 1957 by B. W. Avery, D. W. King and A. J. Thomasson. The memoir was written mainly by B. W. Avery and the maps and diagrams were prepared by D. V. Jones and E. M. Thomson. The analytical data are the work of C. L. Bascomb and Miss A. M. Du Feu; Dr. P. W. Arnold (Rothamsted Experimental Station) supplied the data relating to potash. The chapter on forestry was contributed by Mr. J. M. B. Brown of the Forestry Commission. Professor S. W. Wooldridge, Mr. H. W. Gardner and Dr. J. T. Coppock read parts of the manuscript and the latter gave permission for the reproduction of the maps in Fig. 8. The author wishes to acknowledge the help of Messrs. R. A. T. Harris, P. J. James, R. G. Kerr, W. F. Mackenzie, C. J. Rowe, R. A. Smith and B. Wilkinson of the National Agricultural Advisory Service, who contributed information used in compiling the sections on land use and the agricultural properties of the soils.

The survey could not have been carried out without the permission of landowners and farmers to inspect their land in all parts of the district; permission was always willingly given and the Survey is grateful for their co-operation.

Copies of the 1-inch coloured map are obtainable from Ordnance Survey Agents. Fair copies of the field sheets, at $2\frac{1}{2}$ in. to 1 mile, are kept at the headquarters of the Soil Survey at Rothamsted Experimental Station, Harpenden, Hertfordshire, where they can be inspected by appointment.

D. A. OSMOND

Head of the Soil Survey of England and Wales

CONTENTS

TEXT FIGURES

PLATES

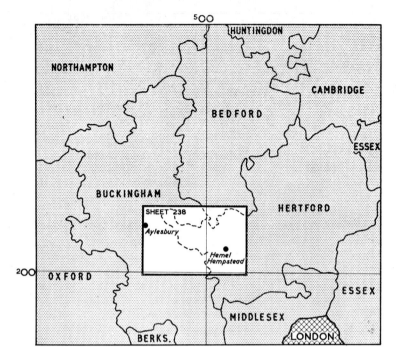

Fig. 1. Location of the Area

CHAPTER I

General Description of the Area

LOCATION AND PHYSIOGRAPHY

The area of 216 square miles extends from Aylesbury and Lacey Green in the west to Redbourn and Abbots Langley in the east, and includes parts of Buckinghamshire, Hertfordshire and Bedfordshire (Figs. 1 and 2). Before the first World War the district was almost entirely rural, but its proximity to London, coupled with the development of light industries, has led during the last few decades to a rapid expansion in population and a corresponding loss of agricultural land for housing and other developments. The part most affected lies around and to the south-east of Hemel Hempstead which, following its designation as a "new town", already has over 50,000 inhabitants; Aylesbury, with some 28,000, is also rapidly expanding, and, of the other towns in the area, Chesham has a population of about 16,000 and Berkhamsted of 13,000.

The chief physical features (Fig. 3) are closely related to geological structure, which will be considered in detail later. As illustrated in Fig. 4, three main physiographic regions may be distinguished, the boundaries of which extend north-eastwards and south-westwards beyond the limits of the area.

1

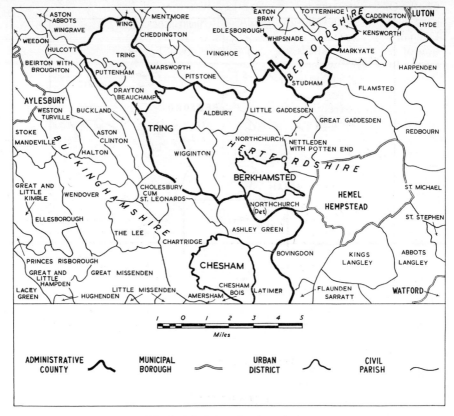

Fig. 2. Administrative Boundaries

1. The Chiltern Plateau

About two-thirds of the district is formed by a segment of the Chiltern Plateau. This Chalk upland, covered by a variety of clayey superficial deposits, is trenched by numerous sub-parallel valleys and presents a steep scarp face to the north-west (Frontispiece). Within the area of survey the scarp is much indented and is breached by several through-valleys or wind-gaps, the chief of which are flanked near their outlets by lateral valleys, so reducing the highest part of the dip-slope plateau to a series of narrow ridge-tops and outlying bastions. South-eastwards from the summit ridges, which rise to over 800 ft. O.D., there is an appreciable descent in the general level of the plateau to about 650 ft., where the surface flattens and extends some eight or nine miles to elevations below 400 ft. The underlying strata of the Chalk are inclined in the same direction at a rather steeper angle (see Fig. 5, p. 9), and towards the south-east, as at Cowcroft, near Chesham, outliers of the succeeding Eocene beds (Reading Beds and London Clay) form low hills rising a little above the flat-topped ridges on either side.

Running water is rare on the Plateau, but spring-fed streams arise in the principal dip-slope valleys where they intersect the plane of saturation in the

Chalk. Of the streams in the area, the Misbourne, Bulbourne, Gade and Ver have their sources in valleys communicating with wind-gaps at Wendover, Tring, Dagnall and Dunstable respectively; whereas the Chess emerges near the junction of several dry valleys, none of which breach the escarpment crest. Except for the Bulbourne, which serves as a feeder for the Grand Union Canal and joins the Gade below Hemel Hempstead, all these rivulets are tributaries of the Colne. Their upper courses are frequently dry for long periods, but every few years, after seasons of exceptionally heavy rainfall, intermittent "winterbournes" flow for a time from springs well above the normal levels.

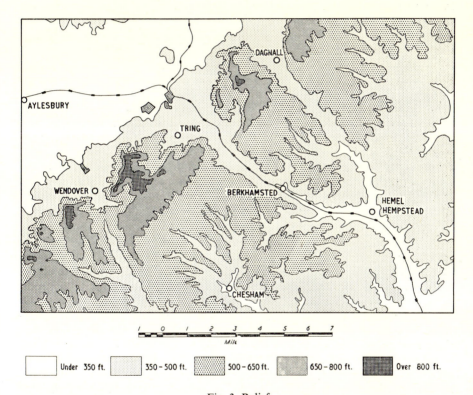

Under 350 ft. 350 – 500 ft. 500 – 650 ft. 650 – 800 ft. Over 800 ft.

Fig. 3. Relief

The branching dry valleys which originate as shallow depressions on the interfluvial plateaux have a general south-easterly trend and, together with the main valleys, become shallower and less steep-sided towards the north-east. Most of the valleys have narrow bottoms and predominantly convex or even slopes (Plate I), but the upper reaches of the through-valleys and their major tributaries are distinctly broader, and generally have well defined foot-slopes of relatively low gradient, underlain by flinty Coombe Deposits, and backed by steeper, convex slopes (Plate VIa). Both types of dry valley are typically asymmetrical, the south-west facing slopes being steeper and shorter and having a thinner drift cover than those exposed to the east or north-east; whereas in the occasional valleys which follow a direction at right angles to the dip of the Chalk, the north-western exposure is much the steeper.

2. The Icknield Belt

The escarpment is bounded at its foot by a varying breadth of well-drained, rolling or gently sloping land on Middle and Lower Chalk, lying mainly between 400 and 500 ft., and traversed throughout its length by the upper and more ancient branch of the Icknield Way (Plate II). This "Icknield Belt" is narrowest in the south-west and widest opposite the Tring and Dagnall gaps, where in each case the floor of the dip-slope valley is continued north-westwards as a gently rising platform, which fans out in front of the escarpment and terminates in bluffs overlooking the Aylesbury Vale.

3. The Vale of Aylesbury

In the north-west a part of the Vale of Aylesbury presents a contrasting land-scape of subdued relief, floored mainly by Gault and Kimmeridge clays, and rising northwards to the low boulder-clay covered plateau that occupies a large part of north Buckinghamshire. Most of this Vale country is drained by head-waters of the Thame, and so belongs, together with the Chiltern Plateau, to the Thames Catchment Area, but east of a low watershed near Cheddington about five square miles belong to the basin of the Great Ouse.

The part of the Vale nearest the foot of the hills constitutes a sub-edge plain up to four miles wide, based chiefly on Gault, and drained by small streams which rise at intervals along the Icknield Belt. From Aston Clinton north-eastwards to Edlesborough, the plain commonly extends from the Gault across the Upper Greensand on to the Lower Chalk outcrop, with but little change in relief, to terminate in a distinct break of slope between 300 and 400 ft. O.D. The Upper Greensand thickens south-westwards, and the presence of malm-stone rock-bands around Ellesborough and Wendover has led to the preserva-tion of bench-like features at 350–400 ft. (Plate VIIIa), which may be considered to belong physiographically to the Icknield Belt. For the present purpose, how-ever, it is convenient to regard the Upper Greensand outcrop as part of the Vale, as the associated soils are generally slow-draining, in contrast to the dry chalky soils at the foot of the scarp.

The sub-edge plain is narrowest and least well defined in the region of the Thame-Ouzel watershed, where it is surmounted by an outlier of Lower Chalk and merges north-westwards into a broad expanse of undulating clay-land. South-westwards from the watershed, the various spring-fed streams and ditches converge on a tract of ill-drained low-lying ground between Bierton and Putten-ham, and pass thence into the Thame, either by way of the Thistle Brook or by the stream which runs through the lower part of Aylesbury. Between these two streams the ground rises to a low ridge, discontinuously capped by Portlandian limestone and terminated north-westwards by a minor scarp. North of the Thistle Brook the landscape assumes a more rolling aspect and culminates around Wingrave in flat-topped hills capped by glacial drift.

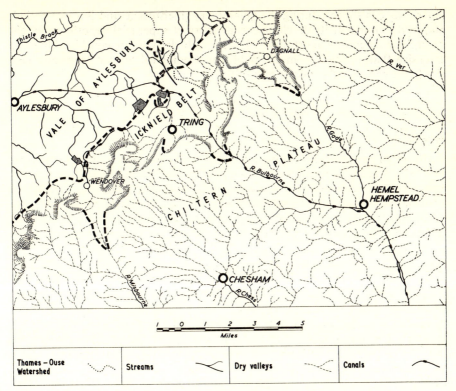

Fig. 4. Physiographic Regions

GEOLOGY

The following geological formations are represented at the surface (cf. Sherlock, 1922):

Recent and Pleistocene	Alluvium
(Superficial Deposits)	Valley Head and River Gravels
	Glacial Drift and High-level Gravels (with far-travelled stones)
	Clay-with-flints and Plateau Drift
Eocene	London Clay
	Reading Beds
Cretaceous	Upper Chalk
	Middle Chalk
	Lower Chalk
	Upper Greensand and Gault
Jurassic	Portland Beds
	Kimmeridge Clay

The pre-Pleistocene or "solid" formations have a general south-easterly dip, imparted by slow and intermittent tilting movements that began during the Cretaceous and culminated in post-Eocene (Miocene) times (Fig. 5). The existing landscape was shaped during the Quaternary (Pleistocene and Recent) period, and in the course of its development a variety of superficial deposits were laid down. These deposits, most of which are locally derived, are considerably more extensive than appears from the published Geological Survey Map, and give rise to the soil over the greater part of the district.

SOLID FORMATIONS

Jurassic System

Upper Jurassic rocks, comprising beds of the Kimmeridge and Portland formations, come to the surface in the north-west. The *Kimmeridgean* stage is represented for the most part by dark grey, shaly clay containing occasional nodular calcareous layers and crystalline gypsum. The uppermost beds are micaceous and glauconitic sandy clays, named Hartwell Clay after a village west of Aylesbury where they were formerly used for brick-making.

Overlying the Kimmeridge Clay is a series of yellow and greenish sands and sandy clays and bluish grey and cream-coloured limestones of *Portlandian* age, which emerge from beneath the Gault at Walton, Aylesbury, and form an irregular outlier extending from the centre of the town through Bierton. Other small outliers occur at Burcott and at Groveway Farm, Weedon. The base of the formation is marked by the Lydite Bed, consisting of glauconitic sandy limestone in which are embedded small pebbles of black chert (lydite) and vein quartz, together with rolled and phosphatised fossils. Above this stratum, which weathers to an ochreous, pebbly sandy clay, are some 8–10 ft. of sandy glauconitic beds, followed by a similar thickness of pale-coloured, more or less rubbly limestone. Higher beds of sand and limestone also occur at Aylesbury (Sherlock, 1922), but are nowhere well exposed at present.

Cretaceous System

The marine Cretaceous rocks which underlie the greater part of the area include the Gault, Upper Greensand and Chalk. On account of the overlap of the Gault on to the Jurassic rocks, the Lower Greensand does not appear at the surface, but has been proved north of Tring by several borings.

The strata distinguished as *Gault* and *Upper Greensand* are grouped as Selbornian on the Geological Survey Map. In the Vale of Aylesbury the Gault is represented by about 200 ft. of stiff grey clay, containing occasional seams of phosphatic nodules or coprolites, which at Puttenham, Cheddington and elsewhere were formerly worked for making fertilizer. The unweathered clay is normally paler in colour, more calcareous and less fissile than the Kimmeridge Clay, and contains little bituminous or pyritic matter, but north-east of Bierton, where the two formations overlap, the boundary between them is difficult to locate precisely.*

---

* On the Old Series Geological Map (Sheet 46) the valley of the Thistle Brook as far as Rowsham is indicated as Gault; although this interpretation is almost certainly incorrect, the form of the ground between Bierton and Hulcott is consistent with the presence of a northerly extension or outlier. When the Leighton Buzzard–Aylesbury road was straightened in 1956 a temporary section near Corner Farm (grid ref. SP/846160) showed Portlandian rocks overlain by up to four feet of stiff grey-green glauconitic clay which can hardly be other than the base of the Gault. It also appears, from deep auger borings, that Gault overlies Portland Beds at Groveway Farm Weedon (grid ref. SP/823183).

The Gault becomes increasingly calcareous and silty as the Chilterns are approached and finally passes into the Upper Greensand. This variable formation is here represented by grey, fine sandy, micaceous marl with interbedded malmstone, succeeded at the base of the Chalk by green, sandy strata (the true greensand) containing much glauconite, a fine-grained, ferriferous, mica-like mineral rich in potassium. The Upper Greensand rocks, nowhere more than about 35 ft. thick, thin out and lose their identity towards the north-east, until at Ivinghoe Aston the Gault is only separated from the overlying Chalk Marl by less than 5 ft. of greenish, fine sandy marl. The malmstone is a fine-grained siliceous rock, often resembling chalk in appearance, and containing variable amounts of sponge spicules and globular opaline silica, together with quartz, muscovite, glauconite, and clayey or calcareous matter. Alternating beds of sandy marl and malmstone rock were formerly exposed to a depth of 15–16 ft. at Little Kimble, and Sherlock (1922) records a thickness of at least 12 ft. near Nash Lee, but towards Aston Clinton and Buckland the rock bands fade out into impersistent seams and nodules.

The great *Chalk* formation is represented in the Chilterns by nearly 700 ft. of strata, but only the lower zones of the Upper Chalk are present, the remainder having been removed by denudation before the Eocene beds were deposited.

The *Lower Chalk*, here about 180 ft. thick, outcrops along the lower part of the Icknield Belt and caps the outlying hill at Cheddington. Rather more than half is taken up by the *Chalk Marl*, consisting of compact marly chalk alternating with occasional beds of hard grey chalk. The thickest and most persistent band, lying 50–60 ft. above the base, has been named the "Marl-Rock" or Risborough rock-bed and, as noted by Whitaker (1889), is "*par excellence* the water-bearing stratum of the district where it comes to the surface, its outcrop being marked by a line of frequent springs, most of which are utilized for the growth of watercress". Above the Chalk Marl comes the *Totternhoe Stone*, another hard band largely made up of minute shell fragments which give it a gritty feel. This bed, poorly developed west of Ivinghoe, is followed by a further 30–35 ft. of grey, marly chalk, and finally by tough, whitish, nearly pure chalk containing only a few thin marl bands, and locally with a rock-bed ("rag") at its base.

The succeeding *Middle Chalk* forms the face of the escarpment and underlies the bottoms and sides of the dip-slope valleys for several miles to the south-east. This division, 200–225 ft. thick, consists mainly of tough white chalk with few flints and occasional seams of marl. At the base is a 9–10 ft. thick band of hard nodular chalky limestone known as the *Melbourn Rock*, which crops out regularly along the Icknield Belt near the crests of projecting knolls and ridges.

The *Upper Chalk* or Chalk-with-flints outcrops at the crest of the scarp and underlies the whole of the dip-slope plateau, but is largely buried under Clay-with-flints and other superficial deposits. Its base is marked by the *Chalk Rock*, consisting of two or three bands of hard creamy limestone each about one foot thick, containing scattered green grains of glauconite, and separated by layers of hard nodular chalk in a soft matrix. Above this is normal white chalk, generally softer than that of the Middle Chalk, and including much flint, some as nodules disposed in more or less regular layers and some in tabular sheets following bedding planes or cracks.

At the crest of the scarp very little Upper Chalk has escaped denudation, but higher beds come in gradually down the dip-slope until in the south-east it underlies the bottoms of the valleys and attains a maximum thickness of about 230 ft. The outlying hills at Pitstone and Ivinghoe (Plate II) are capped by the Chalk Rock, which on account of its superior hardness is often associated at its outcrop with a distinct break of slope, conspicuous both on the escarpment and in some of the larger valleys.

Whereas the Chalk Marl may contain up to 40 per cent of non-calcareous matter, normal white chalk (Middle and Upper Chalk) is a very pure form of limestone, usually containing more than 97 per cent calcium carbonate. The non-carbonate residue consists largely of micaceous and montmorillonitic clay; calcium phosphates* (chiefly as collophane) are also present in small amounts, together with occasional rounded grains of quartz and other minerals.

As found in the Upper Chalk, flint is a mesh-like aggregate of colloidal (opaline) silica and microcrystalline (chalcedonic) quartz, and is exceedingly durable, contributing hard angular fragments or water-worn pebbles to most of the succeeding formations. Freshly broken flint is typically black or grey, but weathered pieces exhibit a considerable range of colours, and are often stained brown, or even red, by traces of adsorbed iron oxide. Flints are very slowly attacked by carbonated water, which results in preferential removal of the relatively soluble opaline component, leaving a porous, whitish rind or patina. On account of its porosity, patinated flint absorbs iron solutions much more readily than most fresh flint, and while weathered flints derived directly from the Chalk have a white patina, those in river gravels generally have ochreous hues due to ferruginous staining.

Eocene System

In this area the Eocene succession begins with the *Reading Beds*, a variable formation mainly of fluviatile or deltaic origin, comprising irregular and impersistent beds of pale-coloured, current-bedded sand and of red and grey clay, with subordinate lenses or seams of flint pebbles. The basal or Bull-Head Bed, typically consisting of green or black-coated flint nodules and small pebbles in a matrix of glauconitic sandy clay, was laid down during a short-lived incursion of the sea and normally rests with an even junction on the Chalk.

The succeeding *London Clay* begins with a loamy and locally pebbly basement bed, but the bulk of the formation consists of dark grey marine clay, with occasional layers of concretionary calcareous nodules. At its outcrop there is generally a brown weathered zone several feet thick resulting from the oxidation of iron compounds, chiefly sulphides, present in the original sediment.

These soft and incoherent beds were later progressively denuded, and now only survive on the Chiltern dip-slope as occasional outliers. Once surface water gained access to the Chalk, disintegration of the cover was aided by underground solution and swallow-hole formation. In Pleistocene times the remaining mantle of residual and transported materials was further re-arranged by solifluxion or glacial action, with the result that much Eocene-derived detritus is incorporated

---

* Certain of the nodular hard bands, including the Totternhoe Stone and the Chalk Rock, are often notably phosphatic.

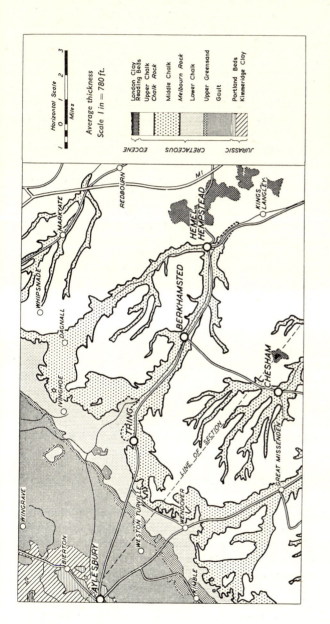

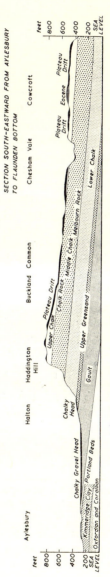

Fig. 5. Solid Geology (Stratigraphy and Structure)

in superficial deposits and only the larger outliers retain an undisturbed core. Of these outliers, that at Cowcroft was dug through for brick-making during the 19th century, and exhibited a complete section from the London Clay to the Chalk, described by Prestwich (1854) in a classical paper on the Woolwich and Reading Series. About 16 ft. of London Clay were then exposed, below which some 30 ft. of Reading Beds, represented chiefly by pale-coloured sands with interleaved seams of clay, rested on an even surface of Chalk, showing that here, at least, the beds are *in situ*. London Clay was also formerly exposed in a brick-yard at Bennetts End, Hemel Hempstead, but here the beds were let down against the Chalk by twin faults, trending north and south, and bounded by hard, polished, slickensided surfaces. Similar irregularities, whereby masses of more or less reconstituted Eocene materials have been protected from denudation, are exposed from time to time in brick-pits, and are probably attributable in part to the still-recurrent phenomenon of subsidence following underground solution.

Besides the outliers at Cowcroft and Bennetts End, of which the age and identity are proved by cappings of fossiliferous London Clay, several other ill-defined patches of Reading Beds, generally obscured by drift, are indicated by tentative boundaries on the New Series Geological Map. The chief of these lie south-east of Hemel Hempstead where, at Abbots Langley and Bedmond in particular, the form of the ground and the nature of the subsoil leave little room for doubt that the beds are present in appreciable thickness, even if somewhat disturbed. Pale-coloured sands with clay lamellae, similar to those at Cowcroft, have been identified near Bedmond (grid ref. TL/102032), and many of the slopes in this locality are underlain by impervious Reading Beds clay.

As noted by Sherlock (1922), the remaining outliers shown on the map are of more doubtful origin. Near Gaddesden Row, where "brick-earth" containing a few flints and pebbles was worked to a depth of 45 ft., Smith (1916) obtained Paleolithic implements from a "floor" 20 ft. below the surface, showing that the deposits, although resembling Reading Beds, were reconstituted in Pleistocene times; while at Little Heath, east of Berkhamsted, the beds overlying the Chalk include up to 21 ft. of stratified sands and gravels, first described by Gilbert (1920) and now generally accepted, following Wooldridge (1957), as littoral deposits of early Pleistocene age.

LANDSCAPE DEVELOPMENT

The present landscape is believed to have been sculptured from an uplifted plain which resulted from long-continued sub-aerial denudation in later Tertiary (Mio-pliocene) times. At the beginning of the Pleistocene period, slight down-warping allowed the sea to transgress westwards into the London Basin across the plain to cut a bench at c. 550–650 ft., still perceptible as a distinct shelf on both the Chiltern Plateau and the dip-slope of the North Downs. In places on the bench, and capping hills of Eocene rocks at similar levels, are surviving patches of sand and shingle containing large "beach-battered" pebbles of flint and Hertfordshire Pudding-stone with a yellowish patina. Most of these accumu-lations, including that at Little Heath, are unfossiliferous, but, according to Wooldridge and Linton (1955), each contains a characteristic mineral suite found in deposits at Netley Heath, Surrey and at Harpenden, Herts. from which marine fossils of Red Crag age have been obtained. Beyond the presumed shore-line, the summit ridges of the Chilterns survive as truncated relics of a Pliocene land-surface, while the intervening wind-gaps have been interpreted as the contemporary outlets of consequent* streams which originated north-west of the present escarpment.

Since the Red Crag sea retreated, successive "uplifts" relative to sea-level have allowed the rivers to deepen and widen their valleys; but as reduction of the pervious Chalk by erosive agencies failed to keep pace with that of the impervious Gault and Kimmeridge clays, the Chiltern Plateau remains in a state of arrested dissection. As streams antecedent to the Thame and Ouzel and their tributaries cut back from progressively lower base levels across the Gault outcrop, the Chalk escarpment slowly receded and gained in height, while the consequent drainage lines were progressively captured and truncated, leaving the upper parts of the major dip-slope valleys high and dry. Some indication of the order in which the dip-slope streams were beheaded and ultimately ceased to erode their upper courses can be gained from the altitude and form of their associated wind-gaps (Davis, 1895). In the high-level gaps at Chequers (620 ft.), Longdown (604 ft.) and Wendover (510 ft.), the land falls away rapidly north-westwards from the watershed, which in each case is located in the neck of the gap, whereas at Dagnall (440 ft.) and Tring (410 ft.) dissected remains of the former valley-floors extend beyond the general line of the escarpment, suggesting that drainage through these gaps ceased at a later date.

At intervals during the Pleistocene period, the course of denudation was profoundly modified by marked oscillations in climate, phases of arctic cold alternating with interglacial phases when temperate or even sub-tropical conditions prevailed. With the onset of each glacial period, ice-sheets spread out from the British and Scandinavian mountains, displacing and transporting surface materials as they advanced, while melt-waters from the ice-fronts fed the ancestors of today's rivers, carrying down masses of glacial drift and depositing the coarser materials as spreads of gravel and sand.

Deposits of at least three distinct glacial periods have been recognized in East Anglia and the Midlands, and tentative correlations established with the Elster, Saale and Weichsel glaciations of north-west Europe (West, 1958; Bishop, 1958). In the last (Hunstanton or Weichsel) glaciation, the main ice-fronts lay well to the north of the present area, but in one or more earlier glaciations it appears that ice extended into the Vale of Aylesbury, where its southward progress was checked by the Chiltern escarpment. Further east, however, the escarpment was over-ridden, allowing lobes of ice to advance into the Vale of St. Albans, and Wooldridge (1957) considers that the country south-east of the escarpment was also affected in the first glaciation by ice which entered by way of the Goring Gap. Weathered, clayey deposits containing Triassic pebbles and other far-travelled stones, which occur in a belt on the lower part of the Chiltern dip-slope at levels between 300 and 450 ft., are regarded as a product of this early glaciation. It seems more probable, however, that ice came through the Hitchin gap, and the further possibility remains that the foreign stones in certain of the deposits were introduced from a westerly direction by the ancestral Thames, whose pre-glacial course lay well to the north of the present valley.

---

* Streams which follow the original slope of an uplifted land surface.

Beyond the margins of the main ice-fronts, tundra conditions prevailed, and local snow-caps developed on the hills; stresses caused by alternate freezing and thawing of the ground caused contortion and disintegration of the surface layers, and with a sparse vegetation solifluxion was greatly facilitated. This process, now characteristic of certain sub-Arctic regions, consists essentially in the mass movement, often down very gentle slopes, of waterlogged soil and frost-disintegrated rock, while the substratum remains permanently frozen and so prevents melt-water sinking in. It was probably under such conditions, when the frozen water in the Chalk rendered it impervious, that many of the minor dry valleys in the Chilterns were initiated or enlarged, while torrents of melt-water released during short seasonal thaws carried down stones and mud to be deposited as great spreads or fans in the larger valleys and at the base of the escarpment. Unstratified or roughly stratified deposits of this kind, to which the general term *Head* was applied by Dines *et al.* (1940), accumulated in each glacial period beyond the limits of the main ice-fronts, and are accordingly found in various stages of weathering and dissection depending on their age.

Since the final retreat of ice from the area, the older land surfaces and deposits have been subject to weathering and denudation, both under normal temperate conditions and under the conditions of intense cold obtaining during the last (Weichsel) glaciation. Apart from renewed solifluxion on hillsides, the Chiltern landscape appears to have undergone comparatively little modification during this period. In the Vale, however, much of the surface was lowered by erosion and stream action, and the older drift sheets were extensively dissected, mainly as a result of headward erosion by springs. Reduction of the drift-capped plateaux around Wingrave has evidently proceeded by this means, and similar effects are apparent along the Icknield Belt, where fans of gravelly drift, spread out from the escarpment during an earlier cold phase, have been dissected by spring-fed streams. The heads of the valleys in which springs occur are now frequently dry, and some, like Incombe Hole and Coombe Hole (Plate IVb) near Ivinghoe, and the Happy Valley at Kimble, are deeply entrenched into the face of the escarpment. Sherlock (1922) considered that these striking escarpment valleys resulted from channelling by torrential melt-waters from snow-caps on the plateau above, but the occurrence of right-angled bends, and the gentle talwegs terminating abruptly against the main scarp, are difficult to explain on this hypothesis, and later authors (Oakley, 1936; Arkell, 1947) have attributed them primarily to spring-sapping when the water-table was higher than at present. In contrast to the smooth outlines of the dip-slope valleys, they are characteristically sharp-edged and steep-sided, suggesting that they belong to a later erosion stage. Sparks and Lewis (1957) have shown that the floor deposits in similar valleys near Pegsdon, Hertfordshire contain moisture-loving mollusca indicating that springs were still active during the Recent (post-glacial) period, but in view of the size of the valleys it seems probable that they were initiated during or before the last glaciation.

The most recent phase of erosion and deposition, which still continues, is largely attributable to man's activity in clearing the dense forests which spread over the ground after the period, some 10,000 years ago, when the country was last subjected to sub-arctic conditions. Wherever sloping land was brought into cultivation, the direct impact of rain on bare ground, coupled with the effects of tillage, accelerated erosion on the upper parts of the slopes, with consequent deposition of "hill-wash" in hollows and against field boundaries. Accumulations of this kind are generally looser and more uniform in colour and texture than those of earlier periods, and their recent origin is sometimes betrayed by the inclusion of bricks, cinders, or other artifacts, or by the occurrence of buried soil horizons.

Also of recent origin are thin deposits of alluvium alongside streams. Although regular deposition has now largely ceased, occasional flooding takes place from the Thistle Brook and its tributaries (Plate III), and place-names like Long Marston, Marsworth and Fen Barn testify to the swampy condition of low-lying parts of the Vale before certain of the streams were straightened and artificial drainage became general.

SUPERFICIAL DEPOSITS

Owing to the importance of the superficial deposits as soil parent-materials, their nature and origin are treated below in some detail. The drift geology presents problems of great complexity, and the deposits are not easily placed in a chronological sequence. For the present purpose, however, they are conveniently grouped as follows, and are shown similarly on the accompanying sketch-map (Fig. 6):

(1) Plateau Drift and associated Clay-with-flints.
(2) High-level Gravels.
(3) Glacial Drift of the Vale.
(4) Head Deposits and River Gravels.
(5) Alluvium.

(1) Plateau Drift and associated Clay-with-flints

These deposits cap virtually all the high ground of the Chiltern Plateau and extend some distance down the sides of the valleys, covering in all more than one half of the area.

The term "Clay-with-flints" was first applied by Whitaker (Hull and Whitaker, 1861) to "a deposit of stiff brown and reddish clay with large unworn flints that . . . lies very irregularly on the Chalk, filling pipes in that rock, and never occurring as an even overlying bed (like the Thanet Sand or the Reading Beds)". At the same time he distinguished as "brick-earth"* an overlying and more heterogeneous deposit of stony clays and loams which were regarded as the "waste" of Reading Beds clays and sands. On the Old Series Geological maps of this and adjoining areas, the Clay-with-flints and "brick-earth" were shown separately, the latter as covering the broader ridge-tops and the former as an emergent fringe on slopes and spurs. Owing to difficulties of boundary location, this separation was later abandoned and the meaning of the name Clay-with-flints was extended to include the bulk of the former "brick-earth", while the remainder, characterized by a predominance of flint pebbles, was grouped with certain other pebbly drifts under the name of "Pebbly Clay and Sand" (Sherlock, 1924).

---

* The name "brick-earth" is now generally restricted to more or less weathered, loamy or silty superficial deposits with few stones.

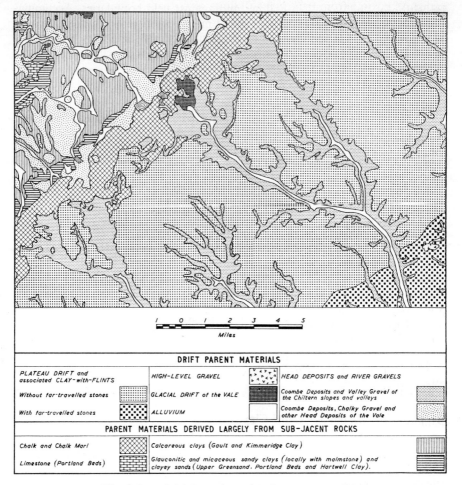

Miles

DRIFT PARENT MATERIALS

PLATEAU DRIFT and associated CLAY-with-FLINTS		HIGH-LEVEL GRAVEL		HEAD DEPOSITS and RIVER GRAVELS	
Without far-travelled stones		GLACIAL DRIFT of the VALE		Coombe Deposits and Valley Gravel of the Chiltern slopes and valleys	
With far-travelled stones		ALLUVIUM		Coombe Deposits, Chalky Gravel and other Head Deposits of the Vale	

PARENT MATERIALS DERIVED LARGELY FROM SUB-JACENT ROCKS

Chalk and Chalk Marl		Calcareous clays (Gault and Kimmeridge Clay)	
Limestone (Portland Beds)		Glauconitic and micaceous sandy clays (locally with malmstone) and clayey sands (Upper Greensand. Portland Beds and Hartwell Clay).	

Fig. 6. Superficial Deposits and Soil Parent Materials

Since Whitaker made his observations, there has been much discussion concerning the nature and mode of formation of these deposits, and the differing meanings attached to the term "Clay-with-flints" have given rise to a certain amount of confusion. That the Clay-with-flints proper does indeed display distinctive properties was emphasised by Barrow (1919), who showed that, whatever the texture and stone content of the plateau deposits, it emerged on slopes as a markedly tough, tenacious clay containing large unworn and often unbroken flints. These observations have since been confirmed and extended, and it is therefore proposed to retain the term "Clay-with-flints" for the characteristic material in contact with the Chalk, while the thicker and more heterogeneous accumulations above it are grouped under the general name of Plateau Drift (Loveday, 1962).

The Plateau Drift consists predominantly of yellow-red, more or less stony clay, often with greyish coatings around stones, or lining fissures and root-paths. As distinct from the Clay-with-flints proper, it usually contains appreciable amounts of sand, localized to some extent in pockets, and has a characteristic sub-plastic consistency when slightly moist, tending to crumble under gentle pressure before moulding. Where exposed in brick-pits, the content of stones is often seen to be extremely variable, patches of almost stoneless clay alternating with seams or irregular masses of clayey gravel. Although clay-size particles often account for over 60 per cent of the matrix, it is distinctly more friable and pervious than undisturbed Eocene clays, probably as a result of the intensive weathering it received either before or after its deposition (Avery *et al.*, 1959; Loveday, 1962).

The drift may be 30 or 40 ft. thick beneath the broader ridges, but its base is known to be very uneven, and such thicknesses seem generally to be associated with hollows or "pipes" in the Chalk, of which little indication exists at the surface, and in which relics of older formations are sometimes preserved. Besides slumped masses of Reading Beds clay or sand, the surviving marine gravels at Little Heath were believed by Gilbert (1924) to occupy a hollow of this kind, and in addition there are numerous inlying pockets of finely laminated, virtually stoneless, clay and loam, apparently consisting of relaid Eocene materials. These "laminated brick-earths" were clearly deposited in water and may occupy swallow-holes formed when the cover of Eocene rocks was only partly destroyed. In several places, however, they have yielded flint implements of Acheulian type (Oakley, 1947), indicating that deposition took place at a relatively late (mid-Pleistocene) stage.

At elevations above about 400 ft., the stones consist almost entirely of broken and corroded flints and flint-pebbles, but whereas drift with angular flints predominant is found at all levels, flint-pebbles only become abundant in certain localities below 650 ft., corresponding in most cases to the areas mapped as Pebbly Clay and Sand by the Geological Survey. Small white quartz pebbles often accompany the flint pebbles, and large fragments or boulders of sarsen and Hertfordshire Pudding-stone are locally present, the latter chiefly east of Chesham and sarsens further to the west (Davies and Baines, 1953). These silicified masses, which resemble silcretes found in sub-tropical regions (Kerr, 1955), appear to have formed as a result of local cementation by silica of Reading Beds sands and flint-pebble beds.

The deposits on the lower part of the dip-slope (mapped as Glacial Gravel by the Geological Survey) contain Triassic pebbles and other far-travelled stones, but otherwise resemble the Pebbly Clay and Sand at higher levels, and are accordingly described, following Loveday (1962), as Plateau Drift with far-travelled stones. Although a substratum of gravel is present in places, the dominant component is a red or yellowish, more or less stony clay, apparently including masses of little-disturbed Reading Beds, which thins out on slopes and spurs to reveal irregular accumulations of Clay-with-flints. This essentially clayey drift, overlain by stony soil of lighter texture, covers the ridges on either side of the Gade valley at heights of 350–400 ft., and descends, often with a distinct break of slope, to the low plateaux south and east of Abbots Langley. The stones include sub-angular flints and flint-pebbles, rounded or sub-angular pieces of vein quartz, Hertfordshire Pudding-stone and hard Palaeozoic sandstone; and occasional weathered fragments of crystalline rocks, notably felsite.

The considerable thickness and heterogeneous constitution of the Plateau Drift, and the manner in which it over-rides or incorporates the remains of older formations led Sherlock and Noble (1912) to postulate a glacial origin for the bulk of the material, and Wooldridge (1957) concludes, from evidence of deep-seated disturbances near Cowcroft, that certain of the pebbly deposits in that area were overthrust by an early Pleistocene ice-sheet which advanced eastwards from the Goring Gap. Except below 400 ft., however, all the constituents could have been derived locally, and essentially similar irregularities have been observed in analogous deposits south of the Thames, where a major ice-sheet can hardly be invoked. It therefore seems reasonable, following Dines et al. (1940) to regard the higher lying drift as a type of Head, representing the weathered remains of Chalk, Eocene and later sediments, more or less mixed and re-arranged under the influence of a local snow-cap or ice-field. Although, apart from the angular flints, all the constituents could have come from the local Reading Beds, Wooldridge and Linton (1955) consider that a considerable proportion of the flint pebbles, as well as the small quartz pebbles, are derived from earlier Pleistocene gravels of marine or fluviatile origin.

The deposits at lower levels—referred to as Chiltern Drift by Wooldridge and Linton (1955)—appear to have been re-arranged by glacial action, and Sherlock (1922) believed that they were laid down by an ice-sheet which came through the Hitchin Gap. It is possible, however, that the Triassic pebbles they contain were at least partly derived from pre-existing river gravels, the remains of which were subsequently mixed with Eocene detritus by local snow and ice.

The surface layers of the Plateau Drift are normally loamy, and although it appears from soil-profile studies (Avery et al., 1959; Loveday, 1962) that this loaminess results largely from weathering or downward migration of clay-size particles, there is clear evidence that in most places the texture has also been significantly modified by accessions of silty material resembling loess. In a number of profiles on the Chiltern Plateau, horizons to depths of up to three feet have been shown to contain a distinctive assemblage of minerals, including epidote, chlorite, hornblende, garnet and feldspar, which are rare or absent in underlying horizons. These minerals must therefore have originated in a separate deposit, and their association with an abundance of coarse silt-size (e.s.d. 0·05–0·02 mm.) grains makes it highly probable that the source was wind-borne dust (loess). As similar material occurs as a constituent of Coombe Deposits at lower levels, the probability is that it accumulated before or during the cold phase when these deposits were laid down, and was subsequently re-arranged by solifluxion or allied processes. Over most of the plateau, it appears to have been incorporated to a greater or lesser extent with the subjacent drift to form a mixed, silty layer which is normally thickest and least stony on level or in slightly depressed sites, and is thin or absent on sloping land at the edges of ridges, where owing to differential erosion of finer material the surface is often extremely stony.

Wherever the Plateau Drift thins out on slopes or spurs, the Clay-with-flints proper appears as a dark brown or reddish, highly tenacious clay, enclosing entire or broken flints, and resting with an irregular junction on the Chalk. The clay is remarkably moisture-retentive, and breaks down when dry into hard, sharp-edged, blocky aggregates, the surfaces of which, together with the flints, are often blackened by a manganiferous film. Besides occurring as a lining to the Chalk surface beneath the ridges, Clay-with-flints of a similar type extends down valley sides to far lower levels, and is also found as isolated residual patches in the major dry valleys and wind-gaps, separated by chalky slopes from the main sheet of Plateau Drift on the ridges above. In either case, it is rarely more than three or four feet thick and, except where exposed by accelerated erosion, is normally covered by a variable thickness of less tenacious flinty or pebbly soil.

Recent studies (Avery *et al.*, 1959; Loveday, 1962) have shown that the morphology, composition and mode of occurrence of this deposit are broadly consistent with the view, held by Whitaker and others, that it represents the weathering products of chalk. It seems certain, however, that even the limited thicknesses involved could not have formed *in situ* from the Chalk alone, for normal white chalk (Upper or Middle Chalk) contains only 1–2 per cent of clay residue, and as, from the position of the Eocene outliers, the surface of the Chalk can hardly have been lowered by post-Eocene solution to any considerable extent, accumulation of residues on the scale demanded is inconceivable.

A more satisfactory explanation of its origin, propounded by Barrow (1919), is that it results from slow solution of Upper Chalk beneath a protective cover of drift or other material which permits free percolation of rain-water. On this view, which is afforded some confirmation by micromorphological studies, the Chalk by solution yields unworn flints and a little insoluble clay, but the bulk of the matrix is derived from the overlying materials, either by the more or less selective infiltration of semi-fluid clay into spaces left by solution, or by deposition from descending suspensions or solutions. Whichever process is primarily involved, the constant occurrence of Clay-with-flints as a lining to the irregular Chalk surface beneath deposits which show evidence of advanced weathering, suggests strongly that sub-surface solution, accompanied by translocation of clay, has taken place over wide areas. It also seems clear, from its present distribution, that more than one phase of Clay-with-flints formation is represented, the earliest, Tertiary accumulation having been largely denuded or incorporated in the Plateau Drift. The greatest recorded thicknesses* of Clay-with-flints occur beneath the summit ridges, and may well include relics of a Tertiary generation, but similar accumulations at lower levels are associated with deposits and surfaces which originated after the Red Crag stage, and must therefore have formed in Pleistocene times, presumably during one or more interglacial periods when normal, humid weathering proceeded undisturbed. Much of this lower-lying Clay-with-flints occurs beneath valley sides, and frequently extends on to the virtually flint-free Middle Chalk, so that although there is evidence that some, at least, has formed *in situ*, the greater part has undoubtedly been moved down-slope from the point where it originated, either by solifluxion, or by normal soil-creep under temperate conditions.

(2) High-level Gravels

As indicated above, stratified gravels and sand occur locally on the Chiltern Plateau in association with the predominant stony clays. They are nowhere

---

* Loveday (1962) studied in detail a profile exposed at Ibstone, Bucks., showing Upper Chalk overlain by 13 ft. 6 in. of Clay-with-flints, and this in turn by 5 ft. 6 in. of Plateau Drift containing appreciable quantities of sand and flint-pebbles.

extensive, and are best represented at Bedmond, where coarse gravel with layers of current-bedded sand rests on Reading Beds clay, and is exposed to a depth of 15 ft. Elsewhere, as at Little Heath and around Abbots Langley, discontinuous rafts or lenses of gravel occur within or below masses of clayey drift, but are rarely exposed at the surface.

The gravels at Bedmond consist chiefly of sub-angular flints and Eocene pebbles, but resemble the adjacent Plateau Drift in also containing numerous pebbles of Bunter quartzite and vein quartz, together with a few of sandstone, felsite and other rocks. These foreign stones can be matched in the Bunter Pebble Beds and other Palaeozoic outcrops of the Midlands, but the way in which they were introduced and mixed with locally derived materials remains a matter for controversy. Since the deposits occur at 425–450 ft. O.D., and are clearly water-laid, they must have been emplaced before the adjacent valleys existed, possibly by a fore-runner of the Thames at the so-called Pebble-Gravel stage (Wooldridge, 1957).

(3) Glacial Drift of the Vale

The great sheet of glacial drift which covers a major part of the Ouse basin extends into the area from the north around Wingrave, and quartzose pebbles of northern origin are common in the soils of the Vale as far south as a line extending from Aylesbury by way of Hulcott and Long Marston to the entrance of the Tring Gap. Except around Wingrave, the drift is rarely more than three feet thick, and the far-travelled constituents appear in most cases to have been derived by solifluxion or stream action from older deposits, relics of which survive locally on hill-tops and in upper slope positions. It is possible, however, that products of both Elster and Saale glaciations are represented, the former being confined to the high ground, and the latter extending on to lower surfaces which were not in existence at the time of the earlier ice-advance.

The deposits at Wingrave include weathered flint and quartzose gravels similar to those at Bedmond, resting on or channelled into the Gault; and east of the village, at 425 ft. O.D., typical blue-grey Chalky Boulder Clay has been identified. Thin outlying patches of stony drift with quartzose pebbles occur at comparable heights on the hill-tops north and east of Rowsham; and, nearer the escarpment, on Southend Hill, Cheddington; north of Dagnall (grid ref. SP/987185), and on the bluff east of Marsworth (grid ref. SP/928148). The last-mentioned point lies on the up-raised, terminal edge of the fan-shaped platform at around 425 ft. which extends southwards to the neck of the gap near Tring station. Beneath the surface of this flat is a brown clay containing scattered sub-angular flints and quartzose pebbles, resembling weathered Chalky Boulder Clay, and resting on chalky drift with gravelly and sandy layers, the whole being mapped as Valley Gravel by the Geological Survey. The presence of foreign stones indicates that the clay, at least, came from the north, and almost certainly derives from an early incursion of ice into the gap.

(4) Head Deposits and River Gravels

This division comprises drifts of variable composition, including those previously mapped by the Geological Survey as Valley Gravel or "Gravel opposite Chalk Gaps", all of which contain materials derived from pre-existing formations (either solid or drift), more or less mixed and re-arranged during transport from higher to lower ground. The deposits are of various ages, ranging from recent "hill-wash" on slopes and in dry-valley bottoms to older, dissected sheets of Head coeval with either the Saale or the Elster glaciation. They often appear to incorporate accessions of wind-borne silt or sand and, although usually unsorted, pass locally into true river gravels.

For convenience in description, they may be grouped according to their area of occurrence as follows:

(1) Coombe Deposits and associated fluviatile gravels of the Chiltern slopes and valleys.
(2) Chalky Gravel and other Head deposits of the Vale.

Coombe Deposits and Valley Gravels. The name "Coombe Deposit" refers to unstratified or roughly stratified Head, occurring for the most part in Chalk valleys, and containing flint, chalk and other materials in proportions depending on their source. At the foot of the escarpment, and wherever Chalk is exposed on valley sides, the deposits are chiefly of the type known as Coombe-Rock, consisting of sub-rounded chalk fragments and shattered flints in a pale-coloured chalky matrix; elsewhere the drift is non-calcareous, at least in the surface layers, either because it has been decalcified by prolonged leaching, or because little or no chalk was originally incorporated. In either case the hard materials of the drift have clearly been derived from nearby higher ground, but the matrix frequently contains a high proportion of silt, which is partly of non-local (loessial) origin. In exposures the stones and fine material are often irregularly arranged in pockets or festoons; crude banding suggestive of down-slope movement is sometimes apparent, and the underlying Chalk is commonly disturbed or disintegrated to depths of several feet (Plate VIIa).

The oldest Coombe Deposits occur in the upper parts of the main valleys, and appear to have originated as more or less confluent fans, spread out from coombes at times of great mass wastage. Since they were laid down, the watersheds in the wind-gaps have retreated south-eastwards, and the ancient drift-mantled valley-floors have been truncated and dissected by younger coombes draining towards the Vale. In the Wendover Gap, where the deposits were formerly dug for gravel, a section (grid ref. SP/874067) described by Sherlock (1922) showed up to 20 ft. of "dirty gravel" containing angular flints, sub-rounded chalk fragments, and a few Eocene pebbles in a loamy calcareous matrix. The top few feet consist of brown or reddish, non-calcareous, loamy and clayey gravel, deeply piped into the underlying chalky gravel, and apparently resulting from long-continued decalcification. It seems probable, however, that the pipes represent fossil ice-wedges (Zeuner, 1959) rather than solution hollows, suggesting that the surface materials have been disturbed by frost action in a cold period subsequent to that in which the chalky Head was laid down, and that they may incorporate the products of a later phase of solifluxion (cf. Evans and Oakley, 1952).

Non-calcareous or decalcified Head resembling that in the upper part of the Wendover section occurs on foot-slopes in most of the broader valleys. Where slopes are gentle it often appears to pass uphill into Clay-with-flints, whereas on steeper (8–12°) slopes it usually gives place at the surface to thinner, chalky Head. The characteristically asymmetrical pattern of slopes and superficial

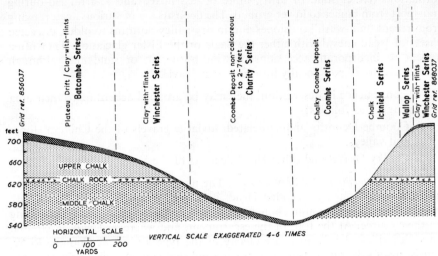

Fig. 7. Cross-section of the valley east of Manor Farm, Little Hampden

deposits found in many of these dry valleys is illustrated in Fig. 7 by a cross-section of the valley east of Little Hampden, studied recently by Ollier and Thomasson (1957). A similar pattern is repeated on a smaller scale by numerous minor spurs and re-entrants, one side being blanketed by Clay-with-flints which passes down-hill into non-calcareous, loamy Head, while on the other the drift is thin and chalky. Ollier and Thomasson concluded that this kind of asymmetry resulted from uniclinal shifting of a down-cutting stream in response to differences in the intensity of weathering and erosion on opposing sides of the valleys. The ultimate cause of such differences is difficult to ascertain, but as the more intensely eroded slopes face west and south it seems probable that aspect in relation to insolation* and/or wind direction may have been a controlling factor. Variations in insolation related to aspect would have been most effective under cold conditions when vegetation was scanty, and one possibility is that snow accumulated in larger amounts and thawed out less frequently on the north-east facing lea slopes than on the opposing slopes, with the result that erosion by either solifluxion or surface wash was more intense on the latter.

In certain of the tributary valleys, including that at Little Hampden, there is no trace of fluviatile deposits, but narrow strips of coarse flint gravel occupy the bottoms of the main valleys above the points at which springs arise, and pass lower down beneath finer-textured alluvium. Similar gravel, usually covered by loamy hill-wash, is also found in many of the dry 'bottoms' which head on the plateau, and appears to have been deposited by streams, possibly of melt-water when the substratum was frozen. 'Dry-valley gravel' of this type is thickest and most continuous in the bottoms east of the Gade valley, where the slopes are gentle and are generally underlain by Clay-with-flints. At Kinsbourne Green, in

* According to Geiger (1950), in temperate latitudes afternoon sun is generally more effective than morning sun in warming the ground, so that there is a tendency for maximum ground temperatures to occur on south-west facing slopes.

the Harpenden Valley, it is locally over 15 ft. thick, and contains occasional quartzite pebbles, suggesting that melt-water may have passed down this valley from an ice-front further north.

The lower parts of the Gade and Ver valleys appear to have been rejuvenated by headward erosion since the older Coombe Deposits were laid down, and the former valley-floor deposits survive in places as rudimentary terraces, more or less obscured at the surface by loamy Head or rain-wash. Sherlock (1922) records 10 ft. of coarse flint gravel at Redbourn, where it forms a low terrace at the convergence of several dry valleys, and similar deposits were formerly worked at Kings Langley and Huntonbridge in the Gade valley.

Head Deposits of the Vale. At the foot of the escarpment, patches of unsorted Coombe-Rock resting on Lower Chalk give place at lower levels to gently inclined sheets of poorly stratified, gravelly drift containing sub-angular and shattered flints and water-worn chalk fragments, set in a matrix of sand and clay. In its main occurrences, the gravel rests on Gault and is covered by 18–30 in. of sandy clay or loam with scattered flints; its thickness varies greatly, the gravel filling hollows in the underlying clay although the surface remains flat, and in places, especially towards Aylesbury, it is replaced by clayey or chalky sand with few stones. This "Chalky Gravel Head" is most widespread around Weston Turville and Stoke Mandeville, and also extends over the Upper Green-sand and Gault at Gubblecote, north of Tring, where it has been described by Oakley (1936) as "a chalky, gravelly sludge, spread out from the escarpment, during a late glacial phase, by the combined agencies of solifluxion and melting snow". A similar spread occurs north of Ivinghoe, but here occasional quartzite pebbles are present, presumably derived from a former cover of glacial drift.

The gravels at Gubblecote and north of Weston Turville lie little above the present streams and run down into low parts of the Vale, whereas those around Stoke Mandeville occupy terrace-like features and probably represent relics of an older and more extensive spread. Although the deposits appear everywhere to have formed as Oakley suggested, the quartz sand they contain in significant amounts is difficult to account for from local sources, and may have been brought in by wind, as postulated for similar drift at the foot of the Cotswold escarpment (Arkell, 1947). On flat or gently sloping land between the gravel areas, the Gault is commonly covered by clayey Head 2–4 ft. thick, the disturbed character of which is shown by the inclusion of scattered flints and chalk fragments, and by the intermittent occurrence at the base of thin seams and pockets of gravel. Layers of a similar type, with a composition closely related to that of the substratum, are also found overlying the Upper Greensand and the Chalk Marl, interspersed with the more obvious gravelly drift. The distribution of these thin and variable deposits can generally be related to minor features of relief, and in places a markedly asymmetrical pattern is discernable, one side of a shallow valley or low ridge being virtually drift-free, while the other bears a continuous layer of re-worked material.

Other thin and irregular spreads of more or less loamy or gravelly drift overlie the Kimmeridge Clay further north. In places, as on the low hill north of Bierton (grid ref. SP/842171), there are patches of stony clay mapped as Boulder Clay by the Geological Survey. Generally, however, their distribution in relation to the existing topography suggests that most of the material has been sludged or washed from nearby higher ground. This is clearly evident north of Aylesbury, where on even foot-slopes the Kimmeridge Clay is covered by brown loamy Head containing lydite pebbles and occasional limestone fragments of Port-landian origin. Elsewhere, particularly on either side of the Thistle Brook, the clay is modified at the surface by appreciably sandy drift, with scattered sub-angular flints and quartzite pebbles, which locally becomes gravelly at the base.

(5) Alluvium

The Chiltern streams are bordered by narrow but well-marked belts of allu-vium which consists for the most part of water-worn flint gravel, overlain in places by calcareous silt, and occasionally, as at Huntonbridge, by thin beds of peat. Much of this valley ground has been disturbed by the construction of watercress beds, gravel workings, or urban and industrial developments and, in the Bulbourne and Gade valleys, by the making of the Grand Union Canal. At the heads of the valleys and in tributaries, the alluvium grades indefinitely into dry-valley gravel.

Of the streams in the Vale, the Thistle Brook and the brook which runs west-wards from Broughton have fairly well-marked alluvial flats underlain by fine-textured flood deposits, often with a substratum of chalk gravel or calcareous silt. Similar deposits extend as ill-defined strips along present or former stream courses in the sub-edge plain, becoming loamier and more chalky as the scarp-foot springs are approached. These alluvial tracts commonly lie little below the general level, and the associated deposits are sometimes difficult to distinguish from the older sheets of flinty and chalky Head which they frequently border. Usually, however, the material is more calcareous, with fewer and smaller flints, the overlying soil is more or less peaty, and fragmented snail shells are commonly present. In certain low-lying areas at the edge of the Icknield Belt, notably around Ivinghoe Aston and south of Aston Clinton, there are very gently inclined spreads of drift consisting largely of finely divided chalk and marl, and similar tracts probably occupied the sites of the Canal reservoirs north of Tring. Much of this material seems to have been laid down by spring-fed streams, but some may have been derived, in a late glacial phase, as local Head or hill-wash from the slopes above.

CLIMATE

Although climatically the area is broadly representative of the Eastern Midlands, the relative elevation of the Chiltern Plateau is reflected in a higher than average rainfall, and its dissected topography produces local variations, particularly of temperature, dependent on relief, aspect and exposure.

Temperature

Monthly averages of maximum and minimum daily temperatures at Berk-hamsted, a centrally situated station, are given in Table 1 for the standard period 1881–1915. The mean annual temperature is about that of central England generally, and the annual range of 23·7°F. between January and July indicates a distinct approach towards continentality, compared with the more equable conditions obtaining near the western sea-board, where annual ranges of less than 20°F. are normal.

The effect of increasing altitude and exposure is shown by a comparison of records obtained at Rothamsted Experimental Station (1½ miles east of Redbourn) and Whipsnade Zoo (Table 1). Both stations are on plateau sites, and that at Whipsnade, located on the windswept brow of the escarpment, is exactly 300 ft. higher than Rothamsted. For the period given, both maximum and minimum temperatures were lower at Whipsnade in every month of the year, the difference averaging 1·4°F.; and if it is assumed that most plants make little growth until the mean daily temperature exceeds 42°F., this corresponds to about a fortnight's difference in the length of the growing season. Further local variations, particularly of ground temperature, may arise in the Chiltern valleys from the influence of aspect on the intensity of insolation and exposure to prevailing winds, and from the tendency for the valleys to function as frost pockets on still, clear nights. A classic example of a frost pocket has been recorded by Hawke (1944) in a dry valley at Rickmansworth, three miles south of the southern boundary of the survey area. The valley is dammed at its lower end by a railway viaduct, so that it undoubtedly represents an extreme case, but the data in Table 2, comparing temperature conditions at Rickmansworth and Rothamsted for the same period, illustrate the kind of variations to be expected between upper slope and valley-bottom sites. The records (Bilham, 1938) show that whereas daily mean temperatures are about the same at each station, the mean daily maximum at Rickmansworth is consistently higher and the mean daily minimum 4–5° lower in all months. There is consequently a great difference in the average diurnal range of temperature, and an even more striking difference in the frequency of ground frosts, which occurred at the Rickmansworth station in every month of the year. The importance of such local variations, particularly to horticulture, can hardly be over-emphasized, for, as Bilham shows, the night climate of the Rickmansworth valley is similar to that of the Aberdeenshire plateau, which is about the coldest inhabited region in the British Isles.

Rainfall, Snow and Fog

Mean monthly and yearly rainfall figures for six selected stations, based on the 35-year period 1916–50, are given in Table 3. The annual average exceeds 27·5 in. over most, if not all, of the Chiltern Plateau, but falls below this value in the Vale of Aylesbury. On average, November is everywhere the wettest month and March generally the driest. Taking the year as a whole, the wettest four consecutive months are October–January, whereas the spring months from February to June inclusive are notably dry, receiving only 32–34 per cent of the yearly total, as against 41 per cent if the distribution were uniform.

Snow, recorded as falling on 16 days in an average year at Rothamsted, and as lying on 9 days, normally accounts for only a small proportion of the annual precipitation, but the proportion increases with altitude, the higher parts of the Chilterns receiving significantly more frequent and persistent falls.

The incidence of fog is also affected by relief. Radiation fogs, common under anticyclonic conditions in autumn and winter, are most persistent in the valleys; whereas with advection fogs, resulting from the influx of warm, moist, Atlantic air during the same period, the reverse effect is commonly observed, the Chiltern summits being enveloped in a pall of low-lying cloud while the valleys remain relatively clear.

TABLE 1

Average Values of Maximum and Minimum Temperature (°F.) at selected Stations*

Station	Jan.	Feb.	Mar.	Apr.	May	June	July	Aug.	Sept.	Oct.	Nov.	Dec.	Year
Berkhamsted (450 ft. O.D.)						Period 1881–1915							
Mean daily max.	41·7	43·9	47·8	54·0	61·2	67·0	70·3	69·4	64·8	55·7	48·1	43·2	55·6
„ „ min.	33·3	33·4	34·4	38·0	43·2	48·6	52·2	51·5	48·2	42·5	37·4	34·6	41·4
„ „ av.	37·5	38·6	41·4	46·0	52·2	57·8	61·2	60·4	56·5	49·1	42·7	38·9	48·5
Rothamsted (420 ft. O.D.)						Period 1943–50							
Mean daily max.	42·7	44·0	49·7	57·3	62·0	66·2	70·2	70·1	64·6	57·1	47·3	42·9	56·2
„ „ min.	32·9	33·7	34·6	40·0	43·2	49·1	51·9	52·6	50·0	43·7	38·0	33·6	41·9
„ „ av.	37·8	38·8	42·1	48·6	52·6	57·6	61·0	61·3	57·3	50·4	42·6	38·2	49·0
Whipsnade (720 ft. O.D.)						Period 1943–50							
Mean daily max.	41·4	43·1	48·4	56·0	60·5	64·7	68·8	68·4	63·1	55·4	44·6	41·3	54·6
„ „ min.	31·6	32·4	33·9	38·6	42·0	47·9	51·7	51·2	46·3	43·1	37·0	32·2	40·7
„ „ av.	36·5	37·7	41·1	47·3	51·2	56·3	60·2	59·8	54·7	49·2	40·8	36·7	47·6

* Supplied by Meteorological Office (Air Ministry).

TABLE 2

Comparison of Temperatures at Rickmansworth and Rothamsted 1931–35

Station	Jan.	Feb.	Mar.	Apr.	May	June	July	Aug.	Sept.	Oct.	Nov.	Dec.	Year
Mean daily maximum													
Rickmansworth ..	44·5	46·0	51·4	55·7	63·2	70·7	75·2	74·7	67·3	58·0	49·6	44·6	48·4
Rothamsted ..	42·7	43·2	48·5	52·3	59·3	66·5	71·0	70·0	63·5	54·7	47·5	43·1	55·2
Mean daily minimum													
Rickmansworth ..	28·7	28·2	28·3	34·6	39·5	45·2	48·5	47·4	43·8	37·2	33·6	30·9	37·2
Rothamsted ..	33·2	32·7	33·8	38·6	43·3	49·8	53·6	52·7	49·1	42·7	38·1	35·1	41·9
Mean daily range													
Rickmansworth ..	15·8	17·8	23·1	21·1	23·7	25·5	26·7	27·1	23·5	20·8	16·0	13·7	21·2
Rothamsted ..	9·5	10·5	14·7	13·7	16·0	16·7	17·4	17·3	14·4	12·0	9·4	8·0	13·3
Nights with ground frost 1935													
Rickmansworth ..	26	21	28	20	15	2	4	6	6	20	23	25	196
Rothamsted ..	12	9	17	9	6	0	0	0	0	5	14	16	88

TABLE 3

Average Monthly and Yearly Rainfall (in.) at selected Stations (Period 1916–50)*

Station	Altitude ft.	Jan.	Feb.	Mar.	Apr.	May	June	July	Aug.	Sept.	Oct.	Nov.	Dec.	Year
Aylesbury (Sewage Works)	251	2·35	1·17	1·58	1·92	2·04	1·58	2·61	2·20	2·17	2·48	2·68	2·22	25·54
Hampden House	695	2·78	2·00	1·78	2·20	2·29	1·70	2·84	2·54	2·49	2·85	3·09	2·69	29·25
Tring (Cowroast Lock)	390	2·87	2·08	1·84	2·36	2·25	1·84	2·82	2·38	2·44	2·83	3·18	2·69	29·58
Hemel Hempstead (Apsley Mills)	268	2·80	1·99	1·80	2·22	2·10	1·83	2·73	2·40	2·34	2·76	3·16	2·65	28·78
Rothamsted Exp. Stn.	420	2·70	1·88	1·68	2·10	2·07	1·71	2·67	2·29	2·32	2·62	3·03	2·51	27·58

* Supplied by Meteorological Office (Air Ministry).

Evaporation and Percolation

In order to assess the adequacy of rainfall to support crop-growth and its capacity for leaching the soil, it is necessary to take account of losses by evaporation. Direct measurement of evaporation from ground surfaces or from growing plants is almost impossible under natural conditions, but useful indirect estimates are obtainable, either from measurements of percolation, by stream gauging, or by calculation from meteorological data, using formulae devised by Penman (1950, 1962).

Measurements of percolation were undertaken in the survey area as long ago as 1836. In that year, as appears from an article by Josiah Parkes (1845), rainfall and drainage gauges were set up at Nash Mills, Abbots Langley by "the eminent paper manufacturer Mr. John Dickinson", to whom, "having several mills on the river Colne and its tributaries, it was a matter of importance to calculate the power of water on which he might depend for use at different periods of the year". The drain gauge, of a pattern "invented by the illustrious Dr. Dalton many years before", consisted of a cylinder 3 ft. long and 1 ft. in diameter with a perforated metal bottom from which drainage water could be collected in a calibrated tube provided with a tap. The cylinder was sunk in the ground right up to its rim, "filled with the sandy, gravelly soil of the district, and had grass continually growing on it". Parkes records the first eight years' observations and the results in Table 4, quoted by Greaves (1876) refer to an 18-year period beginning in 1854, when new gauges were installed.

Later in the century, three drain gauges, 20 in., 40 in. and 60 in. in depth, were constructed at Rothamsted Experimental Station by building cemented walls around blocks of soil *in situ*, each $\frac{1}{1000}$ acre in area. These gauges have always been kept free of vegetation and so provide estimates of evaporation from bare soil. Over a period of more than 60 years, percolation through the 60 in. gauge has been about the same as through the 20 in., results from which are summarized in Table 4.

TABLE 4

Rainfall and Percolation (in.)

	Period	*Rainfall*	*Percolation*	*Loss*
A. Percolation through 3 ft. of soil at Nash Mills (1854–72)[1]	Winter (October–March)	13·8	8·6	5·2
	Summer (April–September)	12·8	0·5	12·3
	Year	26·6	9·1	17·5
B. Percolation through 20 in. of soil at Rothamsted[2]	Winter (October–March)	15·1	11·0	4·1
	Summer (April–September)	14·0	4·1	9·9
	Year	29·1	15·1	14·0

[1] From Greaves *et al.* (1876).

[2] Supplied by H. L. Penman.

So long as water is supplied to the evaporating surfaces fast enough, the rate of evaporation, both from plants and from soil, is governed by the radiant energy available and by the ability of the air to take up more vapour, as determined by temperature, humidity and wind-speed. During the summer months, under the conditions obtaining in south-east England, water normally evaporates from bare moist soil more rapidly than it can be supplied from below, and once a thin surface layer has become dry the rate of loss is markedly restricted. But wherever plants occupy the ground, their roots are able to withdraw water from greater depths, so that evaporation continues at or near the potential rate for very much longer periods than from bare soil, and the amount of percolation is thereby reduced. The results from the Nash Mills and Rothamsted gauges demonstrate this difference clearly, and those from the former station show that where the ground is covered by vegetation there is normally little percolation during the summer half-year.

From a study of the physics of natural evaporation, Penman (1950, 1962) has derived methods of using standard weather data to estimate the "potential transpiration" rate. This potential rate, which depends only on meteorological factors, is considered to be the actual rate of evaporation from an extended area of a short green crop, actively growing, completely shading the ground, and adequately supplied with water around the roots.

TABLE 5

Potential Transpiration and Rainfall at Rothamsted[1]

(*Average for* 1946–57 *to nearest* 0·05 *in.*)

	Rainfall	Potential Transpiration	Accumulated Soil-moisture Deficit	Percolation
Jan. ..	2·25	0·10	—	2·15
Feb. ..	2·25	0·45	—	1·80
Mar. ..	1·80	1·20	—	0·60
Apr. ..	1·45	1·95	0·50	—
May ..	2·10	2·95	1·35	—
June ..	2·10	3·50	2·75	—
July ..	2·10	3·25	3·90	—
Aug. ..	2·75	2·50	3·65	—
Sept. ..	2·35	1·70	3·00	—
Oct. ..	2·20	0·50	1·30	—
Nov. ..	3·10	0·10	—	1·70
Dec. ..	2·25	0·00	—	2·25
Year ..	26·7	18·2		8·5

[1] Supplied by H. L. Penman.

By computing potential transpiration on a monthly basis, it is possible to assess the seasonal cycle of water conditions in a well drained soil (unaffected by a water-table or by accession of water through seepage) with a close cover of short vegetation. Thus, from data for Rothamsted (Table 5), it appears that potential transpiration normally exceeds rainfall from April to July inclusive, so that from April onwards the soil-moisture reserve is progressively depleted until, at the end of July, there is an accumulated deficit of almost 4 in. The deficit is finally made good some time in November, when the soil is recharged to field capacity* and percolation is resumed. In making such an assessment it is assumed that no surface run-off occurs, and that the accumulated soil-moisture deficit is at no time sufficient to reduce transpiration appreciably below the potential level. The reserve of water held in the soil on which plants can draw in a rainless period is limited by their depth of rooting and by the quantity of water available per unit depth. Most well drained loamy and clayey soils are capable of supplying between 1 and 2·5 in. of water per foot, so that the reserve available to deep-rooted crops will commonly exceed 4 in., but for shallow-rooted crops or seedlings, and on shallow soils or soils with a low moisture-storage capacity, the limiting deficit will be considerably less.

LAND USE

HISTORICAL

In prehistoric times, the greater part of the area was almost certainly covered by deciduous forest or scrub, and apart from lynchets (terraces where the soil has been displaced by cultivation) of uncertain age near Cheddington, Edlesborough and Chesham, there is as yet little direct evidence of primitive agriculture. It seems likely, however, from the distribution of barrows, hill-forts and other artifacts, that both Neolithic and Bronze Age peoples settled near the Icknield Way and in certain of the Chiltern valleys, where springs and light, easily cleared land occurred in close proximity (Head, 1955). These early settlers were primarily pastoral, and it was probably through the grazing of their flocks and herds that the first small clearances were gradually extended. Their cultivations were undoubtedly of a sparse and shifting character, but the Belgic tribes who colonized the area in the 1st century B.C. are believed to have introduced a more intensive type of husbandry, based on permanent cultivation strips and the use of ox-drawn ploughs.

The Belgae occupied the hill-fort at Cholesbury and established a capital at Verulamium (St. Albans). Under the Romans this became a thriving city: villa sites have also been unearthed near Kimble and Wendover, and in the Chess and Gade valleys, suggesting that the lower part of the Chiltern Plateau, as well as the Icknield Belt, was partly cultivated in Romano-British times. It seems probable, however, that the Vale of Aylesbury and much of the Chiltern Plateau were still densely forested, and the cleared land may well have reverted in part to scrub and forest after the Roman withdrawal.

To judge from the evidence afforded by the Domesday Survey of 1086 (Darby and Campbell, 1962), the Icknield Belt and the Vale of Aylesbury were largely cleared by the Anglo-Saxon invaders who settled in the area from the 6th century onwards. Besides establishing the existing pattern of nucleated villages, they introduced the open-field system of cultivation that formed the

---

* Defined as the moisture content of the soil when it is holding all the water it can against the force of gravity.

basis of rural economy throughout medieval times. In the 15th and 16th centuries enclosure for sheep pasture resulted locally in the depopulation or even destruction of pre-existing settlements, including Pendley (grid ref. SP/940110), Burston (grid ref. SP/837187), Bedgrove (grid ref. SP/838125) and Tiscott (grid ref. SP/885180; Plate IVa). Elsewhere, however, common arable fields survived in most parishes until the period of Parliamentary enclosure in the 18th and early 19th centuries (Tate, 1946, 1947).

The Chiltern Plateau, by contrast, remained sparsely populated and heavily wooded in the 11th century: the few Domesday settlements were mainly in the watered valleys and piecemeal clearance of the intervening ridges and plateaux during and after medieval times eventually gave rise to a pattern of scattered hamlets and isolated farms with few nucleated villages. The acreage of common arable fields seems never to have been large (Beresford, 1953), and by the 16th century the aspect of the country was such that Leland contrasted the wooded Chilterns "full of enclosures" with the almost treeless "champain" of the Vale (Taylor, 1936).

The rural economy in the early part of the 18th century was described by William Ellis of Little Gaddesden in his "Chiltern and Vale Farming Explained", first published in 1733. Hertfordshire was then the foremost corn-producing county, devoted to supplying the ever-growing requirements of London, and its farmers were among the first to introduce turnips and clover into their rotations. In the more remote country of the Vale, where the arable fields were still unenclosed, cropping was mainly based on the ancient 3-course rotation of wheat or barley, beans and fallow; few dressings were used, and both Ellis and the Swedish traveller Kalm (Lucas, 1892) considered the standard of crop husbandry distinctly inferior to that on the Chilterns. The Vale was chiefly famed, however, for its livestock farming; its pastures had a high reputation for fattening cattle and the drier soils of the Icknield Belt for the production of fine wool. Foot-rot in sheep was prevalent on the wetter land, and it was consequently the custom to sell off ewes in the autumn, often to Chiltern farmers who in their turn supplied young cattle to the graziers of the Vale.

In the 18th century, as appears from contemporary maps* and records (Mansfield, 1952), there existed on the Chilterns, besides enclosed woods of beech and oak, considerable areas of unenclosed commonland surviving from the medieval "waste". Much of this consisted of more or less wooded "scrubs" used for grazing and fuel by cottagers and small-holders whose habitations often bordered the commons and represented earlier encroachments. In the period of "high farming" that followed the Napoleonic wars, extensive commons in Princes Risborough, Great Missenden, Lee, Aston Clinton, Buckland, Wigginton, Northchurch and Flamstead parishes were enclosed for agriculture, while former scrublands on the Hampden Estate and elsewhere were converted into enclosed woodland.

When annual agricultural returns were instituted in the 1860's the acreage of farmland was probably greater than at any other time before or since, for the movement for the appropriation of common lands had by then been brought to a close, and the succeeding century has seen the increasing diversion of land to urban and other non-agricultural uses. Around 1870, according to Coppock

---

* Notably Thomas Jefferies' map of Buckinghamshire, published in 1769.

(1957), more than four-fifths of the agricultural land on the Chiltern Plateau and the Icknield Belt was arable, with sheepwalks on the steeper slopes and other areas of permanent grass in parks, around farms, and as strips along the few streams. Variants of the Norfolk 4-course rotation involving an additional corn crop were generally practised, and the principal products were wheat, barley and sheep; the sheep being mostly folded on turnips, green crops and "seeds". In the Vale tillage was less extensive, and most of the farms were devoted either to dairying or to meat production; both cattle and sheep were fattened on grass, and on dairy farms butter-making was already giving place to the sale of liquid milk, the district having been among the first to supply milk wholesale to London. Another important industry, carried on mainly by small-holders as a part-time occupation, was the rearing and fattening of ducks for the London market. This rose to prominence around Aylesbury with the coming of the railway, but underwent a marked decline at the time of the First World War.

In Hertfordshire, the main dressings used in the 1870's were home-produced dung and London stable-manure, and in addition large quantities of chalk were excavated to ameliorate the lime-free soils of the Chiltern Plateau. This practice was already long established in the 18th century, and may have been initiated in Romano-British times (Gardner and Garner, 1953). Chalk was dug from pits, or "dell-holes", which occur in nearly every field along the sloping margins of the valleys, usually where the drift becomes thin (Plate VIb). Some of the dell-holes, now often overgrown by a small copse or "spring" may have originated as solution hollows, but the majority are clearly artificial. On the more extensive level tracts it was customary to sink shafts through the clay until the Chalk was reached. A bell-shaped cavity was then excavated, and the chalk hauled up by a windlass. When the roof threatened to collapse the hole was filled up with brushwood and waste soil, and eventually ploughed over, leaving a saucer-shaped depression.

Subsequent changes in the agriculture have been studied in detail by Coppock (1954, 1957, 1960), and are illustrated in Fig. 8 by maps showing the distribution of arable land in c. 1875, 1931 and 1951 respectively.

As in other parts of England, the decline in prices, first for grain and later for fat stock, led from the late 1870's onwards to a steady conversion of arable to grass which persisted almost uninterrupted until the 1930's. The proportionate reduction in tillage land was greatest in some of the Vale parishes (e.g. Wingrave), where considerable acreages of wheat and beans had previously been grown, and least on the Chiltern Plateau east of the Gade valley, which remained predominantly arable. The conversion of arable to grass was associated with a steady decline in sheep-folding, and was everywhere accompanied by an increase in the number of cattle. Milk production, already predominant in the Vale, became a major enterprise on the Chilterns, where specialist poultry and game farms, relying on cheap imported feeding stuffs, were also established.

With the outbreak of war in 1939, the area under tillage was rapidly increased, parks and commons were ploughed up, and much unproductive land was rehabilitated by ditching, mole and tile draining, and liming. The change was again greatest in the Vale, where between 1939 and 1945 more than 40 acres in every 100 were ploughed, and the area of permanent grass in several parishes was reduced to below the 1870 level. Apart from limited acreages of potatoes, the

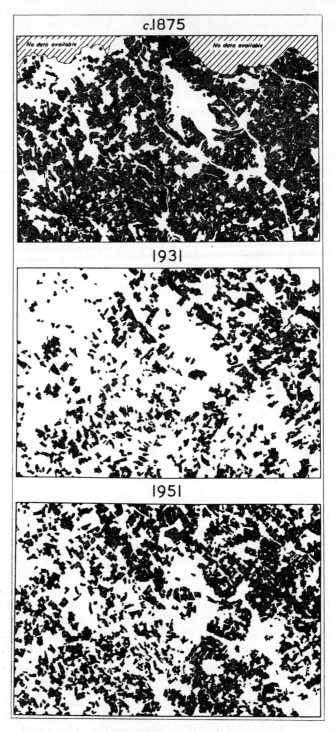

Fig. 8. Distribution of arable land in c.1875, 1931 and 1951
(After Coppock, 1957)

new arable was mainly devoted to cereals, with emphasis on oats and mixed corn to replace imported concentrates for stock-feeding, but by 1943 the need to rest land which had carried two or more successive corn crops led to a marked increase in the acreage of temporary grass. Owing to the high priority assigned to milk production in war-time, the population of dairy cattle increased nearly everywhere, whilst the numbers of other livestock generally declined, and sheep disappeared altogether from some parishes.

LAND USE IN THE POST-WAR PERIOD

In 1960, according to the annual agricultural returns, crops and grass (excluding rough grazings) occupied about 90,000 acres, or roughly 65 per cent of the area;

TABLE 6

Crops and Livestock per 100 acres of Agricultural Land in Four Groups
of Parishes* in June, 1960

	Chiltern Parishes		Icknield† Parishes	Vale Parishes
	Herts. & Beds.	Bucks.		
Acreage of Crops and Grass (including rough grazings)	38,085	17,216	23,021	13,055
CROPS (Acres)				
Wheat	13·2	12·5	9·6	8·3
Barley	24·2	12·4	15·7	6·8
Oats	5·3	5·7	5·1	3·3
Beans and peas ..	0·2	0·1	0·1	0·3
Mixed corn and other grain	0·2	0·5	0·4	0·3
Potatoes ..	0·7	0·2	0·4	0·1
Fodder roots	0·3	0·2	0·2	0·3
Kale, cabbage, etc.	2·1	3·1	1·8	0·6
Vegetables and other crops	1·2	0·9	0·4	0·4
Total tillage, including bare fallows	48·8	37·9	35·4	21·3
Temporary grass, with lucerne and sainfoin ..	20·2	21·2	17·4	12·7
Permanent grass	29·2	36·8	42·1	65·5
Rough grazings (in individual occupation)	1·1	2·2	2·9	0·2
Orchards and small fruit ..	0·7	1·9	2·2	0·3
LIVESTOCK (Numbers)				
Cows and heifers in milk and cows in calf but not in milk ..	10	11	9	10
All other cattle ..	20	23	22	34
Sheep	20	15	43	45
Cow-equivalents‡	26	27	29	40
Pigs	32	29	35	19
Poultry ..	789	645	579	2,832

* Excluding those with less than one-half their area in the district under review.

† Including Edlesborough, Ivinghoe, Cheddington, Marsworth, Pitstone, Aldbury, Tring Urban, Drayton Beauchamp, Buckland, Aston Clinton, Halton and Wendover, and Ellesborough.

‡ 1 cow-equivalent equals 1 cow, 6 sheep or 2 young cattle.

about 8 per cent was under woodland (including scrub), leaving 27 per cent as rough grazing, commons, houses with gardens, and agriculturally unproductive land.

The Farming Pattern

Since the war, the proportion of tillage land has fallen little below the 1945 level in most of the Chiltern parishes, and many Vale farmers who invested capital in machinery have found it advantageous to maintain a moderate acreage of cereal crops for sale. Temporary grass continues to occupy a much greater proportionate acreage than in pre-war years, and improved water supplies, coupled with the advent of the electric fence, have encouraged the spread of ley-farming, particularly on the Chilterns. The numbers of dairy cows have fallen in most parishes since 1945, and the farming pattern has everywhere become increasingly diversified by other livestock enterprises. The numbers of pigs have risen rapidly; there is much intensive production of eggs and table poultry, and beef and lamb production off grass have become increasingly important.

The present-day utilization of agricultural land is illustrated by the data for four groups of parishes in Table 6. Reference to the figures for total tillage and "cow-equivalents" indicates that whereas the Vale is primarily devoted to milk and meat production, livestock enterprises are either supplemented or replaced on the Chiltern Plateau and in the Icknield Belt by the production of arable crops for sale. Although milk production is still a major source of income on the average holding, there are few pure dairy farms, and the importance of dairying in relation to other livestock enterprises varies widely. Broadly speaking, however, beef cattle and sheep are more important in the Vale, while pigs are of greater significance on the Chilterns. In interpreting these statistics it is important to recognize that, although they serve to establish broad differences in land use between the regions represented, they give no indication of the many local diversities in farming practice, or of the manner in which different enterprises are combined on individual farms.

The distribution of holdings according to size in the area is as follows:

Size (Acres)	< 5	5–50	50–150	150–300	300–500	> 500
Per cent of total	28	38	18	11	4	1
Area occupied (per cent)	1	14	24	33	19	9

From these figures it appears that whereas over 60 per cent of the holdings are of less than 50 acres, more than half the land is in farms of 50–300 acres and 30 per cent in farms of over 300 acres; only two farms, both on the Chilterns, exceed 1,000 acres, and there are no farms in the Vale parishes of more than 500 acres. The distribution of small and medium-sized farms varies from parish to parish and determines in some measure the type of farming practiced. Thus, in Buckinghamshire, as shown by Cook and Gill (1956), 70 per cent of milk-selling farms are of between 50 and 300 acres whereas the great majority of very small farms (< 20 acres) do not sell milk and have relatively high populations of pigs and poultry: on larger farms, dairy cows become less numerous per acre as the size of farm increases and, in the Vale particularly, store cattle and sheep become of greater importance. The size of farm also affects the emphasis placed on tillage crops as a source of income, because where the acreage is small the capital charge on mechanical equipment becomes unduly high. Roughly half the holdings are now owned by their occupiers, and in 1960, according to the parish returns, one regular worker was employed for every 49 acres of crops and grass, as compared with one for every 63 acres in England and Wales.

The majority of farmhouses and buildings are over eighty years old and some, like those erected in the late 19th century on the former Rothschild and Brown-low estates, are notably substantial and commodious. Typical layouts are rectangular in plan, with buildings fronting on three or four sides of an open yard, one side being occupied by a large, wooden or (in the Chilterns) flint-built, threshing barn, and the remaining sides by stables, boxes and cowhouses, and sometimes by the farmhouse. Since the war, many of the older steadings have been redesigned to meet modern requirements and new buildings, particularly for housing intensive pig and poultry units, are appearing in increasing numbers. The old barns have been put to a variety of uses, including storage of grain in bins or silos and the accommodation of poultry in batteries or on deep litter; cowsheds have been replaced on many farms by yard-and-parlour units, and Dutch barns are in general use for the storage of hay and straw.

Except in parts of the Icknield Belt, the fields are generally bounded by hedges, which on traditionally arable land are rarely stock-proof and have commonly been supplemented by wire fences in order that leys may be grazed. In the Chilterns drainage generally presents no serious problem, and there are few ditches. On most of the Vale soils, however, both arable crops and grass are dependent for optimum productivity on adequate artificial drainage. Formerly the effects of waterlogging were mitigated by the practice of ploughing in narrow high-backed "lands", and during the 19th century much of the land was drained by bush- or stone-drains, and later by tiles, usually laid at depths of three or four feet. Despite government grants, intensive tile-drainage is now generally considered too expensive and fields where the soil is suitable are mole-drained, the mole being pulled at depths of 20–24 in. over a tiled main.

Arable Crops

The proportion of farming land devoted to arable crops in 1960 ranged from over 50 per cent on parts of the Chiltern Plateau to less than 20 per cent in some of the Vale parishes. Of the groups of parishes for which data are summarized in Table 6, the eastern group of Chiltern parishes in Hertfordshire and Bedfordshire had the highest aggregate acreage under tillage and the Vale parishes the lowest, the intermediate figures obtained for the parishes of the Buckinghamshire Chilterns and the Icknield Belt being attributable, at least in part, to the occurrence of unploughable slopes and, in the latter group, to the inclusion of appreciable areas of Vale country.

Except on small or mainly grass farms, cereals occupy at least four-fifths of the tillage acreage in all districts and are commonly grown for periods of two to four years in succession, alternating with leys of variable duration and occasional crops of kale or roots. Where livestock farming is based on leys, a more or less regular rotation of 2–3 years of corn followed by 2–4 year's ley is often practiced, but elsewhere, particularly in the Hertfordshire Chilterns, the succession of corn crops is only punctuated by short-term leys which are mostly mown. There is generally a fairly even division between winter and spring corn sowings, with divergencies depending on season and soil, autumn-sown crops being preferred on the heavy soils of the Vale. The use of sprays to control weeds in cereal crops is steadily increasing, although bare fallowing is still quite common, especially in the Vale.

Only limited amounts of farmyard manure are produced on the average mixed farm and most of it is applied to kale and root crops, or to grassland intended for hay. Small quantities of sewage sludge are used locally and occasional crops of rape or mustard and of clover aftermath are ploughed in, but to a large extent the organic-matter status of the soils is dependent on the duration and management of leys. Fertilizers are now in general use and the average rates of application have increased steadily since the war, particularly on the Chilterns. A few farmers still use nitrogen alone and slag on occasions, but the majority use compound fertilizers and most of the larger farmers have combine drills. According to a Fertilizer Practice Survey carried out in the Chiltern district of Buckinghamshire in 1957, 90 per cent of all cereals and virtually all the spring barley received fertilizers, the average rates of application being $0 \cdot 33$ cwt. N, $0 \cdot 30$ cwt. P_2O_5 and $0 \cdot 40$ cwt. K_2O per acre. Similar dressings, amounting to rather less than 3 cwt. per acre of complete fertilizer at seeding time, are common practice in Hertfordshire also, but on the best corn-growing farms substantially heavier rates are used, and most autumn-sown crops receive an additional top-dressing of nitrogen in spring at rates up to $0 \cdot 60$ cwt. per acre.

Wheat and barley are now the chief cereal crops, wheat predominating in the Vale and barley elsewhere. Except on thin chalky soils, wheat is generally taken as the first crop after ley, while barley is favoured as a second or third straw crop. Oats and mixed corn for stock-feeding generally account for 11 to 15 per cent of the tillage acreage, but the proportion varies from 10 per cent in primarily arable parishes like Flamstead to over 40 per cent in Bierton-with-Broughton and Hulcott, where livestock husbandry is predominant and cash crops represent only a minor item in the average farm income. Cereal yields have greatly increased since pre-war years as a result of varietal improvements and the more widespread use of fertilizers. On typical mixed farms in the Hertfordshire group of Chiltern parishes, at least 29–30 cwt. per acre of winter wheat, 26–28 cwt. of barley and 24–25 cwt. of oats are commonly obtained. The thin chalky soils common on slopes in the Buckinghamshire Chilterns and in the Icknield Belt generally give somewhat lower yields, while on the more moisture-retentive soils of the Vale very heavy crops, particularly of wheat, are obtained in favourable seasons.

Potatoes account for less than one-half per cent of the total tillage acreage, and are largely confined to the eastern half of the area. In 1960 the chief potato-growing parishes were Redbourn (55 acres), Abbots Langley (44 acres), Edlesborough (39 acres) and Harpenden Rural (31 acres). Sugar beet, limited to a few acres in Harpenden Rural and Wendover, has never been an important crop.

Of the non-cereal crops grown for winter stock-feeding, kale is now by far the most popular and, together with cabbage, rape and other green crops, occupies considerably more than five times the acreage of beans and roots combined.

Kale is more often drilled than broadcast, little hand hoeing is done, and strip grazing of dairy cows on the growing crop is standard practice on many farms. Most of the Vale soils are well suited to beans, but weed-control difficulties and the prevalence of chocolate-spot disease in wet years have hastened the decline of this once important crop and only a small acreage is now grown. Turnips and swedes, mainly for sheep-feeding, are now encountered in only a few parishes, and mangolds are grown in very limited quantities, chiefly on dairy farms where little or no silage is made. As a rule, both root and green crops are more liberally manured than cereals, kale in particular commonly receiving at least 3 cwt. per acre of fertilizer, either compound or nitrogenous, in addition to a dressing of dung.

Arable crops grown for seed occupy only a very small acreage, but a few farms specialize in the production of herbage seeds, and a second cut for clover seed is sometimes taken from short-term leys.

Fruit, Vegetable and Salad Crops

Horticultural crops are not generally important and, apart from occasional nurseries and small-holdings devoted to vegetable or salad-crop production, are mainly concentrated in the south-east, where the cultivation of watercress has also long been established in the river valleys.

Orchards occupy about 1 per cent of the cultivated land, and are chiefly located on the Chiltern Plateau, notably at Ashley Green (218 acres), and on the fringe of the Vale from Edlesborough south-westwards to Aston Clinton. The orchards at Prestwood and in the country east of Chesham are mainly of cherries, which owing to the high cost of picking have tended to become an uneconomic crop. Many orchards thereabouts have been grubbed up in recent years, and in those which remain the trees are often old and many have been killed by bacterial canker. There are, however, some outstanding cherry orchards around Ashley Green, and both here and in the Langleys a number of orchards have been planted or replanted in recent years, chiefly with dessert apples, but also with plums, cherries and soft fruit.

In the scarp-foot zone there are a number of old orchards of the Aylesbury Prune, a small, black, late-maturing variety of plum, originally propagated by seedlings and suckers, and well adapted to the heavy calcareous soils of the district. Many such orchards were planted during the 19th century by small-holders whose major occupation was duck-rearing. Although the trees cropped prolifically only once every four or five years, they furnished a shady run for the breeding birds, while the fruit, formerly in demand as a source of dye, provided a useful additional income. Favourable returns were obtained from these old orchards during the 1939–45 war, but they are now on the decline and, as on the Chilterns, have been replaced to a limited extent by plantations of apples and plums, of which well-managed orchards exist at Cheddington.

Market-garden crops, including brassicas, peas, parsnips and beetroot, are grown to any appreciable extent only in Ashley Green, Bovingdon, Hemel Hempstead, Markyate and the Langleys, each of these parishes having between 50 and 100 acres under vegetables in 1960. A considerable proportion of the acreage is occupied by brussels sprouts, cabbages and peas grown in arable rotations, and intensive production is localized on a few specialized holdings, the largest lying between Ashley Green and Bovingdon.

Grassland

Despite the war-time increase in tillage, grass is still by far the most important crop on most farms, for even in those Chiltern parishes where the acreage of arable crops is highest, nearly half the agricultural land is under grass, and the proportion increases to over 75 per cent in the Vale. The proportion of grassland (excluding rough grazing) classed as "permanent" is also greatest in the Vale, and least in the Hertfordshire and Bedfordshire group of Chiltern parishes, where between 40 and 50 per cent of the total is represented by leys of varying duration. In all districts, however, a good deal of the "permanent" grass has been seeded down during the last fifteen years, either directly from old pasture, or after a period of arable cropping.

The management of permanent grassland has generally improved since the war; both nitrogenous and compound fertilizers are commonly used in addition to slag, and notable increases in productivity have resulted from liming and drainage, but odd fields or groups of fields with low-quality swards remain in most parishes. These fields, often without proper fences, include pastures, which are either understocked in the flush period or over-grazed and poached in winter and spring, and permanent meadows with no water supply, in which continual late mowing has depressed the clovers and encouraged the proliferation of tall-growing weeds, as well as accentuating manurial deficiencies. Throughout the area, apart from undergrazed chalk-land swards dominated by upright brome-grass (*Zerna erecta*), unimproved pastures and meadows usually contain bent-grasses (*Agrostis* spp.) and fine-leaved fescues (*Festuca ovina*, *F. rubra*) in varying proportions, with subsidiary species and weeds dependent on management, soil and drainage conditions. In the Vale, where the best old pastures are chiefly of ryegrass—*Agrostis*—white clover type, tufted hair grass, (*Deschampsia caespitosa*), meadow barley (*Hordeum secalinum*), red fescue and buttercups (*Ranunculus* spp.) are frequent contributors to the poorer swards and, where drainage is especially defective, sedges (less commonly rushes) and meadow-sweet (*Filipendula ulmaria*) are characteristic species of pastures and meadows respectively.

Over the whole area, short (1–1½ years) and long (3–4 years) leys occur in about equal proportions, the former predominating on mainly arable farms in the Chilterns and the latter in the Vale. Undersowing is still the favourite method of establishment, but the advantages of seeding long leys either alone or with a consumable nurse-crop of cereal or rape are appreciated by many dairy farmers, and this practice is gaining ground, especially in the Vale. Except where limitations are imposed by lack of water, both permanent and temporary grass are used either for grazing or for hay. Strip grazing behind an electric fence is now general practice, and on the more progressive dairy farms a variety of special-purpose leys are grown and managed with a view to providing a continuous supply of nutritious herbage for grazing and silage-making throughout the season. As a rule leys are more liberally fertilized than permanent grass; thus, according to the Fertilizer Practice Survey (1957), 68 per cent of the leys in the Chiltern district of Buckinghamshire received nitrogen, 43 per cent had phosphate and 42 per cent potash, whereas the corresponding figures for permanent grass were 29, 20 and 10 per cent.

The most popular mixture for short leys, used to give a break from cereals and to provide hay and a little grazing, is of Italian ryegrass and Broad Red clover, undersown with a spring corn crop. Special mixtures including Italian or H1 ryegrass, occasionally with rye, are also sometimes grown on dairy farms in the Chilterns for early bite, and are usually sown directly as a catch-crop in September for use the following spring. For long leys, relatively simple grass/white clover mixtures, containing either cocksfoot, timothy or meadow fescue as the dominant grass, are tending to supplant the old ryegrass—dominant mixtures. Lucerne is being grown on an increasing scale in the Chiltern and Icknield parishes, either alone or in admixture with cocksfoot or meadow fescue. Although used mainly for hay or silage, this crop is particularly valuable for late-summer grazing on the drier soils. Sainfoin is also well adapted to the dry, chalky soils of the Icknield Belt and the Buckinghamshire Chilterns, to which it is virtually indigenous, but only a limited acreage is grown at the present time, mainly on farms where sheep are kept.

Grass is conserved either as hay or silage, there being little artificial grass-drying in the area. Before the 1939–45 war, hay was an important cash crop, and on Hertfordshire farms was second only to wheat as a source of income (University of Cambridge, 1931), but most of it is now consumed on the farm. Silage, mainly from leys, is made, using buckrake or forage harvesters, on at least half the dairy and beef farms in the Chiltern district, but is less popular in the Vale. Pits or surface clamps predominate, and although self-feeding is not widely practiced it is becoming common to find the silage being made at the buildings, using a part of the Dutch barn as a covered silo.

Woods, Commons and "Rough Grazing": Semi-natural Vegetation

The total extent of woodland remains much as it was at the end of the 19th century, although the proportionate area under coniferous plantations has considerably increased, locally at the expense of agricultural land. The chief wooded areas lie on the slopes of the escarpment and on the higher parts of the Chiltern Plateau south-west of the Gade valley. West of a line through Dagnall and Berkhamsted the main type of woodland, apart from coniferous plantations, is high-forest dominated by beech (*Fagus sylvatica*), whereas the few woods east of this line are frequently of the coppice-with-standards type, with oak (chiefly *Quercus robur*) as the dominant canopy-forming tree.

Semi-natural vegetation other than woodland is represented on the escarpment and certain of the steeper valley sides by chalk grassland and scrub, and on the plateau by parts of the remaining commons, the most extensive of which, between Ivinghoe and Berkhamsted, are now included in the National Trust's Ashridge estate. Only a few of these commons have been intensively grazed in the present century, and as a result the majority show various stages in the natural succession from acidic grassland with bracken (*Pteridium equilinum*) to scrub and woodland, a process which has become more rapid since the rabbit population was greatly reduced by myxamatosis.

The invasion of former sheep-walks and commons by woody vegetation enabled Watt (1934) to elucidate the course of natural succession. Two seres (characterized respectively by hawthorn and juniper scrub) were recognized on the escarpment and four (A_0, A, B and C) on the acid soils of the plateau, each culminating in characteristic beechwood associations, later grouped by Tansley (1949) as follows:

Fagetum calcicolum: beechwoods on chalky soils, including sanicle and mercury types.

Fagetum rubosum: beechwoods on non-calcareous loams characterized by a field layer of brambles.

Fagetum ericetosum: beechwoods on podzolized loams and sands with impoverished, acidophile, ground-flora.

More recently, Brown (1953) and Avery (1958) have stressed the influence of exposure to westerly winds in modifying both vegetation and edaphic characteristics.

CHAPTER II

Soil Formation, Classification and Mapping

The formation and evolution of soils involves three main groups of processes, namely (1) addition and decay of organic residues; (2) physical and chemical weathering of the original rock material; (3) redistribution of soluble or finely dispersed constituents by soil-water movements.

(1) Wherever the ground is stabilized beneath a cover of vegetation, plant remains are continually being added to the surface and sub-surface layers, either directly or through animals, and are used as sources of food and energy by an interdependent population of soil-inhabiting organisms. Part of the organic material added to the soil normally undergoes oxidative decomposition (mineralization), with the result that the nitrogen and mineral nutrients it contains become available to nourish successive generations of plants, while part is transformed into dark-coloured humus which becomes more or less incorporated with the mineral particles, and decomposes in turn at a much slower rate. The amount of organic matter accumulated in or on the soil represents the balance between addition of residues and losses by mineralization, and this is governed in turn by the nature of the vegetation, and by various environmental factors, including moisture conditions, aeration, temperature, and nutrient supply, which regulate the composition and activity of the soil population.

(2) The mineral particles of the soil are also subject to more gradual disintegration and decomposition, and it is through these *weathering* processes that nutrient elements are released in forms available to plants. Except in initial stages of soil formation on hard rocks, where physical break-down predominates, the prime agent of weathering is rain-water charged with oxygen and carbon dioxide. As this acidulated water percolates through the soil it causes various reactions to take place at the surface of mineral particles: thus, fragments of chalk or limestone are gradually dissolved; micas and other minerals present in sedimentary rocks take up water molecules to form more hydrated minerals; ferrous and sulphide ions are oxidized; and primary silicate minerals such as feldspar are subject to hydrolysis, whereby alkali and alkaline-earth cations and silica pass into solution. The rates of decomposition vary greatly with the size and constitution of the particles concerned, but normally increase with the quantity and temperature of the percolating water.

(3) Wherever the annual rainfall exceeds evaporation, soluble products of weathering are removed in the drainage water, whilst other products, including clay minerals and hydrated ferric oxides, tend to accumulate, together with quartz and other resistant minerals inherited from the parent rock. The principal cations, calcium, magnesium, potassium and sodium, can be held in exchangeable form on the surface of clay and humus particles after being set free, but are relatively easily removed by continued leaching, so that unless they can be

replaced by weathering of less soluble minerals the soil tends to become acid in reaction. In addition to dissolved ions, clay minerals and other finely dispersed weathering products undergo downward translocation under certain conditions, but are generally redeposited in sub-surface horizons, where they are held either in fine pores, or by coagulation and drying on the surfaces of larger particles or fissures.

Restricted drainage, by hindering or preventing removal of decomposition products, affects the type and intensity of weathering and leads in particular to the prevalence of reducing processes. Well drained soils are normally characterized by free aeration, so that oxidizing conditions predominate, but where water stagnates in the soil for appreciable periods micro-organisms and plant roots use the dissolved oxygen as fast as it can be renewed. Under the anaerobic conditions so produced, accessible ferric ions are readily dissolved and reduced to the ferrous state, either by microbial action or by direct reaction with soluble products of plant decomposition (Bloomfield, 1951). This process, known as *gleying*, causes the development of grey or bluish colours in contrast to the characteristic browns and reds of ferric oxides formed in well drained soils by oxidative weathering. As the reduced iron compounds are relatively soluble, they tend to migrate in the soil, either in seepage water or by capillary diffusion towards zones of higher moisture tension, and where waterlogging is intermittent are commonly re-oxidised to form ochreous deposits or concretions which impart a mottled appearance to the layers concerned. Manganese, if present in appreciable amounts, is similarly subject to mobilization and redeposition (as manganese dioxide) in seasonally waterlogged soils.

The weathering and translocation processes affecting the inorganic fraction of the soil are intensified to varying degrees by the solvent action of plant roots and of organic acids and other compounds derived from plant residues. Concurrently, however, plant roots are continually removing nutrient elements and other products of weathering including silica from the subsoil and incorporating them in their leaves and stems, which are eventually returned to the surface. By this means the vegetation produces a continuous circulation of mineral substances in the soil, and so counteracts to some extent their removal by leaching. In many soils earthworms and other burrowing mammals also bring material to the surface and so, in effect, oppose the processes of removal.

The Soil Profile

The continual interaction of these processes is reflected in the differentiation of more or less distinct *soil horizons*, roughly parallel to the surface, which may differ from each other in such features as colour, texture, structure, type and amount of organic matter, degree of root development, or faunal activity. The whole system of layers lying within the zone penetrated by plant roots constitutes the *soil profile*, and the material in which the soil horizons have developed is termed the parent material. The relatively unaltered material below can sometimes be regarded as equivalent to the parent material: commonly, however, the soil horizons appear either to have developed in material different from that lying immediately below, or to be superimposed on a vertical succession of differing materials, forming what is called a composite profile.

SOIL SURVEY METHODS

In order to describe or to map the soils of a given area, it is necessary to adopt some form of classification. Although soils may be classified in many different ways, all modern systems of classification and mapping have in common the recognition of the soil profile as the unit of study. In making a soil survey, profiles are examined in pits, auger borings and exposed sections, and information is assembled on relationships between soil properties and other features of the terrain, including land-form, vegetation and geological structure. On the basis of these observations the soils are grouped into mapping units, each characterized by a limited and defined range of profile variation.

The principal mapping unit used in England and Wales for detailed surveys is the *soil series*, defined as a group of soils showing the same or similar succession of horizons in the profile, developed in lithologically similar parent material. In establishing soil series, emphasis is given to relatively permanent features of the profile, such as texture and subsoil characters, and not to ephemeral or transitory features, like the differences in nutrient status, pH and organic-matter content caused by recent fertilization, liming and other cultural practices. It will be appreciated, therefore, that when some soils of a given series have remained under semi-natural vegetation, whilst others have been cultivated more or less intensively for long periods, the upper horizons in particular will vary considerably in both morphology and constitution. The immediate productivity of the soils may also vary widely, depending on recent management history, but areas of the same series, if properly delimited, should present similar problems in management, and respond similarly to weather conditions and cultural practices.

Each established soil series is given a geographic name from a locality where it was first described or is well represented. When appreciable variations in surface texture occur within a series, subdivisions (sometimes referred to as soil types) may be distinguished on this basis and named accordingly (e.g. Wicken clay loam; Wicken clay). Other subdivisions of a series, based on such features as thickness of horizons (including depth to bedrock), average slope, or degree of accelerated erosion, are referred to as *phases* (e.g. deep phase; steep phase; eroded phase). In the present survey the term "phase" has also been applied to variants resulting from differences in land use (e.g. woodland phase, grassland phase; arable phase).

Once the main mapping units have been established by a preliminary reconnaissance, the boundaries between them are determined by boring at frequent intervals with a three-foot auger, and plotted on 6 in./1 mile O.S. maps. The sites of each auger boring and profile pit are also recorded, using appropriate symbols to indicate soil series, surface texture, stoniness, degree of slope and subsoil features. In rolling or hilly landscapes the chief soil boundaries are generally associated with changes in slope and, once the relationships between land-form and soil have been recognized, the lines of traverse may be chosen accordingly. Changes in semi-natural vegetation may also afford guides to boundary location, but on flat or gently undulating, cultivated land reliance has usually to be placed on a regularly spaced pattern of auger borings in each field. Where the soil pattern is so complicated that delimitation of individual soil series is impracticable at the scale used, the areas concerned are mapped as *soil complexes*, and characterized in terms of the constituent series and their proportionate extent. When the survey of the area is complete a draft soil map is prepared on the 1/25,000 (2½ in. to 1 mile) scale, and reduced to the 1 in. to 1 mile scale for publication. Not all the boundaries inserted on the field sheets can be reproduced at this scale, and normally only soil series and complexes are shown separately on the published map.

In order to characterize the soil series, types and phases recognized, representative sites are selected and profile pits dug, generally to a depth of about 4 ft. At each site the location, slope (in degrees), aspect, altitude, land use and vegetation are recorded, and the profile is described in standard terms. The depth, thickness and clarity of recognizable horizons are first noted, and the colour, texture, stoniness, consistence and structure of each horizon are then recorded in turn, together with the kind and distribution of organic matter, the presence and amount of calcium carbonate and secondary mineral deposits, and the distribution of soil fauna and roots. Finally, the parent material and drainage status of the soil may be deduced from a consideration of profile and site characteristics.

The methods and terms used in profile descriptions are based, with slight modifications, on the usage laid down in the U.S.D.A. Soil Survey Manual (Soil Survey Staff, 1951). Soil colours are described using the names and symbols of Munsell Colour Charts designed for this purpose, and textural class names are based on the estimated proportions of sand (2·0–0·05 mm.), silt (0·05–0·002 mm.) and clay (<0·002 mm.) particle-size grades in the inorganic fraction of the soil passing a 2 mm. sieve. Twelve basic textural classes are recognized, and Fig. 9 shows the particle-size distribution range of each class. These basic class names may be modified by adjectival additions indicating the predominant size-grade within the sand fraction (e.g. fine sandy loam; coarse sandy loam), the kind and quantity of stones (e.g. flinty clay; very pebbly loam), or the presence of more than about 13 per cent of organic matter (e.g. humose loam; peaty clay loam). Further details of soil-colour and texture determinations are given in the appendix (p. 205), together with the methods and terms used in describing the depth and clarity of horizons, stoniness, structure and consistency.

To confirm and supplement field observations and to assist in the characterization of mapping units, samples are taken from each horizon of representative profiles for analysis. In this survey, determinations of particle-size distribution (mechanical analysis), pH and calcium carbonate (where present) were made on all samples. Other investigations, carried out on selected profiles, include determinations of carbon and nitrogen (in upper horizons), exchangeable cations, percentage base-saturation, total and citric-soluble phosphate, potash-supplying power, free ferric oxide and clay-mineral content.

Soil-drainage Classes

Drainage, as a condition of the soil, refers to the frequency and duration of periods when the profile is wholly or partly saturated with water. This quality is determined by the rapidity and extent of removal of water by surface run-off (external drainage) and by downward percolation (internal drainage), by the general balance of rainfall and evaporation, and by the proximity of subterranean zones of permanent saturation.

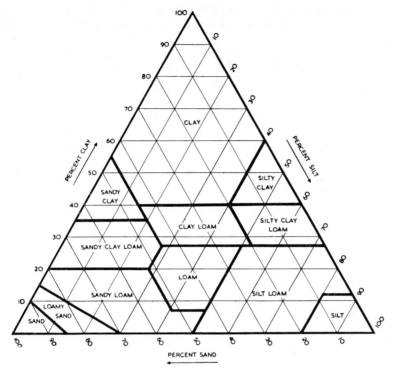

Fig. 9. Soil Texture Diagram

Soil drainage may be assessed in the field by inference from relief and profile morphology, coupled with direct observations of moisture conditions at different periods of the year. In making such an assessment, emphasis is placed on the presence and intensity of mottling and/or grey colours produced by gleying at different levels in the profile, and it is assumed that these effects afford valid comparative indications of differing drainage in profiles of similar constitution. Thus, permanently waterlogged soil horizons are normally pale grey or bluish in colour, depending on the extent to which ferrous compounds have been removed by seepage or accumulated *in situ*, whereas periodically waterlogged horizons are characterized by variegated colours, including ochreous and greyish mottlings, which more or less mask inherited colours and form a pattern related to structural faces and root channels. In interpreting these morphological features, it is important to recognize that for gleying to take place the presence of organic reducing agents is required, and that the colour effects produced vary greatly with the texture, structure and permeability of the soil material, and with the amount and nature of the iron-bearing minerals originally present. There is also evidence that iron is mobilized more readily at lower pH values, so that gley effects may be less marked in calcareous soils than in acid soils of similar texture and drainage status. A further consideration is that where drainage has been improved, either naturally or artificially, the profile may still show features, such as rust stains and mottles, indicative of its former condition. It is therefore necessary, particularly when dealing with agricultural soils, to take account of all available lines of evidence, and to avoid placing undue reliance on morphological features which may be unrelated to the contemporary drainage status of the soil.

On the basis of these observations it is possible to distinguish a sequence of *drainage classes*, ranging from excessive to very poor. Definitions of the six classes recognized in this memoir are given below.*

Excessively drained: water is removed from the soil rapidly, and the amount retained is such that growth of crop plants is severely limited by drought in most seasons†: the soil is often loose or very friable, with a low earthworm population, and may have a high content of organic matter. This class includes shallow soils over hard rock, often on steep slopes, and soils developed on very porous, coarse-textured materials.

Well drained: water is removed from the soil readily but sufficient is retained to allow normal growth of crops and grass except in drought periods. Well drained soils are normally deep and free of mottling throughout the profile (or to at least three feet); they are usually of medium texture, but some fine-textured soils with pervious substrata are included in this class.

Moderately well drained: water is removed from the soil somewhat slowly, so that a part of the root zone may remain saturated for limited periods. Colours typical of the corresponding well drained soil are dominant, but some ochreous and/or paler-coloured mottling is normally present below about 18 in. Soils of this class may be of any texture, but where fine-textured either occur on slopes or have relatively permeable substrata.

Imperfectly drained: water is removed from the soil slowly, so that parts of the root zone remain saturated for significant periods in most seasons, but permanent waterlogging occurs only at depths below about 24 in. Imperfectly drained soils typically show distinct ochreous and/or pale-coloured mottling below about 12 in. and, if not fine-textured, have a relatively impervious layer or a fluctuating water-table at moderate depths. They normally benefit from artificial drainage and often support productive grassland when well managed.

Poorly drained: water is removed from the soil so slowly that the root zone remains saturated for a considerable part of the year, and permanent water-logging may occur below about 18 in. Poorly drained soils normally show pro-nounced ochreous and/or grey mottling throughout the profile. Artificial drainage is necessary for satisfactory crop production and semi-natural vegetation includes hydrophilous species. A high water-table, a very slowly permeable subsoil, addi-tions through seepage, or some combination of these conditions, may be responsible for poor drainage.

Very poorly drained: the soil remains more or less permanently saturated with water, and semi-natural vegetation is of a markedly hydrophilous character. Soils of this class are mainly confined to depressions and wet flushes, and normally have highly organic surface horizons overlying a grey mineral subsoil with or without ochreous mottling. In their natural state they are typically suited only to summer grazing, but their drainage has often been artificially improved.

---

* These drainage classes differ from those in the Field Handbook of the Soil Survey of Great Britain by the inclusion of an additional class, the legend of the map having been decided upon before the Handbook definitions were finalised.

† These indications of plant behaviour refer specifically to conditions in the survey area.

GENESIS AND CLASSIFICATION OF THE SOILS

The properties of the soil at any particular place depend partly on the physical and mineralogical constitution of the parent materials; partly on past and present environmental factors, including climate, vegetation and hydrologic conditions, which regulate the nature and intensity of the soil-forming processes; and partly on the length of time these processes have operated, as governed by the geomorphic history of the land surface concerned.

Under natural conditions the evolution of the soil is closely related to that of the vegetation it supports, both soil and vegetation tending towards a state of equilibrium or *climax*, the nature of which is dependent on climate and physiography. In long-settled landscapes, however, the natural equilibrium between soil, vegetation and other organisms has everywhere been disturbed to a greater or lesser extent by the operations of farming and forestry, and the results of such disturbance are reflected in the soil profile, the upper horizons in particular taking on new characteristics which more or less mask the effects of the primitive vegetation and depend in turn on past and present land use. The replacement of forest by grassland, for example, is attended by considerable changes in the seasonal cycle of moisture and temperature conditions in the surface layers, and in the amount and type of organic residues added to the soil, each of which affects the activities of the soil population and hence the quantity and distribution of accumulated humus. When land is brought into cultivation, the upper horizons are mixed to the depth of ploughing, increased aeration promotes more rapid mineralization of organic residues, and the surface becomes liable to accelerated erosion. Forestry practices, involving modification of the structure and composition of essentially natural woods, and the planting of introduced species, also affect the evolution of the soil, mainly through their influence on the organic cycle and on the type of litter produced.

In this area, as in most of Lowland Britain, climatic conditions are relatively uniform, and the variations in such features as texture, calcium-carbonate content, and subsoil characters, which have been used to distinguish soil series, arise chiefly from the integrated effects of geological and geomorphological factors. Although soils formed *in situ* from the "solid" rocks are of limited extent, these formations everywhere influence soil characteristics, not only by their contribution to the superficial deposits, but also through their variable permeability, which in conjunction with the configuration of the land has largely determined the hydrologic conditions under which the profiles have developed. Differences in parent material and relief also affect the incidence of natural or accelerated erosion, and hence the extent to which horizon development has been inhibited or retarded by removal of material from the surface or by addition of fresh material. Finally, the materials giving rise to the soils have been exposed to the action of soil-forming processes for greatly varying lengths of time, and this is reflected in different degrees of weathering and profile development.

Since all the soils are derived, directly or indirectly, from sedimentary rocks, the materials composing them have already passed through at least one weathering cycle, with the result that primary silicate minerals are rare and play little part in soil formation. Certain of the deposits, notably the Upper Greensand rocks, contain silt or sand-size grains of minerals such as glauconite, mica and feldspar which are capable of yielding clay and/or iron oxides by weathering. For the most part, however, the chief processes affecting transformation of the parent materials are solution of calcium carbonate; oxidation, reduction and translocation of iron-containing minerals; and alteration and translocation of clay minerals present in the original deposits.

Variations in the degree of weathering or of horizon development arise mainly from differences in the constitution and permeability of the parent materials, but may also result from differences in the geomorphic history of the associated land-forms. Thus, profiles in recently deposited alluvium or "rainwash", or on slopes subject to erosion, rarely show well defined soil horizons attributable to weathering and leaching *in situ*, whereas older superficial deposits commonly exhibit clearly differentiated profiles and often appear weathered to depths well below the root zone. Many such deposits, including the Plateau Drift and the older Coombe Deposits, were presumably subjected to weathering in one or more interglacial periods, and may retain the contemporaneous soil horizons. Similarly, much of the Clay-with-flints appears to represent an old soil horizon formed at the expense of dissolved chalk beneath a cover of drift. It seems unlikely, however, that soils formed before the penultimate (Saale) glaciation have anywhere escaped erosion, although some may have been only truncated, and the remaining horizons buried beneath newer deposits. There is also evidence from this and other areas (Hey and Perrin, 1960), that the periglacial conditions obtaining during the last glaciation caused widespread frost heaving and removal of earlier-formed soils by solifluxion. On much of the flat or gently sloping land, however, there was probably no wholesale removal or addition of material, so that profiles in such situations may bear the impress of the fluctuating environmental conditions represented by the last interglacial period, the succeeding cold period, and the mainly temperate climate of postglacial times.

Superimposed on the effects of geological and geomorphological factors are those of varying vegetation and land use during the period of some 5,000 years that has elapsed since Neolithic farmers began to modify and destroy the natural vegetation. Soil variations related to past and present differences in land use are especially pronounced in the district under review, for while some of the Chiltern soils carry old-established beech and beech-oak woods approximating to the natural climax, other soils, especially in the Vale, have been long under grass, and others again have been cultivated more or less regularly for a thousand years or more.

In addition to the effects of cultivation, manuring and chalking, and of maintenance under grass, many of the agricultural soils in the Chilterns have come to differ markedly from their semi-natural counterparts on similar sites as a result of accelerated erosion. Thus, the Clay-with-flints which mantles the Chalk on upper slopes and spurs is normally covered in ancient woodland by a layer of flinty loam, whereas in adjoining long-cultivated fields the profile has commonly been truncated by erosion, so exposing the clay subsoil or, where this is thin, the chalk below. Further evidence of this process is afforded by the occurrence of marked declivities in association with field boundaries following the contour. On the lower side of such boundaries is eroded soil consisting virtually of bare chalk or raw clay, whilst on the upper side there is an accumulation of top-soil material derived from further up-slope.

Photograph by Aerofilms and Aero Pictorial Ltd.

Plate I. Hawridge Vale, an asymmetrical dry valley north of Chesham. Batcombe soils in the right foreground. Winchester soils in the fields sloping to the road, and Coombe soils on the steeper opposing slopes.

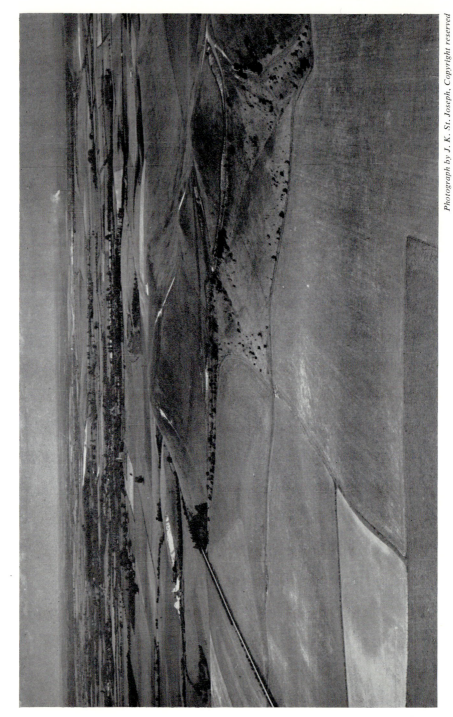

Plate II. The Icknield Belt north-east of Ivinghoe. Beacon Hill (centre) represents a degraded outlier of the Chiltern Plateau, projecting as a bastion between the Tring and Dagnall Gaps.

Plate III. Flooding on Mead soils along the Thistle Brook, north of Aylesbury.

Photograph by Aerofilms and Aero Pictorial Ltd.

Plate IVa. The site of a deserted village at Tiscott, north of Long Marston. A variant of the Wicken series with a very thick, dark-coloured A horizon was identified in and around the site.

Plate IVb. Coombe Hole, near Ivinghoe. Arable land on the Icknield and Wantage series.

In the Vale country, with its gentler slopes and heavier soils, there is comparatively little evidence of accelerated erosion, but the former practice of ploughing in narrow, high-backed 'lands' has resulted in appreciable modification of the original surface, and in most cases the water relationships of the soils have been altered to some extent by artificial drainage.

TYPES OF SOIL FORMATION

In order to facilitate discussion and comparison of soils it is convenient to designate profile horizons by a letter notation, the same symbol being applied to analogous horizons in profiles of similar type. The notation adopted in this memoir is as follows:

Organic and organo-mineral surface horizons

L	Undecomposed litter.
F	Partially decomposed litter.
H	Well-decomposed humus layer, low in mineral matter.
A	Mixed, mineral-organic layer.
Ap	Ploughed layer of cultivated soils.
Ag	An A horizon with rusty mottling, subject to periodic waterlogging.

Sub-surface horizons

E*	Eluvial horizon, depleted of clay and/or sesquioxides.
Ea	Bleached (ash-like) horizon in podzolized soils.
Eb	Brown (paler when dry), friable, weak-structured horizon depleted of clay, characteristic of *sols lessivés*.
(B)	Altered horizon without appreciable depletion of, or illuvial enrichment in, colloidal material; distinguished from the overlying A horizon and from underlying C horizons of less altered material by colour and structure.
B	Altered horizon containing illuviated material.
Bt	Horizon containing illuviated clay, characteristic of *sols lessivés*.
Bh	In podzolized soils, the horizon of maximum deposition of humus.
Bfe	In podzolized soils, the horizon of maximum deposition of iron.
C†	A horizon that is little altered, except by gleying, and is either like or unlike the material in which overlying horizons have developed (where two or more distinct depositional horizons occur in the lower part of the profile, they are designated C1, C2, etc.).
Cca	A C horizon containing appreciable amounts of redeposited (secondary) calcium carbonate.
(B)g Cg }etc.	Mottled (gleyed) horizons subject to waterlogging: where gleying is only weakly expressed the suffix (g) is used.
A/C (B)/C }etc.	Horizons of transitional or intermediate character.

Because of similarities in parent material or mode of origin, profiles characteristic of different soil series often have important features in common, and by selecting certain of these features it is possible to distinguish a limited number

---

* Such horizons have been commonly designated A_2.

† The C horizon, as here defined, includes contrasting layers of material that have been commonly designated D.

of profile types, or *types of soil formation*, which can serve as a basis for classification into higher categories. In this area ten chief types of soil formation may be recognized (see Plate V), and these fall in turn into four *major soil groups*, designated in Britain as calcareous soils, brown earths, podzols and gley soils respectively. Relationships between soil series, types of soil formation, major soil groups and parent geological materials are shown in Table 7, and the distribution of major groups in Fig. 10 (p. 55).

The morphology and genesis of the types of soil formation included in each major group will now be discussed. Soils of the podzol group occupy very limited areas, and are conveniently considered in relation to those of the brown earth group with which they are closely associated.

TABLE 7

Major Soil Groups and Types of Soil Formation in relation to Soil Series and Parent Materials

Major Soil Group	Type of Soil Formation	Parent Material (Substratum)	Soil Series*
Calcareous	Rendzina	Chalk Chalk Marl Portlandian Limestone	Icknield Wantage Aylesbury
	Brown calcareous soil	Chalky Coombe Deposits Thin, flinty clay Head over Chalk Clayey drift over Coombe-Rock or chalky gravel	Coombe Wallop Tring
	Gley calcareous soil	Coombe Deposits locally gravelly, over Chalk Marl Chalk Marl and associated chalky Head Chalky-Gravel Head	Halton Burwell Gubblecote
Brown Earth	*Sol lessivé*	Non-calcareous or decalcified Coombe Deposits Clay-with-flints High-level Gravels	Charity Winchester St. Albans
	Gleyed *sol lessivé*	Plateau Drift (loamy clay with flints and pebbles) Plateau Drift (Pebbly Clay and Sand) Reading Beds sand with clayey seams	Batcombe Berkhamsted Bursledon
	Undifferentiated (colluvial) brown earth	Loamy Head over dry-valley gravel	Nettleden
	Gleyed grey siliceous soil	Fine sandy micaceous marl with interbedded malmstone Glauconitic marl and clayey sand	Harwell Ardington
Podzol	Humus-iron podzol	Pebbly Clay and Sand or High-level Gravel	Southampton
Gley	Clayey gley soil	Gault clay, superficially re-worked Clayey Head over Gault Kimmeridge (or Gault) clay, superficially re-worked	Wicken Challow Denchworth

TABLE 7 (*continued*)

Major Soil Group	Type of Soil Formation	Parent Material (Substratum)	Soil Series*
Gley	Gley soil with clay substratum	Loamy sand and sandy clay (Portlandian) over Kimmeridge Clay	Bierton
		Chalky-gravel Head over Gault	Weston Turville
		Loamy (locally gravelly) Head over Kimmeridge or Gault clay	Rowsham
		Pebbly Head over Eocene clay	Cowcroft
	Calcareous alluvial gley soil	Silty alluvium over flint gravel	Gade
		Chalky alluvium over clay or marl	Ford End
		Clayey alluvium	Mead

* Only 12 series are shown separately on the soil map (see Table 8, p. 60).

Soils of the Calcareous Group

This major group comprises well drained and moderately well drained, base-saturated soils occurring on limestones and other calcareous materials. As there is a general tendency in humid climates for calcium carbonate to be leached from the surface horizons, the soils are commonly associated with young or relatively unstable land-forms (e.g. steep slopes), and are most widespread on soft, highly calcareous rocks like chalk and marl.

The most distinctive members of the group are shallow soils of the type known as *rendzina* (Plate V, 1), occurring in the survey area on Chalk (Icknield series), Chalk Marl (Wantage series), and soft Portlandian limestone (Aylesbury series). Typical rendzinas under woodland or old grassland have very dark-coloured A horizons with a well defined granular or fine, sub-angular blocky structure, passing into a more or less brashy transition layer (A/C horizon) which grades into the underlying rock. Where sufficiently moisture-retentive, rendzinas are favourable to both earthworms and microbial activity, so that under woodland the litter is rapidly incorporated and decomposed within the soil: neither F nor H layers are normally developed, and the humose A horizons are of mull* type. The dark-coloured, base-saturated humus formed under these conditions is resistant to mineralization, and is strongly bound to the clay fraction in water-stable granular aggregates. Very shallow, clay-deficient rendzinas on hard chalk or limestone are generally too dry for earthworms to flourish, with the result that smaller animals, including insect larvae, millipedes and ants, play a major part in comminuting and ingesting plant residues. In such situations, the humose A horizons are frequently of a type called mull-like rendzina moder by Kubiena (1953): the organic-matter content (present partly as recognizable plant remains and partly as animal droppings) is higher than in typical calcareous mull; the structural aggregates are finer, softer and more crumb-like, and there is little formation of clay-humus complexes.

---

* Well aerated crumbly mineral-organic surface horizons with a diffuse lower boundary, resulting largely from the activity of earthworms.

In this area, uncultivated rendzinas are mainly confined to the Chalk escarpment, where they are associated with sanicle beechwood (Watt, 1934), calcicolous scrub, or semi-natural basic grassland. Where similar soils have been long under cultivation, the organic-matter content of the A horizon is greatly reduced, and the surface appears almost white when dry, especially in situations subject to erosion. The rendzinas on Chalk Marl and Portlandian limestone are almost entirely in agricultural use, and are typically deeper, less friable and more moisture-retentive than the white Chalk soils.

Besides rendzinas, the calcareous group as here defined includes well drained soils with brown-coloured (B) horizons (brown calcareous soils) and moderately well drained to imperfectly drained soils (gley-calcareous soils) transitional to the gley group.

Brown calcareous soils (Plate V, 2) are essentially intermediate in character between rendzinas and leached brown soils from which carbonates, if originally present, have been completely removed. Soils of this type are widely developed in the deeper Chiltern valleys and along the Icknield Belt, either on younger chalky Coombe Deposits (Coombe series) or on thin, irregular spreads of flinty Head with a loamy or clayey matrix (Wallop series). The occurrence of a distinct brown or reddish-coloured sub-surface layer, or (B) horizon, which distinguishes them from typical rendzinas, may be attributed, on the one hand, to partial decalcification and weathering *in situ*, and on the other to the presence of disturbed remains of older weathered horizons, more or less incorporated with the calcareous substratum. Under woodland the soils have dark-coloured, well-structured A horizons similar to those of rendzinas, although in some cases the upper few inches are non-calcareous and slightly acid. Complete leaching of carbonates, followed by progressive acidification of the upper horizons, is accompanied by the development of thinner and less strongly aggregated A horizons and by indications of clay migration, leading to the gradual differentiation of a Bt horizon. Generally, however, the tendency to decalcification is offset by the activity of soil fauna in bringing finely divided chalk to the surface, coupled on cultivated land with the effects of tillage and accelerated erosion.

The term *gley-calcareous soil* has been applied to greyish, medium to fine-textured, rendzina-like soils (Halton and Gubblecote series), developed for the most part on chalky drift which overlies relatively impervious marl or clay. The profiles (Plate V, 3) have very dark greyish brown or grey, calcareous A horizons, followed by greyish brown or light olive-brown, A/C or weakly developed (B) horizons with blocky structure. The chalky subsoil material (C(g) horizon) shows ochreous mottling, resulting apparently from periodic waterlogging.

Soils of the Brown Earth and Podzol Groups

The brown earth group includes well drained and moderately well drained, more or less acid soils with uniformly coloured (generally brown), well aerated sub-surface horizons from which any native calcium carbonate has been leached. Soils with these features in common occur on a variety of pervious materials in humid, temperate regions where moderate leaching is accompanied by an active organic cycle, involving rapid decomposition and incorporation of surface litter. Under these conditions, the clay content of the soil tends to be augmented by weathering of silicate minerals, whilst hydrated ferric oxides, produced by weathering of iron-containing minerals or by oxidation of ferrous-organic complexes, accumulate *in situ* to give characteristic brown colours, more or less masked in the A horizon by incorporated humus. In relatively young brown earths, especially those derived from rocks containing an abundance of readily weatherable silicate minerals, the profile consists typically of A, (B) and C horizons, the crumbly, humose A horizon grading into a brown, weathered subsoil or (B) horizon which merges into the parent rock. But wherever appreciable amounts of fine clay have been produced by weathering or inherited from the parent material, there is a tendency, especially marked where the soil dries out seasonally, for clay-size particles (including ferric oxides) to migrate from the upper horizons in percolating water and to accumulate at lower levels as coatings on cleavage faces and in conducting channels. Continuance of this process leads to the differentiation of brown or yellowish, weak-structured Eb horizons which become paler in colour when dry, followed by denser, finer-textured and brighter-coloured Bt horizons with blocky or prismatic structure. Soils of the brown earth group with texturally differentiated profiles of this type have been distinguished in France and other European countries as *sols lessivés* (Duchaufour, 1960),* and in Britain as "leached brown soils" (Avery, 1956). In contrast to podzolization, the process of eluviation leading to the formation of *sols lessivés* appears to operate under conditions of moderate acidity (pH 5·0–6·0) and is not attended by any appreciable decomposition of the clay fraction, the chemical constitution of which remains nearly constant throughout the profile. Soils of *lessivé* character are frequently derived from calcareous sediments (e.g. loess, Coombe Deposits) as a result of continued leaching, the differentiation of Eb and Bt horizons apparently following complete decalcification and consequent desaturation of the absorbing complex.

Brown earths form naturally under deciduous forest which, by effecting an active circulation of bases from the subsoil to the surface by way of the leaf fall, helps to counteract the leaching of the soil and to promote the maintenance of a mull humus layer, characterized by a high level of faunal and microbial activity. As a rule, however, the A horizons under woodland are thinner than in calcareous mull, well-decomposed humus accumulates in smaller amounts, and the structural aggregates are smaller, more crumb-like, and less stable to water.

Where the soil has become strongly acid, the activity of earthworms in particular is greatly reduced, with the result that more or less humified residues accumulate at the surface, forming L, F and H horizons which are described collectively as mor.† The acid humus formed under these conditions does not

---

* Similar soils in North America have been classed as "gray-brown podzolic" or as "red-yellow podzolic" (depending on the colour, base status and degree of weathering of the Bt horizon) but, as true podzolization appears to play little part in their development, these names have not been generally accepted in Western Europe.

† In typical mor, as found under coniferous forest and occasionally under beech, the superficial organic layers are sharply separated from the mineral soil, and consist largely of partially decomposed litter: the F horizon is therefore strongly developed, and the H horizon relatively thin. Humose layers of a type intermediate between mull and mor, called moder in Western Europe (Kubiena, 1953; Duchaufour, 1960), are common in deciduous woods on well drained, acid soils: although few earthworms are present, decomposition of the litter is more rapid than in typical mor, and the activity of small Arthropods causes the formation of a black friable H horizon in which plant fragments, animal droppings and mineral grains are more or less intimately mixed, merging into a thin humose A horizon with a clear lower boundary.

form stable complexes with the clay, fraction, and water percolating through the slowly decomposing litter extracts soluble organic compounds (which under mull conditions are either quickly decomposed or rendered insoluble by polymerisation) capable of reacting with ferric oxide and with aluminium derived by break-down of clay minerals to give metal-organic complexes which readily migrate in the soil. Continuance of this process leads to the development beneath the superficial organic layer of a bleached, ash-like Ea horizon from which iron and aluminium have been leached, followed by more or less well defined Bh and/or Bfe horizons in which humus and/or iron and aluminium have been redeposited. Soils showing these horizons are classed in the *podzol* group, and are mainly confined to coarse-textured materials rich in quartz. Advanced podzolization may take place under oak or beech (Dimbleby and Gill, 1935; Mackney, 1961), but in Southern England the occurrence of well developed podzols can often be associated with invasion of formerly forested areas by *Calluna* heath, following occupation by early agriculturalists in Neolithic and Bronze Age times.

Most brown earths in Lowland Britain have been modified by centuries of farming, so that the structure and base status of the upper horizons, as well as the amount, nature and distribution of organic matter, are largely determined by past and present land use; added lime is often present, and in many places the original profile has been truncated by erosion, or buried beneath recently accumulated colluvium or "field-wash".

Where well developed podzols have been reclaimed for agriculture, some part of the B horizon(s), at least, generally survive beneath the ploughed layer, but weakly podzolized soils of transitional character, in which morphological evidence of podzolization is confined to the upper few inches, rapidly lose their identity when cultivated, and can usually be distinguished only by the presence of bleached sand grains.

In the survey area, soils of the brown earth group are chiefly confined to the Chilterns, where they are widely developed on Plateau Drift (Batcombe and Berkhamsted series), Clay-with-flints (Winchester series) and non-calcareous or decalcified Coombe Deposits (Charity series). On all these materials the uneroded soils are predominantly of *lessivé* type, with loamy Eb horizons up to 18 in. thick. Immediately below the Eb horizon there is commonly a transitional zone (Eb/Bt horizon) in which the structural aggregates (peds) have sandy or silty coatings indicative of clay removal, followed at lower levels by a layer (Bt horizon) showing marked concentrations of clay-size material as pore-fillings and as oriented coatings on structural faces. In certain cases, notably on chalky Coombe Deposits, the characteristic texture profile seems to result simply from continued leaching and downward translocation of clay, and the horizons are designated accordingly as A, Eb, Bt and C. On Plateau Drift and Clay-with-flints, however, the profiles generally appear composite in origin, the upper horizons having developed in a loess-containing superficial deposit, and the lower in weathered substrata which may represent the truncated or disturbed remains of older soil formations (Avery *et al.*, 1959; Loveday, 1962). These lower weathered horizons normally show signs of clay illuviation and evidently correspond in part to the Bt horizons of *sols lessivés* developed in originally uniform materials.

The soils on Coombe Deposits (Plate V, 4) are normally well drained, and the subsoils are characterized by uniform brown or reddish colours. On thick Plateau Drift, however, drainage is impeded to some extent, especially on level sites, and the subsoils are typically mottled with yellow, grey and red at depths below 18 in. Profiles of this type (Plate V, 5) with characteristics transitional to those of the gley group, are classed as gleyed brown earths (*sols lessivés*).

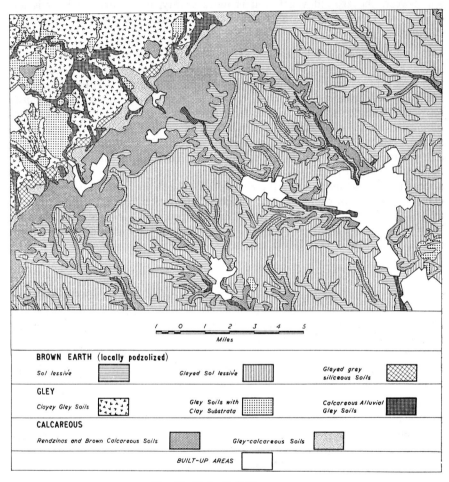

Fig. 10. Major Soil Groups

Under semi-natural beechwoods, both plateau and valley soils are moderately to strongly acid (pH 5·5–4·0) at the surface, and exhibit variations in humus form, degree of leaching, and horizon development which are associated with differences in vegetation. These variations are frequently correlated in turn with differences in parent material or substratum, but are also conditioned by factors such as density of canopy, aspect, and exposure to wind, each of which may affect biological activity on the forest floor by influencing soil moisture and temperature conditions and by regulating the character of the subordinate vegetation (Brown, 1953; Avery, 1958). Thus, mull humus layers are commonest on sloping and valley sites where chalky substrata are encountered at moderate depths and the soils have a relatively high base status. In woods on such sites, corresponding to Watt's (1934) seres A_0 and A, the field layer is commonly dominated by luxuriant brambles (*Rubus spp.*), accompanied by a variety of herbs (e.g. *Asperula odorata, Galeobdolon luteum, Circaea lutetiana*). In dense shade, however, and on exposed slopes and woodland edges exposed to the south-west, the ground vegetation is more scanty, earthworm activity is less evident, and mor formation is common, even where the subsoil is rich in calcium.

On the thicker drift of the plateau, profiles under old-established woods are low in bases throughout (Watt's seres B and C). Mor is of frequent occurrence under mature stands of both beech and oak and is typically accompanied by an impoverished ground flora including such acidophile species as *Deschampsia flexuosa*. Beneath the superficial organic horizons there is usually some morphological evidence of podzolization, but well developed podzols (Southampton series: Plate V, 10) only occur locally on appreciably sandy materials, mainly at the margins of ridges where the surface is often exceedingly stony and strongly depleted of clay. In such situations the characteristic podzol horizons generally appear to have formed within the Eb horizon of a former *sol lessivé* profile, the clayey Bt horizon of which has undergone disintegration from the top downwards as a result of intense eluviation. Elsewhere, with surface horizons of loam or silt loam texture, bleaching is confined to the uppermost inch or so of mineral soil, and the profiles may be classed as weakly podzolized variants of *sol lessivé*.

From comparison of "agricultural" profiles on the Chilterns with their semi-natural counterparts, it is clear that the ploughed layer (Ap horizon) of arable soils normally includes some part of the Eb horizon of the virgin profile and may represent part of the Bt horizon where accelerated erosion has occurred. As a consequence of recent erosion, most of the dry-valley bottoms are occupied by colluvial soils (Nettleden series) composed of material derived from further up-slope. Where originally non-calcareous, these are of brown-earth character, but because of their recent origin the profiles show no well marked horizons, other than those of a depositional nature.

Apart from the *sols lessivés* of the Chiltern Plateau, moderately well drained soils leached of carbonates occur locally on malmstone and associated Upper Greensand rocks. These soils, typified by the Harwell series (Plate V, 6) differ from others of the brown earth group in their predominantly greyish colour and in the highly siliceous nature of their clay fractions, both features being attributable to the high content of alkali-soluble silica in the parent rocks. Because of their distinctive characteristics they are considered to represent a separate type of soil formation, to which the name *grey siliceous soil* has been applied. Typical profiles have olive-grey or light olive-brown sub-surface horizons with blocky or prismatic structure, which are frequently finer in texture than the overlying A horizon and may show evidence of clay illuviation, indicating that they are weakly developed Bt horizons. In the sequel, however, they are described as (B) horizons, as no Eb horizon is distinguishable, and in most instances the possibility remains that the textural difference may be of geological origin. In the present area, where the Upper Greensand is thin, and consists for the most part of relatively impervious, fine sandy marl, the subsoils are usually slightly gleyed, as shown by the presence of faint ochreous and greyish mottling (gleyed grey siliceous soils).

Soils of the Gley Group

Calcareous soils and brown earths are typically soils with free drainage, and as natural drainage becomes poorer they grade into soils with profiles modified to a greater or lesser degree by gleying and other effects of wetness. Those in which horizons below the A show distinct mottling with ochreous and/or pale* or grey colours, considered to result from waterlogging, are grouped as gley soils. This major group may therefore include imperfectly drained, poorly drained and very poorly drained soils as defined above (p. 46). Soils with moderate drainage, in which evidence of gleying is confined to lower horizons, are classed as (slightly) gleyed variants (e.g. gleyed calcareous soils, gleyed brown earths) of the corresponding well drained types.

Gley soils with imperfect and poor drainage are associated naturally with moist oakwoods and meadow-land where the upper horizons dry out sufficiently in summer to permit the formation of normal mull or moder humus layers. Under these conditions, the organic-matter content of the soil may not be significantly greater than in related well drained types, but since subsoil waterlogging tends to restrict root-growth and earthworm activity, it is often less well distributed through the profile. In cold, wet climates, or in places where natural drainage is very poor, the ground remains waterlogged for most of the year, so that decomposition of plant residues is markedly retarded, and more or less humified organic matter accumulates at the surface. Soils containing more than 30 per cent of organic matter to depths exceeding 15 in. are regarded as organic (e.g. fen and bog) soils, but those in which combined organic and organo-mineral layers are less than 15 in. thick are classed as either peaty or humic gley, depending on the extent to which the organic material is humified. Gley soils used intensively for agriculture have usually had their drainage improved. This generally leads to an increase in the depth of soil freely penetrated by roots, and to related changes in the structure and humus content of the upper horizons, but the effects of subsoil gleying tend to persist, and testify to the former condition of the profile.

The gley group includes soils of widely differing morphology for, besides differences in degree of wetness which may be related to relief or climatic factors, their profile characteristics are greatly affected by the texture, composition, and base status of the parent material, and the extent to which leaching has occurred. There are thus many types of gley soil, but a broad distinction may be drawn between soils in which wetness results primarily from the impervious character of the profile itself (surface-water gley), and soils affected by the occurrence of a high water-table in material which would otherwise permit good drainage (ground-water gley).

Soils of the first class have subsoil horizons, either inherited from the parent material or produced by pedogenic processes, which are insufficiently permeable to transmit rain-water without periodic waterlogging. In typical profiles, the more permeable upper horizons are more or less mottled with grey and ochreous

---

* Munsell chroma of 2 or less.

colours, and the impeding layer itself shows pale grey coatings on cleavage faces and root channels, but the interiors of the aggregates, and the more massive material below into which rain-water scarcely penetrates, tend to retain their inherited colours.

In typical ground-water gleys, by contrast, the subsoil horizons are relatively permeable, but the profile is saturated from below by a water-table which rises and falls in wet and dry seasons to produce a zone of alternate reducing and oxidizing conditions with mottled, grey and rusty colouring. Below this zone, in places where the water-table is permanent, lies a constantly wet zone, absent in surface-water gleys, in which iron compounds have been more or less completely reduced, and either pale or bluish grey colours predominate.

Surface-water gleys are chiefly represented in the survey area by fine-textured, calcareous or slightly leached soils with imperfect and poor drainage, overlying Gault (Wicken and Challow series) and Kimmeridge clays (Denchworth series). Although in most cases the upper horizons have formed in solifluxion deposits containing flints and sand of non-local origin, the morphology and water relationships of these soils are dominated by their high content of alumino-silicate clay with well-marked swelling properties, and for this reason they have been grouped in the present work as *clayey gley soils* (Plate V, 7). Their profiles are intersected to depths of several feet by a network of shrinkage cracks, numerous near the surface and more widely spaced below, which open in dry seasons and divide the soil mass into sharp-edged, blocky and prismatic aggregates of varying size. At the surface is a stiff, dark-coloured A horizon, sometimes 12 in. or more thick under old pasture; this is followed by a lighter-coloured, generally olive or greyish brown, tenacious (B)g horizon, more or less distinctly mottled with colours ranging from light grey to brownish yellow. The "solid" clay (Cg horizon), usually encountered at between 18 and 30 in., is dominantly grey, with fine ochreous mottling which gradually fades out with depth as vertical or oblique cleavage faces become rare and the material assumes a massive or laminated condition. The A and (B)g horizons are partly or wholly decalcified and may be slightly acid, but the less weathered horizons below always contain calcium carbonate which is partly present as concretionary or incoherent deposits of secondary origin, reprecipitated in dry periods from saturated solution.

Other gley soils in the area have affinities with the ground-water sub-group. They include *calcareous alluvial gleys* formed in recent alluvium, and more or less decalcified soils derived from older, relatively pervious deposits which overlie clay formations and are affected by local, perched water-tables. Soils of the latter type, grouped here as *gleys with clay substrata* (Plate V, 8) are widely developed in the Vale on Chalky Gravel Head (Weston Turville series) and other thin drifts (Rowsham series), and also on the basal Portlandian strata (Bierton series). Typical profiles have yellowish or olive-brown (B)(g) horizons, distinctly more friable and pervious than corresponding horizons of the associated clayey gley soils. Where the surface has become acid, however, the subsoil often contains more clay than the overlying A horizon, and may represent a weakly developed Bt horizon. Ochreous and pale-coloured mottlings appear at variable depths, and are most pronounced in seasonally waterlogged sandy or gravelly layers in which the ground-water fluctuates freely. Locally, particularly on low-lying ground, water may stand in these relatively pervious layers throughout the year; more commonly, however, free water is removed during the summer by evaporation or lateral seepage. In many of these soils, the water-bearing layers are relatively thin, or are covered by less permeable horizons of clay loam or finer texture, so that their water relationships may approximate more or less closely to those of the clayey gley soils.

The beds of chalky gravel, silt and clay laid down by the small streams of the area give rise to more or less strongly gleyed soils with very dark-coloured, humus-rich A horizons locally containing over 20 per cent of organic matter. The profiles (Plate V, 9), often include depositional layers of variable composition, and where the material consists largely of chalk, rusty deposits and stains often constitute the only visible evidence of periodic waterlogging. Before these soils were reclaimed for pasture, it is probable that most of them carried alder swamps and were much wetter than they are today, so that certain of their morphological features may be unrelated to contemporary conditions. After wet seasons, a water-table is normally encountered at moderate depths, but where alluvium of limited thickness rests on clay the zone of saturation may disappear entirely in dry summers.

THE SOIL MAPPING UNITS

Twelve of the twenty-nine soil series distinguished in Table 7 are shown separately on the published map, one (the Icknield series) being subdivided into phases on a slope basis. The remainder occur as components of eleven soil complexes, each named according to the dominant series present. Fourteen of the series were first described elsewhere; the Icknield, Wantage, Harwell, Ardington, Challow and Denchworth in Berkshire (Kay, 1934); the Wallop, Charity, Winchester, Bursledon and Southampton in Hampshire (Kay, 1939; Green, 1940); the Batcombe in Dorset (Robinson, 1948); and the Burwell and Wicken in Cambridgeshire (Soil Survey of Great Britain, 1951). Besides established soil series, certain of the complexes include unnamed variants of limited extent, which are sufficiently distinct to be considered as separate series, but whose classification has been deferred pending further surveys in adjoining areas.

Table 8 shows the approximate acreage and proportionate extent of each mapping unit, and the soil series recognized as components of complexes: the principal urban areas were excluded from the survey, and are indicated on the map by a separate tint, together with chalk quarries, brick-earth pits and other areas of disturbed ground.

In using the map it is necessary to recognize that soil boundaries are normally diffuse and that an area shown as conforming to a particular mapping unit, besides having a peripheral zone with profiles transitional to those characteristic of adjacent units, will usually also contain small inclusions of abberrant soil series because of limitations imposed by the scale of the map and by the number of points which can be examined. Where a particular soil series is indicated such inclusions should not exceed 15 per cent of the area covered, and in most of the complexes mapped at least 60 per cent of the area is occupied by profiles conforming to the dominant series present.

TABLE 8

Acreage and Proportionate Extent of Soil Mapping Units

Soil Mapping Unit	Acreage (to nearest 100 acres)	Percentage of Area Surveyed
Batcombe series	37,300	29·3
Winchester series	22,200	17·5
Coombe complex (Coombe and Wallop series)	11,300	8·8
Charity complex (Charity and Nettleden series)	10,500	8·2
Berkhamsted complex (Berkhamsted and St. Albans series)	7,800	6·1
Wicken series	7,000	5·5
Icknield series	4,500	3·5
Icknield series (steepland phase)	3,500	2·7
Weston Turville series	3,500	2·7
Wantage series	3,100	2·4
Denchworth series	2,500	2·0
Ford End complex (Ford End and Mead series)	2,400	1·9
Challow complex (Challow and Weston Turville series)	2,200	1·7
Halton complex (Halton and Burwell series)	2,100	1·6
Harwell complex (Harwell and Ardington series)	1,400	1·1
Rowsham complex (Rowsham series)	1,300	1·0
Gade complex (Gade and Ford End series)	1,200	0·9
Mead series	900	0·7
Cowcroft complex (Cowcroft and Bursledon series)	800	0·7
Bierton complex (Bierton series)	700	0·5
Gubblecote series	600	0·5
Tring series	500	0·4
Aylesbury series	200	0·2
St. Albans series	100	0·1
Principal urban areas, disturbed ground, etc.	10,600	

In addition to the series named, the Southampton series occurs in very limited areas as inclusions in the Berkhamsted complex and St. Albans series.

Descriptions of the soil series and complexes delimited on the map are arranged according to their region of occurrence in the two following chapters. The general accounts of the mapping units are supplemented by descriptions of representative profiles; details are given of series occurring as sub-dominant components of complexes, and of local variants and phase differences. Routine analytical data relating to the profiles described are presented in Tables 9 and 10 (pp. 153–163), and are further discussed in Chapter V.

CHAPTER III

Descriptions of the Soil Mapping Units:
1. The Chiltern Plateau and
the Icknield Belt

As shown in Fig. 6 (p. 14), the soils of the Chiltern Plateau are almost every-where derived from superficial deposits, and only on and at the foot of the scarp are there appreciable areas of soil developed directly on the subjacent Chalk. Considered on a major soil group basis (Fig. 10, p. 55), there is a clear division between the naturally acid brown earths on non-calcareous or decalcified plateau and valley deposits, and the calcareous soils on Chalk and chalky drift: gley soils are of limited extent, and are confined to the Eocene outliers and to the narrow strips of alluvium in the main valleys.

Six soil series and five complexes are delimited on this portion of the sheet, and are conveniently grouped for descriptive purposes as follows:

SOILS OF THE CHILTERN PLATEAU

Gleyed brown earths (*sols lessivés*) on Plateau Drift: Batcombe series; Berkhamsted complex.

Brown earths (*sols lessivés*) on High-level Gravel: St. Albans series.

Gley soils and associated gleyed brown earths on Eocene clays and sands: Cowcroft complex.

SOILS OF THE CHILTERN VALLEYS AND THE ICKNIELD BELT

Brown earths (*sols lessivés*) on Clay-with-flints and Coombe Deposits: Winchester series; Charity complex.

Rendzinas on Chalk and Chalk Marl: Icknield series; Wantage series.

Brown calcareous soils on chalky drifts: Coombe complex; Tring series.

Gley soils on alluvium: Gade complex.

In addition to the series named, very small areas of gravelly podzolized soil, classed with the Southampton series, occur as inclusions in the Berkhamsted complex and St. Albans series.

SOILS OF THE CHILTERN PLATEAU

BATCOMBE SERIES

Soils of this series cover most of the flat and gently sloping land of the Chiltern Plateau above 400 ft., and occupy almost 30 per cent of the area surveyed. The series was named in Dorset by Robinson (1948), and it has since been recognized that essentially similar soils are widespread on the dip-slopes of the Chilterns and the North Downs. The areas mapped as Batcombe in the present survey are largely on Plateau Drift classed as Clay-with-flints by the Geological Survey, but soils with similar textures and horizons on Pebbly Clay and Sand are also included, notably at Prestwood and Potten End. The drift is everywhere more than 5 ft. thick, and although as a rule the soils drain fairly well, there are some on flat land that fall into the imperfectly drained class. On the higher ridges, an appreciable proportion of the land is occupied by woods and commons. Elsewhere, the soils are used for mixed farming, diversified in places by orchards and market-garden crops.

The following succession of horizons is characteristic of the Batcombe soil. At the surface is an A horizon of dark-coloured flinty silt loam, less frequently of loam or silty clay loam, overlying a yellowish brown or brown, sub-surface horizon of similar texture, designated Eb. This is followed at 12 to 24 in. by a strong brown to yellowish red, clay subsoil with variegated mottling, which may become appreciably sandy at depth, either in pockets or throughout the mass. Flints, small and shattered in the upper horizons, larger and less broken below, are scattered through the profile in varying amounts, sometimes with a marked concentration in sub-surface and upper subsoil horizons. Flint pebbles may also be present, and in a few localities below 650 ft. are more numerous than angular flints, whereas in scattered small areas the soil is virtually free from stones. Secondary ferri-manganiferous deposits occur in limited amounts in sub-surface and subsoil horizons, either as small concretions or as incoherent segregations. Under semi-natural conditions the soil is acid throughout the profile, but on agricultural land it commonly contains chalk as residues of added dressings, and often has a neutral reaction to depths of 3 ft. or more.

The loamy sub-surface layer may merge gradually into the clay subsoil by way of an intermediate horizon of silty clay loam texture, or the change may be sharper; the boundary often shows considerable undulations, the Eb horizon extending downwards as pale-coloured projections or tongues, sometimes to a depth of 3 ft. The subsoil is characterized by a moderately well developed blocky structure, which in some cases approaches the prismatic form; in the moist state the aggregates are firm, and when pressure is applied will crumble slightly before moulding. Structural faces in the upper few inches are often coated with fine sandy or silty material, whereas at greater depths fissures, flints and old root channels are lined with films of nearly pure clay. Mottling, in shades of red, yellow and brown, is generally faint in the upper part, but becomes more pronounced with depth, and is accompanied by pale grey coatings on cleavage faces and conducting channels. Below about 6 ft. structure is less evident and colours often more uniform, although occasional grey-coated fissures may extend to considerably greater depths. Locally, on level or slightly depressed sites where drainage is classed as imperfect, yellow rather than red subsoil colours prevail, and pale-coloured mottlings, associated in some cases with ferri-manganiferous concretions, may appear at 9–12 in. in the lower part of the Eb horizon.

As indicated earlier (p. 16), particle-size distribution and mineralogical studies of Batcombe profiles from Buckinghamshire and Oxfordshire have shown that they are composite in origin, the characteristic textural change resulting partly from clay migration, and partly from the occurrence of a silty superficial layer which may be up to 3 ft. thick. As the subsoil horizons normally contain segregations of clay-size material as pore-fillings and aggregate coatings, they are designated Bt, although their parent material differs from that of the overlying horizons. In some profiles (e.g. Bu 14 below), however, the upper part of the Bt horizon is a silty clay loam or silty clay with few stones, which appears to have developed in the same material as the Eb horizon.

Although the nature and arrangement of horizons in Batcombe profiles are considered sufficiently uniform for the soils to be classed as one series, a number of phases may be recognized, due either to differences in vegetation or land use, or to variations in parent material and relief. Some indication of the range of variation encountered is given by the six profiles described below, two of which (Bu 14, Bu 13) are from semi-natural beech-oak woods on the Hampden Estate, and four (Bu 57, Bu 58, Ht 60, Ht 61) from agricultural land carrying leys of varying duration.

In old-established woods it is possible to distinguish an acid mull phase and a mor (weakly podzolized) phase, corresponding in general to the beechwood associations grouped by Tansley (1949) as *Fagetum rubosum* and *Fagetum ericetosum* respectively. In the former (Bu 14) the field layer includes abundant brambles and scattered *Oxalis acetosella* and other "mull herbs"; although litter may accumulate locally, neither F nor H layers are continuously developed and the A horizon, which has a friable, crumb structure, may be 2–3 in. thick. In the latter phase, represented by Bu 13, ground vegetation is scanty and an F layer of matted, decaying leaves is followed by a black, friable H layer of comparable thickness, resting on the mineral soil with only slight mixing. Discontinuous bleached patches, betokening slight podzolization, generally occur beneath the humus layer and are bordered below by thin seams of dark or rusty brown, weakly cemented material. As few earthworms are present, and fine roots are largely confined to the humus layer, the sub-surface mineral horizons, including the "micro-podzol" and the succeeding, yellowish Eb horizon, are compact and structureless or weakly laminated, by contrast with the mull phase, in which the Eb horizon is friable and crumbly. A range of humus forms comparable to those under beechwood is also found on the remaining open commons with grass-heath vegetation. Under acidic (*Agrostis-fescue*) grassland there is generally a mat of decaying leaves and stems at the surface, and sometimes a thin H layer, followed by a friable, mull-like A horizon with soft crumb structure, whereas under patches of *Calluna* the soil is firmer, with mor humus and incipient podzolization. Dense bracken also gives rise to a thick layer of unincorporated residues with a black H layer at the base but, owing to the growth and decay of the ramifying rhizomes, the sub-surface horizons are less compact.

On cultivated land the ploughed layer is normally a dark grey-brown, flinty silt loam, which is friable when moist and hard when dry. Moderately well-developed crumb and fine sub-angular blocky structures form under well-managed grassland, but the clods produced by cultivation on old arable land are relatively unstable and are easily broken down by heavy rain, causing the soil to run and cap on the surface. At the same time the soil tends to be washed away from the flints, so that where the land has lain undisturbed for some time the surface appears stonier than it actually is. This structural instability, characteristic of non-calcareous, silty and fine sandy soils, is further shown by a tendency, particularly evident under grazed leys, for the surface and sub-surface layers to become laminated or brick-like, with few visible pores or fissures.

Besides these phases related to land use, the soils show significant variations in such features as stoniness, thickness of horizons, and subsoil mottling, which may be correlated in a general way with the configuration of the land. On level ridge-tops the profile often contains only occasional stones; the silty upper horizons are commonly at least 18 in. thick, with distinct mottling in the lower part; and in scattered small areas, typified by a profile from Hill Farm, Flamstead (Ht 60), the clay subsoil is underlain at no great depth by stoneless, silty or fine sandy material, referred to earlier (p. 15) as laminated brick-earth. Where slopes become appreciable, the surface nearly always becomes more stony, and in many places the subsoil clay is encountered at a shallower depth. At the edges of the ridges there is often a distinct belt of very stony soil, exemplified by another profile from the same farm (Ht 61), which merges downhill into the Winchester series. In numerous localities at and below 650 ft., this "stony edge" is represented by very pebbly loams containing more sand and less silt than the adjoining plateau soils; these pebbly soils are mapped with the Berkhamsted complex where they occupy a zone of sufficient width. Elsewhere, particularly at higher levels, the stones are predominantly angular flints, and the soil is then regarded as a very flinty phase of the Batcombe series, transitional to the Winchester.

Where the Plateau Drift is thick the Batcombe series has been mapped on short slopes of up to 6°, and at the crests of such slopes the soils on long-cultivated land are often eroded, so that the ploughed layer rests more or less directly on the clay subsoil and may itself have a silty clay loam or clay loam texture. This *eroded phase* is typified by a profile at Kings Ash, Wendover (Bu 58), described in the same field as one of the normal phase (Bu 57). The areas shown as Batcombe also include deep colluvial soils of silt loam texture, occurring as narrow strips in the heads of dry valleys, and resembling those which at lower levels have been mapped with the Charity complex.

Descriptions of representative profiles
(*Analytical data in Table* 9, *p.* 153)

PROFILE NO.: Bu 14 (Batcombe series)

Location: Hillock Wood, Great Hampden (grid ref. SP/832021).

Slope: 1° even.   *Altitude:* 775 ft. O.D.

Land Use: woodland (high forest).

Vegetation: beechwood (*Fagetum rubosum*), with some oak (*Quercus robur*) and holly (*Ilex aquifolium*); field layer dominated by bramble (*Rubus* spp.), with scattered herbs, notably *Oxalis acetosella* and *Galeobdolon luteum: Deschampsia caespitosa* common nearby.

Horizons:

L		Litter, mainly beech leaves, up to 1 in. thick.
F/H		Partially decomposed litter, up to 1 in. thick, with traces of black, finely granular humus.
A	0–1½ in.	Dark grey to greyish brown (10 YR 3/1–4/2), friable silt loam with weak crumb structure; occasional small brown-stained flints; abundant woody roots; small worms present; clear irregular boundary.

Plate VIa. View looking down Hampden Bottom towards Great Missenden. Charity series on gentle footslopes; soils of the Coombe complex on steeper slopes in the distance.

Plate VIb. Old arable land in the shallow dry valley leading west from Redbourn (Charity, Winchester and Wallop series). A "dell-hole", now ploughed over, appears as a chalky depression in the left foreground, and chalk has been exposed along the hedge-bank as a consequence of continued cultivation and accelerated erosion.

Plate VIIa. A soil of the Coombe series near Berkhamsted. The underlying "Coombe-Rock" is festooned with pockets of loamy material and shows flow structures towards the base.

Plate VIIb. Fallowing in preparation for wheat on soils of the Ford End and Challow series at Ivinghoe Aston.

Plate VIIIa. The malmstone platform near North Lee, Ellesborough, with the Chiltern Escarpment in the distance. Areas of Harwell soil in the foreground and in the middle distance are separated by a depression cut in Gault (Challow complex).

Photograph by courtesy of the Forestry Commission

Plate VIIIb. Beech, whitebeam (*Sorbus aria*) and yew (*Taxus baccata*) on mid-slope (Icknield series) and crest (Winchester series) of Pulpit Hill, Kimble, viewed from Longdown.

Photograph by courtesy of the Forestry Commission

Plate IX. Old beech on soil of the Winchester series near the summit of Pulpit Hill, Kimble.

Eb   1½–9 in.   Yellowish brown (10 YR 5/6) friable silt loam, pale brown
                            to light yellowish brown when dry, with humose infillings
                            and occasional small flints as above; very weak crumb
                            structure; frequent woody roots; clear boundary.

Eb/Bt   9–16 in.   Strong brown (7·5 YR 5/6), friable to firm, silty clay loam,
                            finely and faintly mottled with redder and with paler colours;
                            small flints more numerous; fine to medium sub-angular
                            blocky structure increasingly well defined; some aggregates
                            have pale-coloured silty coatings, particularly evident when
                            dry; occasional small manganiferous concretions; frequent
                            woody roots; clear, undulating boundary.

Bt1(g)   16–29 in.   Strong brown to yellowish red (7·5 YR—5 YR 5/6), firm
                            flinty silty clay to clay, faintly mottled with light brown and
                            red; flints mainly small and angular; moderate medium
                            blocky structure; aggregate faces smooth, shiny and paler in
                            colour than interior; common small rounded manganiferous
                            concretions; few roots; merging boundary.

Bt2(g)   29–60 in.   Mainly yellowish red, very firm, flinty clay, distinctly to
                            prominently mottled with reddish yellow, red, and pale
                            brown to light grey; occasional large, broken and nodular
                            flints with whitish rinds; blocky structure, ill defined in
                            place; consistency variable through mass; greyish material
                            coating flints and lining fissures and root paths is very plastic,
                            red material relatively friable; few roots; merging lower
                            boundary.

Bt/C(g)   60–90 in.+   Similar mottled flinty clay, becoming rather more uniform in
                            colour and finer in texture with depth, and containing an
                            increasing proportion of large little-broken flint nodules.

PROFILE NO.: Bu 13 (Batcombe series)

Location: Lodge Wood, Great Hampden (grid ref. SP/866014).

Slope: level.   *Altitude:* 650 ft. O.D.

Land use: woodland (high forest).

Vegetation: beechwood (*Fagetum ericetosum*) with some oak (*Quercus robur*) and
holly (*Ilex aquifolium*); no field layer; scattered *Deschampsia flexuosa* and *Chamaenerion angustifolium* nearby.

Horizons:

L   Litter, mainly beech leaves, up to ½ in. thick.

F   Dark brown, partially decomposed, matted litter with
                            abundant fungal mycelium and frequent fine roots; ½–1 in.
                            thick.

H   Very dark brown to black, finely granular and laminated
                            humus with abundant fungal mycelium and fine woody
                            roots; sharp boundary.

A/Ea   0–1 in.   Thin, dark grey, laminated, humose silt loam overlying
                            discontinuous light grey silt loam low in humus, separated
                            by a sharp and irregular boundary from brown silt loam
                            with dark reddish brown streaks; compact and brittle when
                            dry; frequent woody roots.

Eb1	1–6 in.	Yellowish brown (10 YR 5/6) silt loam with occasional small brown-stained sub-angular flints, light yellowish brown (10 YR 6/6) to light yellow when dry; compact in place, but friable when removed, weak platy structure; frequent woody roots; humus mainly confined to root tracks; merging boundary.
Eb2(g)	6–13 in.	Yellowish brown friable silt loam, finely and faintly mottled with paler and with redder colours; occasional small angular flints and flint pebbles; structureless; frequent small manganiferous concretions; frequent roots; clear smooth boundary.
Bt1(g)	13–24 in.	Strong brown to reddish yellow (7·5 YR 5/8–6/8), firm silty clay loam to silty clay with common, distinct, fine, light brown and yellowish red mottling; occasional small stones as above; moderate sub-angular blocky structure with light brown shiny faces to aggregates; small concretions less frequent; few roots; merging boundary.
Bt2g	24–36 in.+	Reddish yellow (7·5 YR 6/6) very firm flinty clay with sandy patches, distinctly mottled with colours ranging from light grey to yellowish red; flints larger and more numerous; weak blocky to prismatic structure, with some grey-coated vertical fissures; few roots.

PROFILE NO. : Bu 57 (Batcombe series)

Location: Great Kingsash Farm, Wendover (grid ref. SP/889057).

Slope: nearly level.   *Altitude:* 760 ft. O.D.

Land use: grass-clover ley.

Horizons:

Ap	0–6 in.	Dark greyish brown (10 YR 4/2) friable flinty silt loam, hard when dry; moderate medium to fine sub-angular blocky and crumb structure; flints mainly small and angular, some brown-stained and sub-angular; abundant fibrous roots; earthworms common; clear boundary.
Eb1	6–18 in.	Yellowish brown (10 YR 5/6) friable flinty silt loam with infilled worm channels; weak fine sub-angular blocky structure; frequent fibrous roots; horizon 9 to 15 in. thick; undulating boundary.
Eb2(g)	18–23 in.	Light yellowish brown to light brown (10 YR 6/3–6/4), friable, flinty, porous and structureless silt loam, faintly mottled with greyer and with redder colours; compact in place and hard when dry; occasional small ochreous and manganiferous concretions; few roots or worm tracks; horizon discontinuous, up to 7 in. thick; clear, undulating boundary.
Bt(g)	23–36 in.+	Yellowish red (5 YR 5/6–5/8), very firm, flinty clay, faintly to distinctly mottled with pale brown and red; flints mainly large, more or less broken, nodules with whitish rinds; medium to coarse sub-angular blocky structure; few roots or worm tracks; upper limit of horizon ranges from 18 to 25 in. below the surface.

PROFILE NO.: Bu 58 (Batcombe series)

Location: Great Kingsash Farm, Wendover, 100 yards east of Bu 57 (grid ref. SP/890057).

Slope: 3–4° convex.   *Aspect:* north-east.   *Altitude:* 750 ft. O.D.

Land use: grass-clover ley.

Horizons:

Ap	0–6 in.	Dark greyish brown to brown (10 YR 4/2–4/3), friable, flinty, silt loam to silty clay loam, pale brown and hard when dry; weak medium to fine sub-angular blocky structure; abundant fibrous roots; clear boundary.
Bt(g)	6–18 in.+	Brown to reddish yellow (7·5 YR 5/4–5/8), firm flinty clay with many humose infillings in upper 3 in., faintly mottled with paler brown and yellowish red, and becoming distinctly mottled with depth; moderate coarse blocky structure; frequent roots; earthworms present.

PROFILE NO.: Ht 60 (Batcombe series)

Location: Hill Farm, Flamstead (grid ref. TL/052139).

Slope: nearly level.   *Altitude:* 520 ft. O.D.

Land use: grass-clover ley.

Horizons:

Ap	0–6 in.	Dark greyish brown (10 YR 4/2), friable, flinty and pebbly, silt loam with weak medium sub-angular blocky structure, tending to platy; some granular worm-casts; stones include brown-stained angular flints and flint pebbles, with occasional small quartz pebbles; abundant fibrous roots; added chalk concentrated with stones at base of horizon; clear boundary.
Eb	6–13 in.	Yellowish brown, friable, flinty and pebbly, silt loam with darker colours on cleavage faces and humose infillings; some faint varicoloured mottling towards base; weak fine sub-angular blocky structure; frequent roots; horizon 6 to 15 in. thick; merging lower boundary.
Eb/Bt(g)	13–21 in.	Strong brown (7·5 YR 5/6–5/8) firm silty clay loam with fewer stones, faintly mottled with pale brown and red; weak blocky to prismatic structure; worm channels and roots less frequent; some soft manganiferous deposits; transitional horizon with merging boundaries.
Bt1(g)	21–35 in.	Reddish yellow, red, and light brown, distinctly mottled, very firm and locally sandy clay with occasional stones and humose infillings; weak blocky to prismatic structure, with texture and consistence variable through mass; few roots; merging boundary.
Bt2(g)	35–43 in.+	Strong brown to reddish yellow (7·5 YR 5/8), weakly platy, silty clay loam with few stones, distinctly mottled with pale brown to light grey, and intersected by vertical fissures and channels lined with grey plastic clay; laminated material less firm and plastic than overlying horizon; roots rare.

PROFILE NO.: Ht 61 (Batcombe series)

Location: Hill Farm, Flamstead (grid ref. TL/057143).

Slope: 2° convex.   *Altitude:* 500 ft. O.D.

Land use: grass-clover ley (first year).

Horizons:

Ap	0–7 in.	Dark greyish brown (10 YR 4/2–4/3), friable, very flinty, loam to silt loam with weak sub-angular blocky structure; hard when dry; stones mainly small angular flints, with some flint pebbles; abundant fibrous roots; clear boundary.
Eb	7–13 in.	Yellowish brown (10 YR 5/4) very flinty loam with darker-coloured aggregate faces and numerous humose infillings; stones as above; weak sub-angular blocky and crumb structure; frequent roots; clear boundary.
Bt1(g)	13–21 in.	Strong brown (7·5 YR 5/6–5/8), very firm, flinty clay, locally sandy, faintly mottled with light brown and yellowish red; stones include large unbroken flints, small shattered flints and flint pebbles; weak blocky structure; few roots; merging boundary.
Bt2(g)	21–42 in.+	Strong brown, very firm, flinty clay to sandy clay loam distinctly mottled with red, yellowish red, and pale brown to light grey, the latter colours becoming more pronounced with depth and associated with very plastic material coating stones and cleavage faces; stones as above; ill-defined blocky structure; roots rare.

BERKHAMSTED COMPLEX

(*Berkhamsted and St. Albans Series*)

The areas mapped as Berkhamsted complex, amounting to about 7,800 acres, are characterized by the dominance of stony, medium- to coarse-textured soils resembling those of the Batcombe series in profile morphology, but distinguished by the presence of numerous pebbles of flint and other rocks, accompanied by varying quantities of sand. This kind of soil, which constitutes the Berkhamsted series, is found on Pebbly Clay and Sand at elevations up to 675 ft., but is most extensive below 450 ft., where it is widely developed on the similar, stony clay drift referred to earlier (p. 15) as Plateau Drift with far-travelled stones. Associated with it, particularly at the lower levels, are lesser areas of considerably coarser-textured soil of the St. Albans series, developed where the underlying drift contains seams or lenses of gravel and sand. Elsewhere, the drift appears to include masses of disturbed Eocene clay, so that, although the surface is pebbly, the subsoil may be virtually free of stones. Depending on the slope, and the relative contents of clay, pebbles and sand in the drift, the drainage of the soils ranges from free to imperfect. Except for built-up areas, the greater part of the land is under arable crops or leys. There are a few semi-natural woods of beech and oak, mainly at the higher levels, and a number of coniferous plantations, the largest being north of Bedmond.

The most extensive soil, to which the name Berkhamsted was originally applied, has friable, pebbly surface and sub-surface horizons of loam or sandy loam texture, underlain between 12 and 30 in. by mottled, red and yellow clay containing variable amounts of sand and pebbles. Three representative profiles are recorded below, under semi-natural woodland, a short-term ley, and from an old grass field respectively.

The semi-natural profile (Ht 47) is sited near Chipperfield in an old oakwood containing some beech. As is common on these soils, the superficial organic layers are of mor type, and signs of superficial podzolization are present, particularly where the ground is bare of vegetation. Beneath the "micro-podzol" there is a brown, weak-structured, very pebbly, Eb horizon with slight evidence of iron enrichment in the upper part. The clayey Bt horizon has at its upper limit a transitional layer of irregular thickness from which clay-size material has apparently been removed, leaving local, pale-coloured zones and aggregates coated with fine sand and silt. Below 18 in., bright red and light grey mottlings become increasingly evident, and bleached clay-skins appear around stones and lining fissures and old root channels. The sand in the subsoil horizons is very irregularly distributed, and there are indications, more marked in other profiles, that the overlying horizons have developed in a disturbed (solifluxion) layer which may have received accessions of silty material, although to a lesser extent than in typical Batcombe profiles.

The cultivated profile from Abbots Langley (Ht 44) contains some quartzite pebbles in addition to rounded and sub-angular flints, and the subsoil clay is rather more sandy, but a closely comparable succession of horizons is represented beneath the ploughed layer. The friable Eb horizon has an irregular lower boundary ranging from 17 to 30 in. below the surface, and where the boundary tongues downwards the depression is occupied by relatively pale-coloured, clay-deficient material with small ferri-manganiferous concretions suggestive of seasonal water hold-up. In the profile under old grassland (Ht 29), a similar succession of pedogenic horizons can be discerned below the greyish brown, weak-structured A horizon but the parent material is clearly non-uniform, the A and Eb horizons having developed in a very pebbly superficial layer which overlies successive sandy (Bt1) and clayey (Bt2) horizons containing comparatively few stones.

At levels above 400 ft. the Berkhamsted soils are chiefly developed on flattened spurs and ridge margins adjoining the main through-valleys. In some places, notably near Flaunden and Chipperfield, the boundary with the Batcombe series is marked by a distinct change in texture and stone content; elsewhere, as at Gaddesden Place, Northchurch and east of Chesham, the two series proved difficult to separate, and in these and other localities the areas mapped as Berkhamsted complex are mainly occupied by moderately stony loams, with only sporadic patches of sandy or pebbly soil. As noted in connection with the Batcombe series, the stoniest and coarsest-textured soils almost invariably occur at the margins of ridges where the slope is increasing, probably because the surface layers have been depleted of finer material by both lateral and downward translocation, a process which Barrow (1919) called "static washing".

On excessively stony upper slopes the soils under semi-natural vegetation are generally somewhat podzolized, and in scattered, small areas show fully differentiated humus-iron podzol profiles which seem to have developed within the clay-deficient upper horizons of a *sol lessivé*, and conform to the Southampton series (Kay, 1939). Although of very limited extent, such profiles are interesting pedologically, and for this reason a description from a small beechwood (*Fagetum ericetosum*) near Prestwood is given below (Bu 80).

On the lower plateaux and ridges in the south-east, the soil pattern is dominated by pebbly loams of the Berkhamsted series, but because of the heterogeneity of the underlying drift there are frequent local variations in texture, stoniness and drainage conditions which are difficult to represent satisfactorily on a map. East of the Gade valley, from Leverstock Green southwards, much of the higher ground is apparently underlain at no great depth by Reading Beds clay, so that drainage tends to be imperfect and the clayey subsoils may be yellow rather than red in colour, with distinct pale mottling at 18 in. or less. Moderately stony loams predominate, but at the plateau edge the surface usually becomes more gravelly, and in places, as at Mansion Farm, there are small patches of pebbly, loamy sand overlying mottled clay. North-east and south-east of the Bedmond outlier, where the ground falls below 400 ft., the soils are generally coarser in texture, and form a complex pattern in which pebbly loams with red-mottled, clay subsoils alternate with lesser areas of gravelly, sandy loam with a subsoil of reddish, clayey, sand and gravel. The latter soils resemble those on the thick deposits of sand and gravel around Bedmond, and are described under the St. Albans series. Also represented, both at the higher and the lower levels, are small, ill-defined areas of silt loam soil which, except for the presence of far-travelled stones, resemble those mapped as Batcombe series. On the ridge-tops west of the Gade valley, soil conditions are rather more uniform and drainage is generally moderately good, but here again, the dominant Berkhamsted soils are associated locally with profiles which conform more closely to either the St. Albans or the Batcombe series.

As with the Batcombe series, the Berkhamsted complex includes limited areas of eroded and colluvial variants. In the eroded phase, occurring at the upper ends of fields and on convex slopes, the brightly-coloured Bt horizon is turned up by the plough, and the surface horizon is accordingly of sandy clay loam or finer texture. The colluvial soils, located in minor dry valleys, are normally deep, pebbly loams or sandy loams, sometimes with a thin layer of gravel at the base.

Descriptions of representative profiles
(*Analytical data in Table* 9, *p.* 154)

PROFILE NO.: Ht 47 (Berkhamsted series)

Location: Scatterdells Wood, Chipperfield (grid ref. TL/047029).
Slope: nearly level.   *Altitude:* 425 ft. O.D.
Land use: woodland (high forest).
Vegetation: oak (*Quercus robur*) with some beech; many beech saplings; field layer, sparse on site, dominated by bramble (*Rubus* spp.) nearby.

Horizons:

L	Litter, mainly oak leaves, up to $\frac{1}{2}$ in. thick.
F/H	Very dark grey, finely granular humus with some bleached sand grains; frequent fine woody roots; up to $\frac{1}{2}$ in. thick.

A/Ea   0–2 in.   Very dark grey to greyish brown (7·5 YR 4/0–4/2), humose, structureless, fine sandy loam with discontinuous flecks and patches of paler material; light brownish grey when moist and near white when dry; abundant woody roots; horizon $\frac{1}{2}$–$\frac{2}{3}$ in. thick; sharp, irregular boundary.

Eb   2–13 in.   Brown to yellowish brown (10–7·5 YR 5/4), friable very pebbly loam, pale brown (10 YR 6/3) and soft when dry; very weak crumb to massive structure; slightly compact and brittle in the upper few in.; stones mainly flint pebbles, with occasional small angular flints and quartz pebbles; frequent woody roots; clear irregular boundary.

Eb/Bt   13–18 in.   Reddish yellow (7·5 YR 6/6–6/8), very pebbly, firm clay loam with patches of pale brown to brownish yellow (10 YR 6/4–6/6), friable, coarser-textured material occurring as inclusions towards upper limit and as coatings to moderate medium sub-angular blocky aggregates; frequent roots; merging boundary.

Bt1(g)   18–28 in.   Reddish yellow, very pebbly, very firm clay, locally sandy, finely mottled with pale brown and red; stones mainly pebbles with some angular flints; ill-defined blocky structure; very hard when dry; texture and consistence variable through mass; few roots; merging boundary.

Bt2g   28–36 in.+   Similar pebbly clay, with red and grey mottling becoming increasingly prominent.

PROFILE NO.: Ht 44 (Berkhamsted series)

Location: Model Farm, Abbots Langley (grid ref. TL/070006).

Slope: nearly level.   *Altitude:* 360 ft. O.D.

Land use: grass-clover ley (first year).

Horizons:

Ap   0–7 in.   Dark greyish brown (10 YR 4/2), very pebbly, friable loam with moderate, medium to fine, sub-angular blocky structure, breaking easily to fine crumb when disturbed; light brownish grey and slightly hard when dry; stones mainly flint pebbles, with some sub-angular flints, quartz and quartzite pebbles; abundant grass roots; added chalk; clear smooth boundary.

Eb   7–20 in.   Yellowish brown (10 YR 5/4–5/6), very pebbly, friable loam; light yellowish brown (10 YR 6/4–7/6) and slightly hard when dry; stones as above; weak fine sub-angular blocky and crumb structure; frequent grass roots and worm tracks; horizon 10 to 20 in. thick; merging undulating boundary.

Eb/Bt(g)   20–27 in.   Brown (10 YR 5/3), very pebbly, porous and structureless loam, faintly mottled with redder and with paler colours and containing numerous small rounded ferri-manganiferous concretions; few roots; texture and consistency variable through mass; relatively plastic reddish material occurring as flecks and patches; horizon discontinuous and variable in degree of expression, up to 12 in. thick.

Bt(g)   27–40 in.+   Reddish yellow, very firm, stony clay, more or less sandy in patches, distinctly mottled with red, pale brown and light grey; stones include pebbles and sub-angular flints; weak blocky structure with pale-coloured plastic clay coatings on cleavage faces; few roots.

PROFILE NO.: Ht 29 (Berkhamsted series)

Location: Little Heath Small Farm, Potten End (grid ref. TL/020084).

Slope: nearly level.   *Altitude:* 560 ft. O.D.

Land use: permanent grassland.

Horizons:

A   0–6 in.   Thin turfy mat overlying dark greyish brown (10 YR 4/2), very pebbly, friable loam; light brownish grey (10 YR 6/2) and soft when dry; stones include flint pebbles, mainly with bleached and brown-stained rinds, occasional sub-angular flints and small quartz pebbles; weak fine sub-angular blocky structure; abundant grass roots; worms present; smooth merging boundary.

A/Eb   6–12 in.   Dark brown (10 YR 4/2–4/3), very pebbly, friable loam with weak crumb structure; abundant roots; smooth merging boundary.

Eb   12–21 in.   Yellowish brown (10 YR 5/4), very stony, friable loam with very weak structure; frequent roots; occasional worm channels; clear undulating boundary.

Eb/Bt1(g) 21–30 in.   Reddish yellow, friable to loose, loamy coarse sand with occasional black pebbles; relatively pale clay-deficient zones alternate with redder, more clayey material which is sticky when wet; structureless; frequent fine roots; clear undulating boundary.

Bt2g   30–38 in.+   Reddish yellow, slightly stony, very firm and plastic clay, more or less sandy, with distinct light grey and red mottling and grey clay-coated cleavage faces, stones include large broken flint nodules and bluish pebbles; weak coarse blocky structure; few roots.

PROFILE NO.: Bu 80 (Southampton series)

Location: Atkins's Wood, Great Missenden (grid ref. SP/885006).

Slope: 3° convex.   *Aspect:* south.   *Altitude:* 600 ft. O.D.

Land use: woodland (high forest).

Vegetation: beechwood (*Fagetum ericetosum*) with some holly (*Ilex aquifolium*); field layer limited to scattered mosses.

Horizons:

L   Litter, mainly beech leaves and twigs, thin on site due to wind.

F   Partially decomposed, matted litter, up to ½ in. thick.

H   Very dark brown, loose, finely granular humus (moder) containing bleached sand grains: abundant fine woody roots and fungal mycelium, ½–1½ in. thick; sharp boundary.

A	0–½ in.	Very dark grey (7·5 YR 3/0–3/1) humose structureless fine sandy loam with abundant roots; horizon discontinuous, up to 1 in. thick, with clear irregular lower boundary.
Ea	½–7 in.	Brown to pinkish grey (7·5 YR 5/2–6/2), very stony, structureless, friable to loose, fine sandy loam with variable humus staining; pinkish grey to pinkish white when dry; stones, including angular and sub-angular flints and flint pebbles, bleached on surface; frequent woody roots; clear boundary.
Bh	7–9 in.	Dark reddish brown (5 YR 3/2), compact, brittle and locally weakly cemented, fine sandy loam, very stony as above; horizon discontinuous and variable in degree of expression, up to 3 in. thick, with clear irregular lower boundary.
Bfe/Eb	9–17 in.	Reddish yellow (7·5 YR—5 YR 5/6), very stony, friable loam with ochreous stains on stones in upper part, tending to become paler in colour below; weak fine sub-angular blocky to crumb structure; distinctly more plastic and sticky than above; frequent woody roots; merging irregular boundary.
Bt(g)	17–30 in. +	Strong brown to yellowish red (7·5 YR—5 YR 5/8), very firm, very stony clay, more or less sandy, faintly to distinctly mottled with colours ranging from pale brown to red, with occasional grey-coated cleavage faces; weak blocky structure; few roots; horizon variable in texture and stone content, appreciably sandy material containing bluish pebbles alternating with tenacious mottled clay; pale-coloured structureless loamy material extends downwards as inclusions and coatings to cleavage faces in the upper part.

ST. ALBANS SERIES

The St. Albans series includes well drained pebbly sandy loams, less frequently loams or loamy sands, overlying water-laid sands and gravels that have been deeply weathered in one or more inter-glacial periods. This soil is unimportant on the Aylesbury Sheet, but is extensive further east on the gravels associated with Chalky Boulder Clay, and also occurs on the higher Thames terraces downstream from the Goring Gap. About 140 acres have been mapped around Bedmond at elevations of 400–450 ft.; a small patch, probably representing a high-level terrace, has been indicated near Langleybury, and other ill-defined areas of similar soil occur as inclusions in the Berkhamsted complex, chiefly below 400 ft. Most of the land carries arable crops or grass; under semi-natural vegetation the soils are usually slightly podzolized, and in small mixed woods east of Bedmond there are well developed humus-iron podzols conforming to the Southampton series, but as only a few acres are involved they were not shown separately on the map.

In typical profiles on agricultural land the dark-coloured A horizon is followed by a brown, friable, pebbly sub-surface (Eb) horizon with weak crumb structure which may be up to 2 ft. thick. Below this the subsoil consists of sand and stones in varying proportions, more or less bound together by reddish clay, which forms coatings round the larger particles and makes the material distinctly sticky when wet. This "dirty" gravel, known locally as "hoggin", may be several feet thick, but when examined in detail the clay component is often seen to be irregularly distributed in coalescing bands, separated by lenses and patches of looser, paler-coloured gravel. At its upper limit there is sometimes a continuous pale layer which, as in certain of the Berkhamsted profiles, is depleted of clay and may at times be saturated with water held up by the more compact material below. In some instances the clayey subsoil horizons may include poorly sorted material of glacial origin, but at Bedmond in particular the deposits were clearly laid down in water and locally show current bedding; it therefore seems probable that much of the clay-size material they contain originated by post-depositional weathering and was subsequently redistributed in percolating water to form one or more textural B horizons.

The St. Albans soils are typically developed where the deposits of sand and gravel are thick and continuous, or are underlain at no great depth by Chalk or other pervious substrata. On the Bedmond plateau the gravel is mainly at least 6 ft. thick, and although it rests on impervious Reading Beds clay there is little sign of drainage impedance in the upper 3 ft.: as it thins out at the margins, drainage becomes poorer, and where the profiles show yellow and grey mottling the soils have been grouped with the Cowcroft complex.

The arable profile described below (Ht 48) is located east of Abbots Langley in an area, mapped as Berkhamsted complex, where the subsoils are variable, reddish coarse-textured materials alternating over short distances with more or less stony, mottled clay. As is usual in this series, the A and the upper part of the Eb horizon contain much more silt, relative to sand, than the succeeding Bt horizon, indicating that they have developed in a loamy superficial layer. The second profile (Ht 69), sited under a mature stand of beech and Scots pine, is representative of the well developed podzols (Southampton series) which occupy limited areas in that locality, mainly at the edges of the plateau where the slope is increasing and the soil is exceptionally coarse-textured. As with the profile (Bu 80) on Pebbly Clay and Sand described above, the characteristic podzol horizons are succeeded below by a textural B horizon, which on this coarser-textured material is encountered at a considerably greater depth.

Descriptions of representative profiles

(Analytical data in Table 9, p. 154)

PROFILE NO.: Ht 48 (St. Albans series)

Location: Home Farm, Abbots Langley (grid ref. TL/105023).

Slope: c. 1° convex.   *Altitude:* 325 ft. O.D.

Land use: arable (roots).

Horizons:

Ap	0–7 in.	Dark greyish brown (10 YR 4/2), very pebbly, very friable, sandy loam with weak fine sub-angular blocky structure; greyish brown (10 YR 5/2) and slightly hard when dry; stones mainly flint pebbles, with some quartz and quartzite pebbles and large sub-angular flints; frequent roots; clear boundary.

Eb	7–15 in.	Brown (10 YR–7·5 YR 5/4), very pebbly, very friable, sandy loam with very weak, sub-angular blocky and crumb structure, and numerous worm tracks with humose infillings; light yellowish brown (10 YR 6/4) and soft when dry; stones as above, but with a higher proportion of small, angular flint gravel (3–4 mm.); few roots; merging boundary.
Eb/Bt	15–30 in.	Yellowish red (5 YR 5/8), very friable, very pebbly, structureless, loamy coarse sand, with patches of paler-coloured loose pebbly sand; occasional worm tracks; few roots; merging, irregular boundary.
Bt	30–35 in.	Yellowish red (5 YR 4/8–5/8), very pebbly, firm coarse sandy clay loam with numerous black specks; hard when dry and sticky when wet; sand grains bound by clayey coatings.
Bt/C	35 in.+	Similar material, becoming looser and less compact with depth.

PROFILE NO.: Ht 69 (Southampton series)

Location: Piecorner Wood, Bedmond (grid ref. TL/103037).

Slope: nearly level.   *Altitude:* 440 ft. O.D.

Land use: woodland, (oak, beech and Scots pine) recently felled; bracken (*Pteridium aquilinum*) dominant on site.

Horizons:

L		Bracken, beech and pine litter 3–4 in. thick.
F/H		Very dark brown to black, fibrous, partially decomposed litter containing increasing amounts of fine crumbly humus; abundant woody roots and bracken rhizomes.
A	0–1 in.	Dark grey to grey, humose sand speckled with bleached grains; abundant roots; horizon discontinuous, up to 2 in. thick; clear boundary.
Ea	1–14 in.	Light brown (7·5 YR 6/4), loose, structureless, very pebbly loamy sand, near white when dry, with variable humus staining; frequent woody roots; clear, undulating boundary.
Bh	14–17 in.	Dark reddish brown (5 YR 2/2–3/2), humose, very pebbly, loamy sand, weakly cemented in places in lower part, which is locally reddish brown; frequent roots; sharp irregular boundary.
Bfe	17–29 in.	Reddish yellow to yellowish red (7·5–5 YR 5/8–6/8), structureless, pebbly loamy sand, locally darker and redder in colour and weakly cemented near upper boundary; few roots; clear boundary.
Eb/Bt	29–36 in.+	Reddish yellow and yellow, irregularly mottled, platy loamy sand, becoming clayey in places.

COWCROFT COMPLEX
(*Cowcroft and Bursledon Series*)

This complex, covering about 800 acres, includes imperfectly and poorly drained, pebbly and loamy soils overlying Eocene clays, together with limited areas of moderately well drained fine sandy loams, derived for the most part from Reading Beds sands. The main occurrences are on London Clay and Reading Beds at Cowcroft, near Chesham, and on Reading Beds south-east of Hemel Hempstead. In both localities the Eocene beds are more or less disturbed and masked by pebbly drift, so that soil conditions are correspondingly variable. To a major extent, however, drainage is restricted at no great depth by impervious clay, and subsoil horizons are in consequence moderately or strongly gleyed. Closely related soils occur sporadically elsewhere on the Chiltern Plateau, wherever the underlying drift is derived largely from Reading Beds clay, but indications of drainage impedance are rarely so marked as on the main outliers.

The Cowcroft outlier is largely under woodland, and much of it has been dug over for brick-making. Around Bedmond and Abbots Langley there are some small oakwoods and mixed plantations, but most of the land is used for agriculture. In this area the soils occupy gentle or moderate slopes, and the prevailing tendency to seasonal waterlogging is mainly a result of seepage from the gravelly deposits at higher levels. Locally, where seepage is concentrated, rushy patches occur in grassland and the ground may remain moist for most of the year. Under semi-natural conditions, the soils are strongly acid and may be slightly podzolized, but on cultivated land they have usually been chalked and have a near-neutral reaction.

The dominant soils of the complex, occurring on London Clay at Cowcroft and on Reading Beds clay around Bedmond, have surface and sub-surface horizons of pebbly loam, less frequently sandy loam or clay loam, underlain at 12 to 24 in. by dense, plastic clay or sandy clay, distinctly mottled with yellow and grey. In most instances the sub-surface horizons are brown or yellowish brown, and may be free of mottling, but under poorer drainage conditions they are pale brown or grey, and rusty mottling extends to the surface. Where the drift is thin the mottled clay subsoil is free of stones; commonly, however, it is more or less pebbly, suggesting that the textural change with depth is mainly pedological in origin.

These soils, which are akin to the Titchfield series (Kay, 1939), are represented below by two profiles near Bedmond, one under oakwood with a mor humus layer, the other in agricultural land carrying a long-term ley. Both are developed in pebbly drift, which in the latter profile is over 36 in. thick, whereas in the former the yellowish red clay below that depth is virtually stoneless, and is apparently Reading Beds in situ. In humus form, texture and stone content, and in the general sequence of horizons, the woodland profile resembles those of the Berkhamsted series under similar vegetation (Ht 47, p. 70), but is clearly more strongly gleyed. There are signs of humus and iron mobilization immediately beneath the H layer, and the succeeding loamy horizon, designated Eg, shows faint rusty mottling. This horizon, which appears nearly white when dry, is waterlogged in wet seasons, and much of the iron it originally contained seems either to have been segregated into concretions, or to have been lost by lateral seepage. The grassland soil (Ht 53) is less strongly gleyed, and the A horizon is finer in texture, probably as a result of accelerated erosion, but below 14 in. the Btg horizon resembles that of the woodland profile.

Both at Cowcroft and at Bedmond, acid gley soils as described above grade into the Berkhamsted series, and are also associated locally with nearly stone-free, sandy soils, developed on outcrops of Reading Beds sand. Occasional borings have revealed deep, well drained, loamy fine sands overlying paler-coloured sand, but more commonly the underlying beds include seams of grey clay, and give rise to soils of fine sandy loam or fine sandy clay loam texture. Profile Ht 67, described on arable land south-east of Bedmond, is representative of these soils, which are usually moderately well drained, and conform to the Bursledon series of Kay (1939). The ploughed layer is a friable fine sandy loam which readily caps and runs when exposed to the rain. Beneath this there is a brownish yellow Eb horizon, followed by a weakly developed textural B horizon of sandy clay loam texture with faint varicoloured mottling. Around the point where the profile was described, free-working sandy soils occupy a fairly well defined area of about 6 acres. At Cowcroft, similar soils occur sporadically on the western side of the outlier, where the Reading Beds, though clearly disturbed, are relatively free of drift. Here, as the boundary with the Chalk is approached, the subsoil consists locally of bright brown or greenish sandy clay with black-coated flints, derived from the glauconitic basal ("Bull-Head") bed.

Descriptions of representative profiles
(*Analytical data in Table* 9, *p.* 155)

PROFILE NO.: Ht 66 (Cowcroft series)

Location: Job's Wood, Bedmond (grid ref. TL/107036).
Slope: 2°. *Aspect:* south-east. *Altitude:* 400 ft. O.D.
Land use: woodland (high forest).
Vegetation: oak (*Quercus robur*) with some ash (*Fraxinus excelsior*) saplings; field layer dominated by bramble (*Rubus* spp.), with patches of bracken and bluebells (*Endymion nonscriptus*).

Horizons:

L		Litter, mainly oak leaves, ½ in. thick.
F		Partially decomposed, matted, litter, up to ½ in. thick.
H		Very dark brown, loose, finely granular humus containing a moderate proportion of recognizable plant remains, and bleached sand grains; abundant fine roots; 1 in. thick.
A/Ea	0–1 in.	Dark grey, friable to loose, humose fine sandy loam with irregular paler-coloured (bleached) and ochreous zones, containing occasional flint and quartzose pebbles and abundant roots; clear irregular boundary.
Ebg	1–7 in.	Grey-brown to brown (10 YR–7·5 YR 5/2), very pebbly loam, with faint, common, grey (10 YR 7/2) and ochreous mottling, humose infillings and humus-staining locally which appears purplish; slightly compact and brittle in place; friable when removed, with very weak sub-angular blocky structure; abundant woody roots; clear boundary.
Bt1g	7–18 in.	Pebbly, very firm and plastic, more or less sandy clay, prominently mottled with light grey to white and strong brown to reddish yellow (7·5 YR 5/8–6/8); grey colours with some humus-staining where stones are embedded; some soft black manganiferous and/or humose re-deposited material on stones and cleavage faces; weak blocky structure evident in less stony zones; frequent woody roots; merging boundary.

| Bt2g | 18–36 in. | Essentially similar, mottled, stony clay to sandy clay with less black staining and a higher proportion of reddish yellow colours; few roots; clear boundary. |
| Cg | 36 in.+ | Very plastic, yellowish red (5 YR 4/6–4/8) clay, prominently mottled with light grey and red, containing only occasional stones (Reading Beds clay *in situ*). |

PROFILE NO.: Ht 53 (Cowcroft series)

Location: Sheppeys Farm, Abbots Langley (grid ref. TL/097033).
Slope: 3°, slightly concave.   *Aspect:* south-west.   *Altitude:* 400 ft. O.D.
Land use: grass-clover ley.

Horizons:

Ap	0–6 in.	Very dark greyish brown (10 YR 3/1–4/2), pebbly, friable to firm, clay loam with some ochreous mottling associated with root channels; stones include flint pebbles and shattered flints and occasional quartzose pebbles; moderate medium sub-angular blocky structure, more granular in upper 2 in.; aggregates hard when dry; abundant grass roots; merging boundary, with humose infillings.
Bt1(g)	6–14 in.	Brown (7·5 YR 5/4) pebbly firm clay, faintly mottled with pale brown and reddish yellow; stones as above; moderate medium sub-angular blocky structure, with relatively pale-coloured aggregate faces; frequent roots; merging boundary.
Bt2g	14–36 in.+	Pebbly, very firm clay, very plastic when wet, prominently mottled with reddish yellow, light grey and red, grey becoming dominant at base; stones as above; structure ill-defined; few roots.

PROFILE NO.: Ht 67 (Bursledon series)

Location: Tenement's Farm, Bedmond (grid ref. TL/103033).
Slope: 2° convex.   *Aspect:* north-east.   *Altitude:* 375 ft. O.D.
Land use: arable (fallow).

Horizons:

Ap	0–8 in.	Dark greyish brown (10 YR 4/2) friable fine sandy loam with occasional flint and quartzose pebbles, clods slightly hard when dry, weak cloddy structure breaking down locally to crumb; frequent roots; added chalk; clear boundary.
Eb	8–16 in.	Brown to yellowish brown (10 YR 5/3–5/4), porous, friable, fine sandy loam with many humose infillings (worm channels); occasional stones as above; very weak fine sub-angular blocky to crumb structure; few roots; merging boundary.
Bt(g)	16–25 in.	Brownish yellow (10 YR 6/6) stoneless fine sandy clay loam with humose infillings, finely and faintly mottled with paler and with redder colours; weak blocky structure; porous, but fairly compact in place; friable when dug out; few roots; merging boundary.

| Bt/C(g) | 25–36 in. | Light yellowish brown, fine sandy loam to fine sandy clay loam with fine, faint to distinct, grey, brown and reddish mottling; compact in place; becoming weakly laminated; occasional worm channels; roots rare; merging boundary. |
| C | 36–40 in.+ | Weakly laminated, brownish yellow, fine sandy loam with thin, interbedded seams of light grey clay, compact in place. |

SOILS OF THE CHILTERN VALLEYS AND THE ICKNIELD BELT

WINCHESTER SERIES

Soils of this series, the most extensive in the area apart from the Batcombe, are formed on Clay-with-flints which rests irregularly on Chalk at depths ranging from 12 in. to 6 ft. or more. Covering about 22,000 acres, they occur for the most part on upper slopes and spurs, bordering the Batcombe and Berkhamsted series, and often extending for considerable distances down the sides of the valleys (Plate I). Where gradients are moderate, they often merge down-hill into soils of the Charity complex, but on steeper, particularly west- and south-facing, slopes they are generally confined to a narrow belt at the crest (Plate VIIIb), and are replaced on the steepest part of the slope by chalky soil (Icknield series and/or Coombe complex).

The surface horizons are variable in texture, depending largely on the extent to which accelerated erosion has occurred. Under semi-natural vegetation there is usually a layer of very flinty or pebbly loam above the clay subsoil, but the cultivated soils are predominantly clay loams, with clays on the most eroded sites. Drainage, though somewhat variable, is generally good, as the Clay-with-flints is sufficiently well fissured to allow percolation, and removal of excess surface water is further facilitated by run-off and down-slope seepage.

Probably as a consequence of their stony and intractable character, coupled with their occurrence on slopes of up to 12°, the soils carry a relatively high proportion of woodland. Some of the woods are of ancient origin, or result from the reversion of former scrublands; whereas others, especially the smaller ones, have clearly been planted and generally obscure one or more dell-holes. On land which has never been cultivated, the soils are moderately to strongly acid at the surface, but the subsoil horizons have a higher base status than in the associated plateau soils. Most of the arable soils contain chalk as residues of added dressings, and the shallower profiles are frequently calcareous throughout.

Morphologically, the Winchester soils are distinguished from those of the Batcombe and Berkhamsted series by the character of their subsoil horizons. In typical profiles, more or less disturbed Chalk is encountered within 5 ft. of the surface, and is overlain by a variable thickness of very tenacious, dark brown or yellowish red clay, which encloses large, nodular or broken flints, and breaks down easily when partly dry into angular blocky aggregates with smooth, slickensided faces. This horizon—the Clay-with-flints *sensu stricto*—contains over 70 per cent of clay-size particles, and is often blackened by manganiferous deposits, but lacks the distinct red, yellow and greyish mottling characteristic of corresponding horizons in the plateau soils. In profiles with chalk at 30 in. or less, unmodified Clay-with-flints may extend to the base of the A horizon, but where the Chalk lies deeper the upper part of the subsoil generally consists of less tenacious clay, which may be sandy or pebbly, either in pockets or throughout the mass. Under semi-natural conditions, and in "agricultural" profiles that have undergone little accelerated erosion, the clay is often overlain in turn by a friable sub-surface (Eb) horizon: on much of the cultivated land, however, this horizon is absent or discontinuous, the Ap horizon resting with a clear boundary on the clay subsoil.

As in the Batcombe and Berkhamsted series, the clayey subsoil horizons are normally designated Bt. Where an Eb horizon is present, the underlying material usually shows relatively pale-coloured clay-deficient zones and sandy coatings on structural faces, indicating that the textural change with depth is due partly to downward translocation of clay-size particles. Such profiles are, however, clearly composite, the immediate subsoil consisting of stony drift which differs in composition from the overlying horizons, and often from the basal Clay-with-flints. The latter layer is generally thickest where it occupies "pipes" and hollows in the Chalk surface, and sometimes appears to form part of an older profile, the truncated remains of which are overlain by a more recent solifluxion deposit.

On slopes where the Winchester series grades into chalky soil (normally of the Wallop series), the boundary may be located precisely by the appearance of the brightly-coloured, non-calcareous clay subsoil. The boundaries with the Batcombe, Berkhamsted and Charity soils are less easily defined, and because of the inherent variability of the substrata, coupled with the difficulty of augering in such stony material, the areas shown as Winchester necessarily include a relatively high proportion of soils representing transitions to one or other of these series. The most obvious inclusions, readily identifiable on the ground, are narrow strips of stony colluvial soil, which occupy depressions in the valley sides, and may be of loam or finer texture, depending on the source of the materials composing them. Elsewhere, especially at lower levels, and in the vicinity of Eocene outliers, the basal Clay-with-flints is only patchily developed, and the subsoils may consist locally of yellow or reddish, mottled clay with few stones.

The main variants encountered are exemplified by the five profiles recorded below, two of which, with chalk at 15 in. and 43 in. respectively, are located in a semi-natural beechwood on the brow of the escarpment, and three on agricultural land under temporary or permanent grass.

In both woodland profiles the upper (A and Eb) horizons to a depth of 7 in. consist of very flinty, friable loam with a crumb structure, resting sharply on the subsoil clay, which in the deeper profile (Bu 54) is faintly mottled and appreciably sandy in the upper part. The sharp lower boundary of these horizons, coupled with their extreme flintiness, suggests that they represent a superficial migratory layer in which the stones have been concentrated by preferential erosion or lateral eluviation of finer material (Avery et al., 1959). The humose layers approximate to the acid mull type, but a tendency to mor formation is apparent, especially in Bu 16, which occupies an exposed slope virtually bare of ground vegetation and dries out strongly in summer. Locally, on similar sites, soils with thicker Eb horizons may show evidence of superficial podzolization;

Photograph by courtesy of the Forestry Commission

Plate X. Mature (160 years old) beech trees in Monkton Wood, Hampden (Batcombe series) with groups of natural regeneration derived from the abundant mast of 1922. The stand has since been several times thinned, and is being further recruited, partly by natural regeneration of beech, and partly by planting larch and other conifers.

Photograph by courtesy of the Forestry Commission

Plate XI. Stand of 52 years old European larch (*Larix decidua*) on soil of the Batcombe series, originating as a row-about mixture of beech and larch. The beech mostly failed and the larch, recently thinned, is due for interplanting with some shade-tolerant tree.

whereas on north-east facing slopes, where soil-moisture conditions are more equable, brambles, herbs and moisture-loving grasses (e.g. *Deschampsia caespitosa*) grow luxuriantly, and the humose layers are generally of mull type.

Profiles Bu 71 and Bu 70, located on the gentler east-facing slopes of the Little Hampden valley (see Fig. 7, p. 20) may be considered as cultivated counterparts of the two woodland profiles. The shallower profile (Bu 71) was described at the upper end of a field under ley, and is evidently eroded, the fine-textured, blocky, Ap horizon resting directly on the clay subsoil. In the deeper profile (Bu 70), from an old grass field further up-slope, the A horizon has a more friable consistency, with finer, more porous structural aggregates, and is under-lain by a loamy sub-surface (Eb) horizon up to 9 in. thick.

Very flinty soils typified by these four profiles occur widely on escarpment spurs and upper valley sides bordering the higher ridges, and isolated areas with similar soils are found on the outlying Pulpit and Pitstone Hills as well as at lower levels in front of the escarpment, notably at Aldbury and Pendley and south-east of Wendover. These lower-lying occurrences usually occupy the gentler side of an asymmetrical knoll or low ridge, and that at Pendley contains occasional quartzose pebbles, suggesting contamination with glacial drift.

Where the Plateau Drift consists of Pebbly Clay and Sand, giving rise to soils of the Berkhamsted series, the upper horizons of the associated Winchester soils contain numerous flint pebbles in addition to angular flints, accompanied, at levels below 400 ft., by quartzites and other far-travelled stones. This pebbly variant is exemplified by profile Ht 43, recorded under ley near Model Farm, Abbots Langley. The Ap horizon is a pebbly clay loam, and from 11 to 36 in., where chalk is encountered, the subsoil consists for the most part of very stiff, yellowish red clay, in which pebbles are progressively replaced by large, more or less broken flints. Similar soils occur widely on gently to moderately sloping land in the south-east, but as the Clay-with-flints layer at the base is rarely more than 3 ft. thick, and follows the undulations of the Chalk surface, the thickness of the overlying soil varies considerably over short distances.

Descriptions of representative profiles
(Analytical data in Table 9, pp. 155–6)

PROFILE NO.: Bu 16 (Winchester series)

Locality: Hillock Wood, Great Hampden (grid ref. SP/828027).

Slope: 6–7°.   *Aspect:* south-west.   *Altitude:* 750 ft. O.D.

Land use: woodland (high forest).

Vegetation: beechwood (*Fagetum rubosum*); closed canopy; field layer sparse (wind-swept site); scattered brambles (*Rubus* spp.) and herbs, including *Asperula odorata*, nearby.

Horizons:

L	Litter, mainly beech leaves, thin and discontinuous.
F/H	Partially decomposed litter, up to ½ in. thick, followed in places by a thin layer of black powdery humus.

A   0–2½ in.   Very dark greyish brown (10 YR 3/2), very flinty, friable loam with bleached sand grains and moderate crumb structure, soft and paler in colour when dry; flints mainly small and shattered; abundant woody roots; clear irregular boundary.

Eb   2½–7 in.   Brown (10 YR–7·5 YR 4/4), very flinty, friable loam to silt loam with weak structure and humose infillings, light brownish grey when dry; flints as above; abundant roots; earthworms present; sharp smooth boundary.

Bt   7–15 in.   Yellowish red, very flinty, very firm clay with brown structural faces and many black specks; flints large, mainly broken nodules; medium to coarse blocky structure; very plastic when wet; frequent roots; sharp irregular boundary.

Bt/C   15–24 in.   Disturbed chalk with patches of reddish yellow chalky loam and yellowish red clay containing unbroken flints.

C   24 in.+   Fissured brown-stained chalk *in situ*, with nodular flints and occasional inclusions of reddish clay.

PROFILE NO.: Bu 54 (Winchester series)

Location: Hillock Wood, Great Hampden (grid ref. SP/829027).

Slope: 5° convex.   *Aspect:* south-west.   *Altitude:* 770 ft. O.D.

Land use: woodland (high forest).

Vegetation: beechwood (*Fagetum rubosum*) with some oak (*Quercus robur*); field layer dominated by bramble (*Rubus* spp.), with scattered herbs, chiefly *Galeobdolon luteum.*

Horizons:

L   Litter, mainly beech leaves, up to 1 in. thick.

F/H   Partially decomposed litter, thin and discontinuous.

A   0–2½ in.   Very dark grey to greyish brown (10 YR 3/1–4/2), very flinty, friable loam with some bleached sand grains and abundant roots; flints mainly small and angular; occasional rounded and sub-angular iron-stone nodules; crumb structure with numerous cavities; earthworms active; clear irregular boundary.

Eb   2½–7 in.   Brown (7·5 YR–10 YR 4/4), very flinty, friable loam with humose infillings and abundant roots, grey-brown and soft when dry; shattered flints and iron-stone nodules as above; weak crumb structure; clear undulating boundary.

Bt1   7–26 in.   Yellowish red (5 YR 4/4–5/8), very firm, flinty clay with few, faint, pale brown and red mottlings and irregular manganiferous deposits which become more prominent with depth; occasional infilled channels; flints mainly large, more or less broken nodules; occasional iron-stone nodules as above; moderate medium to coarse blocky structure; aggregate faces relatively pale-coloured and locally coated with sand; roots less frequent; this horizon includes patches of relatively flint-free sandy clay loam to sandy clay containing numerous small manganiferous concretions; merging boundary.

| Bt2 | 26–43 in. | Yellowish red (5 YR 4/8–5/8), very plastic, flinty clay with faint mottling and manganiferous deposits on cleavage faces and flints, becoming less evident with depth; flints rather less numerous and largely unbroken; breaks down easily when partly dry to fine to medium blocky aggregates with brown shiny faces; few roots; sharp irregular boundary. |
| C | 43 in.+ | Soft weathered chalk containing unbroken flint nodules and seams of reddish yellow clay. |

PROFILE NO.: Bu 71 (Winchester series)

Location: Manor Farm, Little Hampden (grid ref. SP/862038).

Slope: 6° convex.   *Aspect:* east.   *Altitude:* 595 ft. O.D.

Land use: grass-clover ley.

Horizons:

Ap	0–9 in.	Dark greyish brown (10 YR 4/2), very firm, very flinty, silty clay loam, very hard when dry; flints mainly angular, shattered; moderate medium blocky structure, becoming finer and more granular in the upper 3 in.; abundant fine roots; added chalk; clear boundary.
Bt	9–23 in.	Yellowish red (5 YR 4/6) to dark brown (7·5 YR 4/4), very firm, very flinty clay with black manganiferous deposits on structural faces and flints; numerous large slightly broken flints in addition to shattered fragments; moderate, medium to coarse blocky structure; infilled worm tracks; roots frequent to 18 in., occasional below; sharp irregular boundary, extending downwards locally to 50 in.
Bt/C	24–42 in.	Transitional layer containing yellowish red clay and large flints, mixed with increasing amounts of rubbly chalk; zones consisting almost entirely of either clay or chalk are readily distinguishable, together with seams of pale brown, more friable, chalky material.
C	42 in.+	White chalk with few flints.

PROFILE NO.: Bu 70 (Winchester series)

Location: Manor Farm, Little Hampden (grid ref. SP/861038).

Slope: 3–4° convex.   *Aspect:* east.   *Altitude:* 650 ft. O.D.

Land use: permanent grassland.

Horizons:

| A | 0–7 in. | Dark greyish brown (10 YR 4/2), very flinty, firm clay loam, hard when dry; flints mainly angular, shattered; moderate medium sub-angular blocky structure; abundant fine roots; earthworms active; added chalk; clear, irregular boundary. |
| Eb | 7–15 in. | Brown (10 YR 4/3–5/4), very flinty, firm loam to clay loam with humose infillings and darker-coloured aggregate faces; weak fine sub-angular blocky structure; frequent roots and worm channels; horizon variable in degree of expression, up to 9 in. thick; clear undulating boundary. |

Bt   15–26 in.+   Yellowish red (5 YR 4/6–4/8), very firm, very flinty clay with
                          black manganiferous speckles and some faint paler-coloured
                          mottling; flints mainly large broken nodules; moderate
                          blocky structure; some worm channels; few roots; chalk at
                          50 in.

PROFILE NO.: Ht 43 (Winchester series)

Location: Model Farm, Abbots Langley (grid ref. TL/063003).

Slope: 4° convex.   *Aspect:* south.   *Altitude:* 325 ft. O.D.

Land use: grass-clover ley (first year).

Horizons:

Ap   0–6 in.   Dark greyish brown (10 YR 4/2), very pebbly, firm clay loam,
                          hard when dry, with moderate, medium to fine, sub-angular
                          blocky and granular structure; stones mainly flint pebbles,
                          with some quartz and quartzite pebbles and angular flints;
                          abundant roots; clear boundary.

Eb   6–11 in.   Brown to dark brown (7·5 YR 4/2–4/4), very pebbly, firm,
                          clay loam to loam with many humose infillings; medium to
                          fine, sub-angular blocky and granular structure; frequent
                          roots; added chalk; horizon variable in thickness and degree
                          of expression; clear or merging boundary.

Bt   11–36 in.   Yellowish red (5 YR 4/8), very firm, flinty clay with black
                          manganiferous staining and brown shiny faces where stones
                          are embedded; moderate, medium to coarse blocky struc-
                          ture; pebbles progressively replaced with depth by angular
                          flints, including an increasing proportion of large unbroken
                          nodules; few roots and worm tracks; sharp irregular boun-
                          dary. (Locally the upper part of this horizon is replaced to a
                          depth of 24 in. by inclusions of dark brown and brownish
                          yellow, faintly mottled, pebbly clay loam, which is friable
                          to firm when moist, and shows well marked clay coatings in
                          pores and around stones.)

C   36 in.+   Soft white chalk with nodular flints.

CHARITY COMPLEX
(*Charity and Nettleden Series*)

Well drained, naturally acid soils formed on Coombe Deposits and "dry-valley
gravel" are grouped with the Charity complex and cover about 10,500 acres, or
roughly 8 per cent of the area surveyed. The dominant soil series, to which the
name Charity* was first applied, consists of flinty and pebbly loams, usually
silty, with finer-textured, more or less gravelly subsoils which rest at variable
depths either on chalky Head (Coombe-Rock), or directly on Chalk. Soils of this
series are typically developed on even or concave foot-slopes of up to 6°, and are
most extensive in the wind-gaps and in the broader dip-slope valleys (Plate VIa),
often occupying the gentler north-east and east facing slopes below the Winchester zone. These deep, well drained soils are largely under arable crops or

---

* Derived from Stoke Charity, a village north of Winchester.

leys, and there are only limited areas of woodland, chiefly on the Hampden and Ashridge estates. On cultivated land they often contain chalk, either as residues of added dressings, or washed down from adjoining slopes where the soil is naturally calcareous.

In the bottoms of many of the dry valleys the Charity soils are accompanied or replaced by superficially similar soils with a substratum of loose, flint gravel. These have been distinguished as the Nettleden series but, as they usually occur only in narrow strips, they are not shown separately on the map. Also included in the complex are small patches of nearly stoneless, silty soil, developed on brick earth-like slope deposits.

The most extensive soil of the complex is characterized by the following sequence of horizons. At the surface is an A horizon of dark greyish brown silt loam, less frequently loam or silty clay loam, containing angular flints with locally variable proportions of pebbles, depending on the nature of the adjacent Plateau Drift. This is followed by a brown, friable sub-surface (Eb) horizon of similar texture with a crumb or fine sub-angular blocky structure. Below 12 in. there is a gradual change to a stiffer, reddish brown Bt horizon which has a more or less well defined blocky structure, and may show black manganiferous staining. It usually becomes finer in texture and more plastic with depth, but is normally less tenacious than the subsoil in the Winchester series, and the flints are smaller and more broken. Even within a short distance, the thickness of the horizons and the depth to chalky material may vary considerably, the variations being frequently accompanied by differences in texture and stoniness. At the one extreme, in soils transitional to the Coombe series, pale-coloured Coombe-Rock is encountered at 15–18 in., the textural difference between surface and subsoil is then only weakly expressed, and the A horizon is commonly a silty clay loam. In deeper profiles the soil may be non-calcareous to 6 ft. or more, the upper horizons are generally thicker and lighter in texture, and the clayey subsoils are often more stony. The most gravelly soils tend to resemble those of the St. Albans series, and mainly occur in the lower parts of the main valleys adjacent to the alluvium, where they may be associated with terrace remnants, as at Redbourn and Kings Langley.

Locally the drift on gentle, north-east and east facing slopes consists of virtually stoneless brick-earth, giving rise to deep, brown, silty soils similar to those which in Hampshire have been classed as the Hamble series (Kay, 1939). These occur north of Redbourn, south of Langleybury church, and in shallow, asymmetrical dry valleys north-east of Bedmond, where they are in marked contrast with the coarser, pebbly soils of the Berkhamsted complex occupying the higher ground. Small patches of similar soil have also been identified in several other localities, notably in the Missenden–Wendover valley.

Three profiles conforming to the Charity series are recorded below. Two (Bu 55 and Bu 56) are in a semi-natural beechwood occupying the high-level wind-gap at Longdown, south-east of Kimble. In this locality the drift-mantled southern foot-slope of the former through-valley is dissected by obsequent* coombes, leaving an isolated patch of Charity soils bounded on three sides by steep chalky slopes. The first profile, with a thin, acid mull A horizon, is most typical of the series, and is sited near the middle of the area mapped, where the

---

* Drainage-lines inclined in a direction opposed to the original inclination of an uplifted land surface.

ground vegetation includes brambles and scattered herbs. In the second profile (Bu 56), sited on the exposed western edge, the upper horizons are exceptionally flinty, presumably through the washing out of finer material; here the forest floor is virtually bare and the humose layers are of mor type, accompanied by signs of superficial podzolization. The third profile (Bu 79), described under ley, is in the Little Hampden valley (see Fig. 7, p. 20), roughly 180 yards down-slope from the lower of the two Winchester profiles (Bu 71) previously described.

The characteristically silty texture of these soils suggests that the parent deposits consist partly of loess, which has been more or less mixed by solifluxion with frost-shattered flints, disintegrated chalk, and Plateau-Drift material of local origin (Avery *et al.*, 1959). In some cases (e.g. Bu 55, Bu 79), the underlying chalky drift may represent the parent material of the soil; elsewhere, however, the processes of leaching and textural differentiation have evidently operated on non-uniform materials which, in the shallower valleys, may have been largely non-calcareous when deposited. It is certain, too, that many of the cultivated soils on concave slopes include the superposed products of more than one phase of solifluxion or rain-wash, the original profile having been buried beneath recently accumulated colluvial material.

The soils classed as Nettleden series are typically developed in narrow, V-shaped dry-valleys, both at higher and lower levels, but also occur in the bottoms of the larger valleys above the points at which streams rise. At Kinsbourne Green, Trowley Bottom and Nettleden, and, further west, in Hampden Bottom, are old pits exposing at least 4 ft. of coarse flint gravel beneath 1 to 2 ft. of stony soil, but in profile pits the gravel was never more than about 2 ft. thick, and consisted largely of finely shattered flint. A profile (Ht 63) in the valley west of Redbourn is described below and others have been recorded in Threegates Bottom, Chartridge, and in the valley below Hampden Common. In all the gravel rests on reddish, flinty clay, and its "washed out" appearance, coupled with the occurrence of small ferri-manganiferous concretions, suggests that it is waterlogged for short periods and functions as a temporary drainage channel. The overlying soil in all three profiles consists of flinty silt loam showing little sign of textural differentiation, which probably accumulated by soil-creep or rain-wash in quite recent times. Elsewhere, the soil in similar situations may be sandy or pebbly, depending on the source of the material.

Descriptions of representative profiles

(Analytical data in Table 9, pp. 156–7)

PROFILE NO.: Bu 55 (Charity series)

Location: Ninn Wood, Monks Risborough (grid ref. 833040).

Slope: c. 2° even.   *Aspect:* north.   *Altitude:* 650 ft. O.D.

Land use: woodland (high forest)

Vegetation: beechwood (*Fagetum rubosum*), with ash (*Fraxinus excelsior*) seedlings in spaces left by felling; field layer, sparse locally, includes *Rubus spp.* and scattered herbs, notably *Chamaenerion angustifolium*, *Circaea lutetiana*, *Oxalis acetosella*.

Horizons:

L	Litter, mainly beech leaves, up to 1 in. thick.
F	Partially decomposed litter, thin and discontinuous.

A   0–3 in.   Dark grey to greyish brown (10 YR 4/1–4/2) friable flinty silt loam, soft and greyer in colour when dry; flints small and shattered; moderate crumb structure with numerous cavities; abundant woody roots; earthworms present; clear irregular boundary.

Eb   3–11 in.   Brown (7·5 YR 4/4–5/4) friable flinty silt loam with occasional infilled worm channels; soft and greyer in colour when dry; weak crumb structure; frequent woody roots; clear undulating boundary.

Eb/Bt   11–17 in.   Dark brown (7·5 YR–5 YR 4/4) friable flinty silt loam with weak fine sub-angular blocky structure; flints as above; roots less frequent; clear undulating boundary.

Bt   17–33 in.   Reddish brown (5 YR 4/4) firm flinty silty clay with some black staining and small manganiferous concretions; flints as above, less numerous with depth; moderate, medium to coarse blocky structure with waxy colloid-rich coatings and channel fillings; increasingly plastic with depth; occasional roots; horizon 12 to 17 in. thick; sharp undulating boundary.

C   33 in.+   Brown to reddish yellow (7·5 YR 5/4–6/6), very calcareous, silty clay loam containing angular shattered flints and numerous sub-angular and rounded chalk fragments; compact in place, but friable when dug out.

PROFILE NO.: Bu 56 (Charity series)

Location: Ninn Wood, Monks Risborough (grid ref. SP/830040)

Slope: 3° convex. *Aspect:* south-west. *Altitude:* 625 ft. O.D.

Land use: woodland (high forest).

Vegetation: beechwood (*Fagetum ericetosum*) with nearly closed canopy; field layer limited to scattered mosses, including *Polytrichum* spp.

Horizons:

L   Litter, mainly beech leaves and twigs, thin and discontinuous.

F   Partially decomposed, matted litter, up to 1 in. thick.

H   Black, very finely granular humus, $\frac{1}{2}$–1 in. thick, with abundant fine woody roots; sharp boundary.

A/Ea   0–1$\frac{1}{2}$ in.   Compact and locally laminated, very flinty silt loam, more or less humus-stained. Includes discontinuous pinkish grey (7·5 YR 6/2) layers and flecks up to $\frac{1}{2}$ in. thick bordered by apparently iron-enriched, dark reddish grey to reddish brown (5 YR 4/2–3) seams; some channels with humose infillings; abundant fine roots, except in bleached zones; sharp irregular boundary.

Eb   1$\frac{1}{2}$–12 in.   Brownish yellow (10 YR 6/6), very flinty, friable silt loam, very pale brown (10 YR 7/4–8/3) and slightly hard when dry; flints mainly small and shattered; very weak crumb structure; frequent woody roots and occasional cavities containing humus; clear smooth boundary.

Eb/Bt	12–17 in.	Reddish yellow (7·5 YR 6/6), friable, very flinty silt loam with some black specks and reddish clayey flecks; weak sub-angular blocky structure, with pale-cloured silty coatings on cleavage faces; roots less frequent; clear, undulating boundary.
Bt1	17–35 in.	Strong brown to yellowish red (7·5 YR–5 YR 5/8), firm clay with black specks, very hard when dry; fewer and larger flints; weak sub-angular blocky structure; few roots; merging boundary.
Bt2	35–41 in.	Yellowish red (5 YR 4/6), very firm to plastic clay with black staining; very hard when dry; occasional large flints; weak blocky structure; few roots; sharp irregular boundary.
C	41 in.+	Compact disintegrated chalk, containing numerous sub-rounded lumps of hard chalk.

PROFILE NO.: Bu 79 (Charity series)

Location: Manor Farm, Little Hampden (grid ref. SP/864038).

Slope: 5° even. *Aspect:* east. *Altitude:* 575 ft. O.D.

Land use: grass-clover ley.

Horizons:

Ap	0–5 in.	Dark greyish brown (10 YR 4/2–4/3), very flinty, friable silt loam, hard when dry; flints mainly small and shattered; moderate fine sub-angular blocky structure; abundant grass roots; added chalk; clear boundary.
Eb	5–21 in.	Yellowish brown to brown (10 YR–7·5 YR 5/4), flinty friable silt loam with infilled worm channels; hard when dry; weak crumb and fine sub-angular blocky structure; frequent roots; merging boundary.
Eb/Bt	21–36 in.	Dark brown (7·5 YR 4/4) firm flinty silty clay loam with redder clayey coatings and flecks; weak medium blocky structure, numerous worm tracks; few roots; merging boundary.
Bt	36–54 in.	Reddish brown (7·5 YR 4/4), very firm, flinty clay with blocky structure; numerous small manganiferous concretions; roots rare; sharp irregular boundary.
C	54 in.+	Pale brown to reddish yellow, compact, calcareous clay loam to clay containing numerous broken flints and chalk fragments; amount of chalk increases with depth and Middle Chalk appears at 86 in.

PROFILE NO.: Ht 63 (Nettleden series)

Location: Flamsteadbury Farm, Flamstead (grid ref. TL/087115).

Slope: nearly level (valley bottom). *Altitude:* 375 ft. O.D.

Land use: arable (fallow).

Horizons:

| Ap | 0–8 in. | Dark greyish brown (10 YR 4/2) friable flinty silt loam, hard when dry; cloddy structure, breaking to fine sub-angular blocky and crumb; flints mainly small and shattered; occasional flint pebbles; few roots; clear boundary. |

(B)/C	8–24 in.	Brown (7·5 YR 4/4) friable flinty silt loam with darker-coloured infillings and aggregate surfaces; crumb structure; occasional small ferri-manganiferous concretions; earthworms active; merging boundary.
C1(g)	24–45 in.	Brown (7·5 YR 5/4) gritty loam to sandy loam, containing abundant angular flint gravel (< 1 in.) and some large broken flints; becomes paler in colour, looser and moister with depth; numerous small ferri-manganiferous concretions and some ochreous mottling below 30 in.
C2	45 in.+	Reddish brown, black-stained, flinty clay.

ICKNIELD SERIES

This series, covering some 8,000 acres, comprises shallow friable soils of rendzina type, formed where the Chalk is virtually free of drift and contains limited amounts (normally less than 5 per cent) of non-calcareous matter. It is most extensive on the face of the escarpment and on the rolling land at its foot, and only occurs in the dip-slope valleys as occasional small patches and narrow belts on steep slopes and spurs. As the land-use potentialities of these thin, chalky soils are largely dependent on relief, a division has been made into a normal (rolling) phase, and a steepland phase characterized by average slopes of more than 11°. Where slopes are moderate the soils are chiefly under arable crops or leys (Plate IVb), but the escarpment slopes and valley sides on which the latter phase is mapped are too steep for regular cultivation and much of the land carries semi-natural grassland or scrub, alternating locally with hanging woods of beech and coniferous plantations (Plate VIIIb).

In this area the Icknield series is mostly developed on Middle Chalk, but extends on to the Upper Chalk in places at the crest of the escarpment. It has also been mapped on the uppermost "white" beds of the Lower Chalk which, although generally containing a little more clay, give rise to soils difficult to distinguish in the field from those formed on the Middle Chalk under similar conditions. The drainage of the soils varies from free to excessive, depending on their depth, their topographic position, and the physical constitution of the underlying chalk.

Typical profiles under woodland or old pasture have very dark greyish brown or dark brown A horizons with a strongly developed granular or crumb structure, which may become somewhat coarser and more blocky in the lower part. This horizon, 4–7 in. thick, contains chalk fragments, and sometimes flints, and rests on a rubbly A/C horizon of more or less humus-stained, chalky loam mixed with fragmented chalk. Fissured chalk in situ normally occurs at from 8 to 15 in. below the surface, although on gentler slopes and in slight depressions there may be 24 in. or more of chalky rubble with a pale-coloured matrix before the solid chalk is reached. In beechwoods the tree-roots are concentrated in the A horizon and few penetrate the fissured chalk below. In typical Chalk grassland, the chief graminaceous species (e.g. *Festuca ovina*) root mainly in the upper few inches, but some of the associated herbs (e.g. *Poterium sanguisorba*) have long tap-roots which exploit the rubbly A/C horizon. The soils support a numerous and varied soil fauna, so that plant residues are rapidly decomposed and incorporated; earthworms are usually present in appreciable numbers, but are scarce under grass in the shallowest and driest soils, the fine humus-rich aggregates of which may consist largely of insect droppings (see Chapter II, p. 51).

On convex slopes where the underlying chalk is soft and erosion relatively active, the A horizons may contain as much as 70 per cent calcium carbonate, but much lower amounts, less than 10 per cent in places, have been recorded on spurs of the escarpment. The less calcareous soils are often stiffer and browner in colour, and clearly incorporate small quantities of Clay-with-flints or Plateau-Drift material; others are distinctly silty, resembling the thin brown soils, distinguished by Robinson (1948) as the Andover series, which occupy considerable areas on the rolling chalk-lands of Wessex, and appear to be partly derived from loess. There is also a tendency, noted by Kay (1934), for low carbonate contents to occur in association with relatively hard strata such as the Chalk Rock, which break down less easily into sand and silt-sized particles than normal chalk: the action of earthworms in bringing finely divided chalk to the surface is much reduced under these conditions, with the result that the fine, humose soil is more prone to decalcification. Mixing by earthworms is also inhibited on the Upper Chalk by the occurrence of numerous flints, which tend to accumulate in a layer at the base of the A horizon, separating it from the chalk below.

The clay content of the soils may amount to over 30 per cent of the mineral fraction but, owing to the large amounts of organic matter and calcium carbonate present, the soils are typically light and friable. Even in the shallowest profiles, the silt and sand fractions include appreciable quantities of quartz and other minerals which can hardly have been entirely derived from the Chalk, and are probably of loessial origin in part.

Three semi-natural profiles are described below, one under beechwood, and two under Chalk grassland on the Ivinghoe hills. The first soil (Bu 20), containing about 70 per cent CaCO₃ and 15 per cent organic matter in the A horizon, is typical of those under sanicle beechwood on exposed upper slopes where ground vegetation is scanty and litter is commonly scattered by the wind. On gentler and more sheltered slopes where the soil is deeper and moister, litter accumulates locally and the A horizons are in general thicker and less calcareous, with a higher total content of organic matter. Profile Bu 7 is representative of the series under semi-natural grassland (now little grazed) on the steeper slopes of the escarpment, where the underlying rock is relatively soft Middle Chalk. The other grassland profile (Bu 8) is developed on Chalk Rock near the summit of Ivinghoe Beacon, under a close turf consisting largely of *Festuca ovina*. Here the soil is less calcareous, and richer in organic matter, and has a softer, more spongy consistency.

When the old grassland soils are ploughed they retain their dark colour and mellow consistency for a few seasons, but with continued cultivation the organic-matter content is rapidly reduced, and the surface horizon, which is greyish brown when moist, appears almost white when dry. The cultivated phase, originally distinguished by Kay (1934) as the Upton series, is typified by profile Bu 115, developed on Lower Chalk. The soil is sticky when wet, but dries out quickly and readily breaks down into friable, granular or fine sub-angular blocky aggregates which are only slightly hard when dry. Because of the lower organic-matter content, the structure is not so well developed as in the semi-natural grassland and woodland phases, but is more stable to water than in non-calcareous soils of similar texture.

On the rolling land of the Icknield Belt most of the soils have been cultivated more or less intensively for long periods, and erosion has been accelerated, so that on convex slopes and knolls the ploughed layers contain much chalky rubble and rest directly on massive chalk. In depressions and at the base of slopes, deeper soils are encountered which are mapped with the Icknield series where the subsoil material consists largely of disintegrated chalk. This deep (colluvial) variant is represented by profile Bu 81 from east of Ivinghoe, where the adjoining ridge-crests bear thin stony soils on Melbourne Rock. In the dip-slope valleys, and wherever the higher ground is drift-covered, the deeper soils on gentler slopes and in minor dry valleys are normally browner and more flinty, and are grouped with the Coombe complex. Thin spreads of flinty drift also occur locally in the steepland phase, but owing to their limited extent are not shown on the map.

Descriptions of representative profiles

(Analytical data in Table 9, p. 157)

PROFILE NO.: Bu 20 (Icknield series)

Location: Ninn Wood, Monks Risborough (grid ref. SP/830042).

Slope: 12° convex.   *Aspect:* north.   *Altitude:* 600 ft. O.D.

Land use: woodland (high forest).

Vegetation: beechwood (*Fagetum calcicolum*), with sparse field layer, comprising scattered *Sanicula europaea* and patches of moss.

Horizons:

L		Litter, mainly beech leaves, sparse.
A	0–5 in.	Very dark grey to greyish brown (10 YR 3/1–3/2), friable humose silty clay loam containing small chalk fragments and very occasional flints; strong granular to fine sub-angular blocky structure; abundant woody roots; clear boundary.
A/C	5–13 in.	Brown-stained chalk brash set in a matrix of pale brown (10 YR 6/4) chalky loam with some infillings of granular humose soil; roots much less frequent; merging boundary.
C	13 in.+	Broken white chalk with occasional brown stains, passing into harder and more massive chalk below 18 in.

PROFILE NO.: Bu 7 (Icknield series)

Location: Ivinghoe Hills (grid ref. SP/959165).

Slope: c. 20°.   *Aspect:* west.   *Altitude:* 675 ft. O.D.

Land use: ungrazed permanent grassland, formerly sheep-walk.

Vegetation: chalk grassland with *Zerna erecta*, *Festuca ovina* and *Poterium sanguisorba*.

Horizons:

A	0–7 in.	Dark brown (7·5 YR 3/2) when moist, to very dark greyish brown (10 YR 3/2) when dry, friable humose loam containing chalk lumps and snail-shell fragments; strong granular (in upper few inches) to fine sub-angular blocky structure; abundant grass roots; worms, ants and moles active; clear smooth boundary.

| A/C | 7–13 in. | Brown-stained chalk brash with a matrix of brown, friable, more or less humose, chalky loam; frequent roots; merging boundary. |
| C | 13 in.+ | Fissured and fragmented white chalk with brown stains, becoming increasingly hard and massive with depth. |

PROFILE NO.: Bu 8 (Icknield series)

Location: Ivinghoe Beacon (grid ref. SP/960168).

Slope: nearly level. *Altitude:* 750 ft. O.D.

Land use: ungrazed permanent grassland, formerly sheep-walk.

Vegetation: chalk grassland dominated by *Festuca ovina*, with yarrow (*Achillea millefolium*) and rib-grass (*Plantago lanceolata*).

Horizons:

| A | 0–7 in. | Very dark brown (7·5 YR 3/2), very friable, humose clay loam, soft when dry, containing occasional fragments of hard chalk and small calcareous particles; fine crumb structure, bound by abundant fibrous roots. |
| A/C | 7 in.+ | Very hard fragmented chalk with a gritty feel (Chalk Rock); humose material and occasional roots in fissures. |

PROFILE NO.: Bu 115 (Icknield series)

Location: Bacombe Lane, Wendover (grid ref. SP/867074).

Slope: 4° convex. *Aspect:* south-east. *Altitude:* 500 ft. O.D.

Land use: arable (fallow).

Horizons:

Ap	0–7 in.	Dark greyish brown (2·5 Y 4/2) friable chalky loam with a few flints; moderate, fine sub-angular blocky and granular structure; frequent roots; clear boundary.
A/C	7–11 in.	Greyish brown (2·5 Y 5/2) friable loam with much chalk brash and some humose infillings; clear irregular boundary.
C	11 in.+	Fissured chalk *in situ*, hard and brown-stained.

PROFILE NO.: Bu 81 (Icknield series)

Location: East of Ivinghoe (grid ref. SP/958165).

Slope: 1° concave. *Altitude:* 525 ft. O.D.

Land use: arable (fallow).

Horizons:

| Ap | 0–8 in. | Greyish brown (10 YR 5/2) friable chalky loam with occasional small shattered flints, light grey (10 YR 7/1) when dry; clods slightly hard when dry, breaking down easily to crumbs when slightly moist; few roots; snail-shell fragments; clear irregular boundary, with frequent worm channels. |

C   8–30 in.+   Pale brown (10 YR 6/3–7/2) chalky silt loam containing frequent chalk fragments and occasional small flints; compact in place but friable when removed; moderate fine sub-angular blocky and granular structure; frequent worm channels; few roots.

WANTAGE SERIES

As the ground falls towards the Vale, the Icknield chalky loams merge into stiffer and greyer soils of the Wantage series, developed on the more argillaceous beds of the Lower Chalk which emerge some 40 to 50 ft. below the Melbourne Rock. In Berkshire, where the series was first described, their outcrop forms an undulating platform 2 or 3 miles wide, but in the Aylesbury district it is considerably narrower and, as it is also more obscured by superficial deposits, the associated soils are much less extensive. The areas mapped, totalling about 3,100 acres, lie mainly on gentle or moderate slopes, and are almost entirely in agricultural use, with a high proportion of arable land. On the Cheddington outlier, and east of Ivinghoe, there are steeper slopes and lynchets with thin, very chalky soils, most of which are uncultivated. These include a shallow, eroded phase, but owing to their limited extent they have been grouped with the Icknield series (steepland phase).

The Wantage soils are normally well drained, yet retain sufficient moisture to withstand a drought. As the underlying rocks include beds of hard grey chalk alternating with softer marl, the depth of soil is somewhat variable, and where hard beds occur fragments may be turned up by the plough, making the surface more or less stony. On footslopes, where the soil is deeper, it often appears to have formed in locally-derived colluvium or Head, containing lumps of chalk and occasional flints embedded in a fine-textured matrix consisting largely of disintegrated chalk. These deeper soils resemble the Blewbury series (Kay, 1934), but they have not been separated in this area, as they are often difficult to distinguish from those formed *in situ* on the softer strata. In depressions and at lower levels they generally grade into either Halton or Ford End soils, and towards the base of slopes the profiles locally show rusty mottling which may be associated with sub-surface seepage above relatively impervious marl bands.

Typical profiles have an A horizon of dark grey, very calcareous, silty clay loam up to 12 in. thick. It may contain fragments of hard chalk, and a few flints are generally present, but as a rule the soil is only slightly stony, the occurrence of flints in any quantity indicating a transition to the drift-derived Tring or Halton series. Under old grassland or woodland a strong granular structure is developed in the upper few inches, grading downwards to fine sub-angular blocky; although the A horizon is thicker than in the Icknield series, its organic-matter content is generally lower, and as the clay content is higher the aggregates are firmer and less porous. On cultivated land the soil is dark grey and very sticky when wet: if ploughed in this condition it dries to hard white lumps, which break down when moisture conditions are favourable to give a fine, stable tilth.

Beneath the A horizon there are usually a few inches of stiff, light brownish grey or pale olive, silty clay loam to silty clay, which grades into unweathered marl or fissured chalk at 15–18 in. This sub-surface (A/C) layer is absent locally, whilst in deeper profiles it may be 12 in. or more thick, when it has a well defined blocky to prismatic structure, and represents a weakly developed (B) horizon. The substratum is paler in colour and more or less brashy, depending on the hardness of the parent rock and the presence or otherwise of colluvial material. It is normally boreable with an auger to depths of 24 in. or more, and hard rock-beds, where present, are usually fragmented.

The non-calcareous residue of the unweathered rock consists largely of clay and silt, with a little fine sand; this is reflected in the mechanical composition of the overlying soils which, except where small amounts of drift are present, are normally of silty clay loam or silty clay texture. The silt and sand fractions may contain glauconite, sufficient being present in the basal beds of the Chalk-Marl to give the material a greenish tinge. The calcium-carbonate content of the surface soil ranges from 20 to 60 per cent in profiles for which estimates are available, and whereas some is sufficiently fine to fall within the clay fraction, most of it is in particles of silt or fine sand size.

Of the three profiles recorded below, the first (Bu 26), on gently undulating arable land near Ivinghoe, is developed on tough marly chalk towards the upper limit of the Chalk Marl outcrop and may be considered as a modal representative of the cultivated Wantage soils. The second profile (Bu 27) is located higher up the same field, adjacent to the boundary with the Icknield series. Here the soil is shallower and more calcareous, and the underlying chalk contains only about 12 per cent insoluble residue as compared with 40 per cent on the lower site.

In the third profile (Ht 71), under old grassland, the thick dark-coloured A horizon is similar in texture, although slightly more sandy, and rests directly on a bed of hard broken rock with a gritty feel, containing approximately 40 per cent insoluble residue. This bed (the Marl-Rock) gives rise to a distinct feature in the country north of Tring, and a similar hard band is conspicuous near Wellwick Farm, Wendover (Frontispiece), where fragments of the rock are scattered over the fields. Other hard beds, known locally as rag, occur at higher levels, notably near Miswell Farm, Tring, where one appears to mark the boundary between the grey and the white chalk. Shallow soils of this nature are not extensive, however, and the outcrop of a particular hard bed can rarely be traced for any considerable distance, either by augering or by surface features.

Descriptions of representative profiles
(*Analytical data in Table 9, p.* 157)

PROFILE NO.: Bu 26 (Wantage series)

Location: Pitstone Green Farm (grid ref. SP/943157).

Slope: 2° even.   *Aspect:* west.   *Altitude:* 390 ft. O.D.

Land use: arable (stubble).

Horizons:

Ap	0–10 in.	Dark greyish brown to grey (2·5 Y 4/2–5/1), friable to firm, silty clay loam containing chalk fragments and occasional small shattered flints; cloddy structure, breaking down easily to moderate, fine sub-angular blocky and granular; abundant roots; clear, smooth boundary.

A/C	10–20 in.	Light olive-grey (2·5 Y–5 Y 6/2) firm silty clay containing numerous fragments of marly chalk and some infillings of darker-coloured soil; weak fine blocky structure; frequent roots; merging boundary.
C	20–30 in.+	Light grey (5 Y 7/2) chalk brash with a friable marly matrix, passing down into fissured grey chalk.

PROFILE NO.: Bu 27 (Wantage series)

Location: Pitstone Green Farm (grid ref. SP/947154).

Slope: 1–2°. *Aspect:* west. *Altitude:* 430 ft. O.D.

Land use: arable (stubble).

Horizons:

Ap	0–7 in.	Dark greyish brown (2·5 YR 5/2), very calcareous, friable silty clay loam containing a few very small flints; hard and nearly white on surface when dry; moderate granular to very fine sub-angular blocky structure; abundant roots; earthworms active; sharp smooth boundary.
A/C	7–15 in.	Light brownish grey (2·5 Y 6/2), friable to firm, silty clay loam to silty clay containing abundant chalk fragments and darker-coloured channel fillings; moderate, fine to medium sub-angular blocky structure; frequent roots; clear irregular boundary.
C	15 in.+	Fragmented, light grey chalk with soil-filled fissures.

PROFILE NO.: Ht 71 (Wantage series)

Location: Little Tring Farm, Tring (grid ref. SP/917133).

Slope: c. 1°. *Altitude:* 375 ft. O.D.

Land use: permanent grassland.

Horizons:

A	0–6 in.	Dark olive-grey (5 Y 3/2) clay loam with occasional sub-angular flints, and strong fine sub-angular blocky and granular structure; aggregates firm, but separate easily; earthworms active; abundant fibrous roots; merging boundary with many infillings.
A/C	6–13 in.	Olive-grey (5 Y 4/2–5/2) firm clay loam with few sub-angular flints and fragments of gritty calcareous rock; strong fine sub-angular blocky structure with dark-coloured structural faces and granular humose infillings; frequent roots; sharp irregular boundary.
C	13 in.+	Hard light grey calcareous rock (Marl-rock), locally stained brown, with olive-grey soil extending down fissures.

COOMBE COMPLEX
(*Coombe and Wallop Series*)

The land mapped as Coombe complex, amounting to about 11,000 acres, is characterized by the dominance of well drained, flinty, calcareous soils, over-lying Coombe-Rock or fragmented Chalk, and distinguished from those of the Icknield and Wantage series by the presence of a distinct, brown or reddish sub-surface horizon. Two soil series, Coombe and Wallop, are recognized as components of the complex and, together with intergrades between them, occupy at least 80 per cent of the area mapped. The Coombe series, which is most extensive, comprises friable medium-textured soils derived from younger Coombe Deposits (including recent hill-wash) that contain chalk rubble and shattered flints in a loamy matrix (Plate VIIa). These soils occur on valley sides and foot-slopes and are typically developed in the upper parts of the major valleys, where they commonly occupy a zone between the Charity and the Icknield series. The Wallop soils, which are stiffer, and often more flinty, are found as a fringe to the Winchester series on upper slopes and spurs, where the Clay-with-flints merges down-hill into thin irregular deposits of flinty clay or clay loam, more or less mixed with rubbly chalk.

Because of their greater depth, the soils of both series are generally more moisture-retentive than the Icknield soils. Most of the moderately and gently sloping land is under cultivation, but there are appreciable areas of woodland, particularly on the Wallop soils, and some of the steeper valley sides carry scrub or rough pasture.

Soils of the Coombe series range in texture from silt loam to clay loam and are normally slightly to moderately flinty. Like the Winchester and Charity series, they may contain pebbles and appreciable quantities of sand where developed on slopes beneath pebbly and sandy plateau deposits. Typical profiles show a dark-coloured A horizon 4–8 in. thick, followed by a brown or yellowish brown (B) horizon of similar texture, which contains fragmentary chalk, and grades at variable depths into chalky rubble (Coombe-Rock) with a pale-coloured, highly calcareous matrix. Both A and (B) horizons are friable when moist, and have a well-developed fine structure, granular at the surface under woodland or old grassland, merging below into fine sub-angular blocky. The chalky substrata are porous, but relatively structureless, and often more compact; on gentle slopes and in minor valley bottoms this unweathered Coombe-Rock material is often several feet thick, but on steeper slopes it may be virtually absent, the soil resting on broken chalk *in situ* at 18–24 in. The chalk content of the soils varies considerably, ranging up to 50 per cent or more on slopes below the Icknield series, where the surface often appears almost white when dry. Less calcareous soils have brighter brown subsoils, and are normally more flinty, and in wood-land profiles transitional to the Charity series the A horizons may be devoid of carbonates. The predominantly silty texture of the soils is partly due to the presence of finely divided chalk, but the particle-size distribution of the non-calcareous residue suggests that, as in the Charity series, the parent materials contain a variable contribution of loess, mixed with chalk, clay, sand and flints of local origin.

Three profiles representative of the series are described below, one under beechwood with typical calcareous mull, and two from arable land. In the first two profiles (Bu 101 and Bu 74), both on west-facing foot-slopes (see Fig. 7, p. 20), the A and (B) horizons appear to have developed, by weathering and partial decalcification, from material resembling the underlying Coombe-Rock. The third profile (Bu 50) shows a dark greyish brown horizon at 22–29 in., designated A', which contains charcoal and is richer in organic carbon and lower in carbonates than the horizons above and below, suggesting that it is an old top-soil buried beneath more recent colluvium.

Soils of the Wallop series are essentially shallow, flinty clays over Chalk. The texture may range from clay to clay loam at the surface, and some pebbles and sand may be present, depending on the nature of the adjoining plateau deposits. Beneath the A horizon there is normally a thin, and sometimes discontinuous, (B) horizon of brown to yellowish red, tenacious clay, which contains chalk fragments and has a well marked blocky structure. This rests either directly on shattered, brown-stained chalk, or on a heterogeneous layer of chalky rubble and flints with clayey or loamy inclusions. Under woodland conditions, as represented by profile Bu 17 below, the A horizon is very dark greyish brown, and often very flinty, with a strongly developed fine sub-angular blocky structure. The profile is at the crest of the escarpment, adjacent to profile Bu 16 (Winchester series, p. 81); on this and similar sites, where ground vegetation is scanty and litter is scattered by the wind, the A horizons are frequently non-calcareous and slightly acid in reaction, and show a distinct tendency to textural differentiation, even with chalk at 12 in. or less. On agricultural land the soils are invariably calcareous, and often appear to have resulted from accelerated erosion of Winchester profiles (Plate VIb). Such soils are heavy to work and, if ploughed when wet, form dense clods which disintegrate only under favourable conditions to give small, sharp-edged, blocky aggregates. A profile (Ht 36) under old grassland at Pendley Farm, Tring, is recorded below.

On the scarp face and on the steepest, west- and south-facing valley sides, the Wallop series is generally separated from the Coombe by a belt of Icknield soils, but the zone it occupies is often too narrow to represent separately on the 1 in. to 1 mile map. In dip-slope valleys where the Icknield series is absent or only locally developed, the Wallop commonly grades down-hill into the Coombe series, and the areas shown as Coombe complex frequently include a high proportion of soils intermediate in texture and consistency, together with small patches of Icknield soil on the steepest and most eroded slopes. In front of the escarpment and in the wind-gaps, the Coombe series occurs on foot-slopes and in dry-valley bottoms, and the Wallop on rising ground, either in association with the Winchester series, or as irregulaɩ, isolated patches which seem to represent disturbed and eroded remnants of former Winchester, Charity or Tring-type profiles. Here again, medium to fine-textured, flinty soils of intermediate character are common, and the Coombe complex includes small areas of Icknield soil in places where the drift is thin and patchy.

Near Halton, and west of Wendover, tracts of stiff, brown, flinty soil are associated with the Wantage series, and are shown as Coombe complex on the map. In these localities, the soils are derived from Coombe Deposits overlying Chalk Marl, and may show slight subsoil mottling, indicating that they are transitional to the Halton series.

Descriptions of representative profiles
(*Analytical data in Table 9, pp. 157–8*)

PROFILE NO.: Bu 101 (Coombe series)

Location: Hobbs Hill, Kimble (grid ref. SP/833044).

Slope: 1–2° even.   *Aspect:* west.   *Altitude:* 625 ft. O.D.

Land use: woodland (high forest).

Vegetation: beechwood (*Fagetum calcicolum*) with some oak, ash and planted larch (*Larix decidua*); field layer dominated by ivy (*Hedera helix*); patches of *Mercurialis perennis* nearby.

Horizons:

L		Litter, mainly beech leaves, less than $\frac{1}{2}$ in. thick, resting directly on mineral soil.
A	0–6 in.	Very dark grey (10 YR 3/1) friable silty clay loam containing fragmentary chalk and a few small shattered flints; strong granular to fine sub-angular blocky structure, consisting largely of worm casts or their residues; abundant fine woody roots; clear boundary.
(B)	6–11 in.	Brown (10 YR 5/3–5/4) friable silty clay loam containing fragmentary chalk, small shattered flints and much infilled top-soil material; strong fine sub-angular blocky and granular (infilled material) structure; frequent woody roots; clear irregular boundary.
C	11–24 in.+	Very pale brown (10 YR 7/4) chalky silty clay loam containing numerous sub-rounded chalk fragments and few shattered flints; compact in place, friable to loose when removed.

PROFILE NO.: Bu 74 (Coombe series)

Location: Manor Farm, Little Hampden (grid ref. SP/864038).

Slope: 5° concave.   *Aspect:* west.   *Altitude:* 550 ft. O.D.

Land use: grass-clover ley (first year).

Horizons:

Ap	0–7 in.	Dark greyish brown (10 YR 4/2) friable silt loam containing shattered angular flints and fragmentary chalk; brown (10 YR 4/3–5/3) and hard when dry; strong, fine to medium sub-angular blocky and granular structure; frequent roots; clear irregular boundary with numerous infillings.
(B)	7–14 in.	Brown to yellowish brown (10 YR 5/3–5/4), friable to firm, flinty silt loam containing fragmentary chalk and numerous darker-coloured infillings (worm channels); moderate, fine and medium sub-angular blocky structure; aggregates finely porous; few roots; clear irregular boundary.
C1	14–32 in.	Light yellowish brown (10 YR 6/4) porous silt loam with much fragmentary chalk and fewer flints than above; structure less well developed; compact in place, but friable when removed; occasional worm tracks; roots rare.
C2	32 in.+	Fragmented chalk, with some pale brown loamy material in fissures.

PROFILE NO.: Bu 50 (Coombe series)

Location: west of Dutchlands Farm, Wendover Dean (grid ref. SP/877035).

Slope: 8°.   *Aspect:* east.   *Altitude:* 600 ft. O.D.

Land use: arable (wheat).

Horizons:

Ap	0–6 in.	Greyish brown (10 YR 5/2) friable flinty clay loam with chalk fragments, hard when dry; moderate, medium to fine sub-angular blocky structure; flints mainly small and shattered; frequent roots; earthworms active; clear, boundary.
(B)	6–22 in.	Brown (7·5 YR–10 YR 4/3), friable to firm, flinty clay loam with frequent chalk fragments and darker-coloured infillings; hard when dry; moderate to strong, fine and medium sub-angular blocky structure; occasional small manganiferous concretions; clear boundary.
A/	22–29 in.	Dark greyish brown (10 YR 4/2), very flinty, clay loam, browner when crushed; infillings of paler-coloured material; structure and consistence much as above; few roots; charcoal fragments; clear boundary.
(B)/	29–36 in.+	Brown (7·5 YR 4/4), firm, flinty and chalky, silty clay loam with a few roots and worm tracks.

PROFILE NO.: Bu 17 (Wallop series)

Location: Hillock Wood, Great Hampden (grid ref. SP/827027).

Slope: 10° convex.   *Aspect:* south-west.   *Altitude:* 725 ft. O.D.

Land use: woodland (high forest).

Vegetation: dense beechwood, field layer absent on site: stunted *Rubus* and scattered herbs nearby.

Horizons:

L		Litter, mainly beech leaves, thin and discontinuous.
A	0–5 in.	Very dark greyish brown (10 YR 3/1–3/2), firm, very flinty clay with strong fine sub-angular blocky structure; aggregates very hard when dry, with dark-coloured organic coatings; abundant woody roots; clear boundary.
(B)	5–11 in.	Strong brown to dark yellowish red (7·5 YR–5 YR 4/6–4/8), very firm, very flinty clay with some inclusions of dark brown, more humose material and occasional brown-stained chalk fragments; moderate, fine to medium blocky structure; abundant woody roots; clear irregular boundary.
(B)C	11–17 in.	Reddish yellow to pale brown, chalky clay loam containing numerous flints and hard chalk fragments; compact in place, friable when removed; merging boundary.
C	17 in.+	Hard white blocky chalk with brown-stained faces.

PROFILE NO.: Ht 36 (Wallop series)

Location: Pendley Farm, Tring (grid ref. SP/945115).

Slope: 2–3° convex.　*Aspect:* west.　*Altitude:* 475 ft. O.D.

Land use: permanent grassland.

Horizons:

A	0–4 in.	Very dark greyish brown (10 YR 3/2), firm, flinty, clay loam to clay containing small chalk fragments; hard when dry; flints mainly small and shattered, with occasional pebbles; moderate fine sub-angular blocky structure; abundant roots; earthworms active; merging boundary.
A/(B)	4–9 in.	Dark brown (10 YR 4/3) flinty clay containing fragmented chalk and much darker-coloured infilled material; strong, medium and fine blocky structure; individual aggregates firm, but separate easily; frequent roots; clear, smooth boundary.
(B)	9–17 in.	Brown (7·5 YR 4/4) firm clay containing large chalk fragments and fewer flints; some humose infillings; moderate medium blocky structure; few roots; sharp irregular boundary.
C	17 in.+	Fragmented chalk with brown clay in fissures.

TRING SERIES

The name Tring has been applied to medium to fine-textured soils with brown clayey subsoils and free to moderate drainage, developed on chalky drift overlying Lower Chalk. Although grouped as brown calcareous soils, they are typically less calcareous and less well drained than those of the Coombe complex, and may be regarded as intergrading to the class of gleyed brown earths. In the type area they are associated with the gently sloping platform at about 425 ft. O.D., which fans out north-westwards from Tring Station and terminates in bluffs overlooking the Vale. Of the 500 acres mapped, the greater part is in arable crops or leys; the fields are large, and some are bounded by deep ditches that are dry in summer, but carry water in wet seasons. Small areas of similar soil, mapped with the Coombe complex, occur near the watershed in the Dagnall Gap, and also near Wendover and Ellesborough, where they are included with the Halton complex.

The drift from which the soil is derived is normally at least 4 ft. thick. Beneath the subsoil the unweathered material contains small sub-rounded chalk fragments and angular flint chips in a yellowish calcareous matrix, and generally has the aspect of Coombe-Rock, but deposits of apparently water-sorted gravel and sand are also present, especially in the lowest ground adjoining the Grand Union Canal. Besides angular flint, the soil and subsoil, and in some instances the chalky material below, contain sub-angular brown-stained flints and occasional pebbles of quartzite, vein quartz and hard sandstone. The presence of these stones, coupled with the topographic relationships of the deposits, indicates that at least part of the drift came from the north and is almost certainly of glacial origin.

A representative profile (Ht 114), examined north of Tring Grove, is recorded below. Generally the A horizons are of silty clay loam or clay loam texture, and are often only slightly stony. The brown or yellowish brown subsoils consist of stiff clay loam or light clay, with a well fissured, blocky or weakly prismatic structure. They generally contain small manganiferous concretions, and may be slightly gleyed, as indicated by the occurrence of faint variegated mottling and pale brown aggregate faces. The chalky substratum is encountered at depths ranging from 15 to 30 in., and the overlying horizons, particularly in the deeper profiles, are more or less completely leached of carbonates. Some of the soils are slightly acid, and others contain added chalk. In the more leached profiles, the subsoils are finer in texture and may be considered as weakly developed Bt horizons. Mechanical analyses of the described profile (Table 9, p. 158) indicate that the A and (B) horizons could have developed, by weathering and leaching, from a deposit resembling the immediate substratum. Elsewhere, however, the underlying material is clearly more sandy.

To north and west, where the drift-sheet is truncated by younger slopes, its eroded edge is marked by the sporadic occurrence of tenacious flinty soil resembling the Wallop series, and thin irregular solifluxion deposits often extend for some distance down the slope, giving rise to soils which are grouped with the Coombe complex. On the south, between Tring Grove and Pendley Farm, the Tring soils merge into brown, flinty silt loams of the Charity series as the ground rises gently towards the southern flanks of the gap.

On the lowest ground adjacent to the canal, and near Marshcroft cottages (grid ref. SP/938127), the soils show indications of imperfect drainage, and appear to have developed in part from thin alluvial deposits associated with the former head-waters of the Bulbourne stream. This land, which must have been wetter before the canal cutting was made, is shown on the map as Gade complex.

Description of a representative profile
(Analytical data in Table 9, p. 158)

PROFILE NO.: Ht 114 (Tring series)

Location: Grove Farm, Tring (grid ref. SP/935133).

Slope: 1°.   *Altitude:* 425 ft. O.D.

Land use: grass-clover ley.

Horizons:

Ap	0–8 in.	Dark greyish brown (10 YR 4/2) firm clay loam containing occasional flints, some small and shattered, some large (>2 in.), sub-angular and brown-stained; occasional small quartzose pebbles; moderate, medium and fine sub-angular blocky structure; abundant fine roots; sharp boundary.
(B)(g)	8–16 in.	Yellowish brown (10 YR 5/4–5/6) firm silty clay with moderate, medium blocky and prismatic structure; aggregates finely porous and faintly mottled internally with pale brown (10 YR 5/3) and ochreous (7·5 YR 5/6) colours; occasional small stones as above; numerous pin-head sized manganiferous concretions; numerous fine roots; clear boundary.

(B)/C(g) 16–25 in. Yellowish brown to light yellowish brown, firm calcareous silty clay loam, faintly mottled with pale brown and strong brown; occasional small stones, including pebbles of pink and brown quartzite and vein quartz; weak, medium to coarse prismatic structure, breaking down easily to moderate medium blocky; occasional roots; clear boundary.

C1(g) 25–36 in. Light yellowish brown (10 YR 6/4) to pale yellow (2·5 Y 7/4), very calcareous loam, coarsely mottled in streaks with light grey and yellowish brown; containing numerous very small (2–5 mm.) rounded chalk fragments and angular flint flakes; occasional small quartzose pebbles; massive or weakly platy structure; more friable and apparently drier than above; abundant fine pores, occasional roots; merging boundary.

C2 36–48 in. Similar material, becoming sandier with depth.

GADE COMPLEX

(Gade and Ford End Series)

The narrow belts of alluvium in the Misbourne, Chess, Bulbourne, Gade and Ver valleys give rise to an assemblage of loamy, gravelly and peaty soils, grouped as the Gade complex. Although some small areas are liable to occasional floods, alluvium is nowhere actively accumulating at present, and most of the soils have well defined, dark-coloured A horizons containing moderate to high amounts of organic matter. The subsoils consist of interstratified beds of water-laid flint or chalk gravel, loam and chalky silt, with occasional peaty layers, forming an intricate pattern which is often related to minor differences in level, the gravels forming low terraces or levees raised a few feet above the lowest ground. Ochreous and/or pale-coloured mottlings, resulting from periodic saturation by rising ground-water, occur in the profiles at various depths but, as the general level of the water-table was higher in the past and the hydrologic regime has also been affected locally by the construction of watercourses and mill dams, the gley effects observed may not be entirely related to contemporary conditions. Some of the land is included in built-up areas and an appreciable proportion of the remainder has either been disturbed by gravel workings, or is used for watercress beds or for sewage disposal. Where it remains in agricultural use it is chiefly under grass, and often provides useful summer grazing when the productivity of higher-lying pastures is reduced by drought.

Owing to their limited extent and variable character, the profiles have not been studied in detail. The most extensive kind of soil, the Gade series, is formed in silty alluvium overlying flint gravel, and may be acid at the surface. A typical profile (Ht 51) under old grass, from the Gade valley near Kings Langley, is described below. At this site, the silty superficial layer is about 38 in. thick, and is appreciably darkened by humus to a depth of 26 in., suggesting that the surface of the soil was gradually raised to its present level by occasional, thin accretions of alluvial silt. In August, 1955, when the profile was sampled, the water-table was below 48 in., but it probably rises to within 24 in. of the surface after a wet season.

On lower-lying sites in each of the valleys, the soils appear to have developed under conditions of poor drainage and the A horizons are more humose. These soils are usually calcareous to the surface, and in places, as at Chesham Bois and in parts of the Gade valley above Hemel Hempstead, the sub-surface layer consists largely of disintegrated chalk, the profile as a whole conforming to the Ford End series (p. 136). In locally depressed sites, where the water-table rises seasonally to near the surface, the A horizons may contain over 20 per cent of well decomposed organic matter, and buried peaty horizons have been identified in a few places, notably at Huntonbridge.

Elsewhere, usually on slightly raised, terrace or levee sites, brown-stained flint gravel is encountered at 18 in. or less, and the A horizon consists of dark brown, more or less humose loam with a fine granular structure. The horizons above the gravel are free of mottling, and are normally acid, and although the water-table may rise occasionally to within 24 in. of the surface, pastures tend to burn in dry summers.

Description of a representative profile
(Analytical data in Table 9, p. 158)

PROFILE NO.: Ht 51 (Gade series)

Location: south of Kings Langley (grid ref. TL/076108).

Slope: level (valley floor).   *Altitude:* 225 ft. O.D.

Land use: permanent grassland with *Agrostis spp.* and some timothy (*Phleum pratense*), ryegrass (*Lolium perenne*) and wild white clover (*Trifolium repens*).

Horizons:

A	0–15 in.	Very dark brown (10 YR 2/2) friable silt loam containing a few small flints; dark grey (10 YR 4/1) and slightly hard when dry; moderate to strong, fine sub-angular blocky structure, grading to granular in upper few inches; numerous grass roots; merging boundary.
A/C(g)	15–26 in.	Grey to greyish brown (10 YR 5/1–5/2), friable silt loam to silty clay loam, faintly mottled with grey, pale brown and yellowish brown; numerous worm channels filled with dark grey humose soil; occasional small flints; weak, fine to medium sub-angular blocky structure; frequent fine roots; merging boundary.
C1g	26–38 in.	Light yellowish brown (10 YR 6/4), friable to firm loam, distinctly mottled with light brownish grey and ochreous colours; frequent worm channels with dark-coloured infillings; weak, fine to medium sub-angular blocky structure occasional roots; clear boundary.
C2g	38–48 in.+	Light brownish grey, moist, calcareous, gravelly loam with prominent brownish yellow mottlings; stones mainly small, slightly worn, brown-stained flints; occasional rounded chalk fragments; becoming increasingly gravelly with depth.

CHAPTER IV

Descriptions of the Soil Mapping Units:
2. The Aylesbury Vale

Over more than half the Vale country, the soils are formed either directly from the solid formations or from thin solifluxion layers composed largely of locally-derived material (see Fig. 6, p. 14). Elsewhere they are derived from variable superficial deposits, including Head, glacial drift and alluvium, which differ more or less markedly in composition from the subjacent rocks. Owing to the generally subdued relief, and the presence of impervious Gault or Kimmeridge clays at no great depth, most of the soils are imperfectly or poorly drained, well drained soils being confined to limited areas on the Portlandian and Upper Greensand outcrops.

The Vale portion of the map shows the distribution of six soil series and six complexes, relationships of which to parent materials and types of soil formation may be summarized as follows:

Rendzinas on Portlandian limestone: Aylesbury series.

Gley-calcareous soils on Chalk Marl and chalky drifts: Halton complex; Gubblecote series.

Grey siliceous soils and associated gley soils on Upper Greensand rocks: Harwell complex.

Clayey gley soils on Gault and Kimmeridge clays and associated clayey drift: Wicken series; Challow complex; Denchworth series.

Gley soils with clay substrata (locally associated with brown calcareous soils or gleyed brown earths) on Portlandian rocks and on loamy and gravelly drifts: Bierton complex; Weston Turville series; Rowsham complex.

Calcareous gley soils on alluvium: Ford End complex; Mead series.

AYLESBURY SERIES

The Aylesbury series comprises well-drained, calcareous, medium to fine-textured soils overlying Portlandian limestone. It covers only between 200 and 300 acres, but is more extensive on similar rocks between Aylesbury and Oxford. The main area mapped, north and west of Bierton, consists of flat or gently sloping land, much of which is under arable cultivation. Tracts of similar soil, now largely built over, occur in the Manor Park and Walton suburbs of Aylesbury, and two small patches were mapped near Groveway Farm, Weedon, where the limestone emerges on slopes from beneath a capping of Gault clay.

The underlying rocks include beds of grey or cream-coloured, fossiliferous limestone, with subordinate sandy and marly layers. Partly weathered limestone, which may be rubbly or earthy, is normally encountered at 12 to 24 in. below the surface, and is usually soft enough to be penetrated, at least a few inches, with an auger. Around Bierton, the boundary of the series corresponds to the junction between the Rubbly or Aylesbury Limestone (Arkell, 1947) and the under-lying glauconitic beds, and where the former are thin it is sometimes possible to bore through weathered limestone into a yellowish or greenish, sandy stratum. The soil horizons contain occasional flints and quartzose pebbles in addition to fragmentary limestone, and may be derived in part from the residues of super-incumbent solid or drift deposits.

Typical profiles have an A horizon of very dark greyish brown clay loam 6–9 in. thick, containing limestone fragments, followed by a stiff, finely fissured, light olive-brown sub-surface horizon of similar texture, which grades into the weathering rock. Under old grassland the A horizon contains moderate to high amounts of organic matter, is friable, and has a well developed granular struc-ture. On arable land, as in profile Bu 114 described below, it is normally stiffer, and distinctly plastic when wet, but breaks down readily under favourable conditions to give a fine, stable tilth. The sub-surface layer is variable in thick-ness and degree of expression, depending on the hardness of the parent rock and the extent to which it has been weathered. As a rule it is 9–15 in. thick and may be considered as a weakly developed (B) horizon ranging in colour from olive to brown, but locally, where the soil is shallow, the A horizon merges into the weathered rock at depths of 9 to 12 in. A deep variant has also been noted, characterized by a thick subsoil of bright brown, sometimes faintly mottled, clay or sandy clay with prismatic structure. This kind of profile, which seems to be associated with pockets or solution-hollows in the limestone, is of very limited extent, and probably represents an older phase of weathering and soil formation, the products of which have mainly been denuded.

Description of a representative profile
(Analytical data in Table 10, p. 159)

PROFILE NO.: Bu 114 (Aylesbury series)

Location: Badrick's Farm, Bierton (grid ref. SP/833157).
Slope: nearly level.   *Altitude:* 320 ft. O.D.
Land use: grass-clover ley.

Horizons:

Ap	0–7 in.	Very dark greyish brown (10 YR 3/2), friable to firm, clay loam containing a few limestone fragments; moderate, fine sub-angular blocky and granular structure; abundant fibrous roots; numerous worm casts; clear smooth boundary.
(B)/C	7–20 in.	Light olive-brown (2·5 Y 5/4) firm stony clay loam with darker colours associated with structural faces and worm channels; fragments of soft light yellow limestone, increasing in size and amount with depth; moderate, medium and fine sub-angular blocky structure; local inclusions of yellowish calcareous fine sandy material; frequent roots; clear boundary.
C	20 in.+	Brown-stained, grey-hearted, impure limestone with yellowish sandy intercalations.

HALTON COMPLEX
(*Halton and Burwell Series*)

This complex, which covers about 2,100 acres, consists for the most part of stiff, calcareous, clay loams and silty clay loams with rust-mottled, flinty and/or chalky subsoils, overlying Chalk Marl. The dominant soils, classed as the Halton series, are derived from thin deposits of flinty Head resembling Coombe-Rock, patches of which occur at intervals on even, very gentle slopes from Ellesborough north-eastwards to Pitstone, extending in places on to the Upper Greensand. The deposits contain fresh shattered flints derived from the Chilterns, although in places, as at Ellesborough and Drayton Beauchamp, they occupy terrace-like features separated by later erosion from the higher ground to the south. The drift on such sites is variable in composition and, although generally unsorted, passes locally into roughly stratified chalk and flint gravel.

Elsewhere along the Chalk-Marl outcrop, the surface horizons are similar in morphology, but the subsoils contain few flints, and appear to have developed either directly on the solid formation or on locally-derived Head or colluvium consisting largely of marl and chalk. These soils, which may be correlated with the Burwell series of Cambridgeshire, generally occupy foot-slope sites and often grade into the Ford End series. They are chiefly represented around Marsworth, Ivinghoe, and Edlesborough, but are also found further west in association with the Halton series, notably near World's End, and south of Aston Clinton Park.

Both the Halton and Burwell soils are closely related to those of the Wantage series, but normally occupy flat or more depressed sites with moderate or imperfect drainage. As run-off is slight, and the underlying marls are only slowly permeable, the subsoil horizons are subject to seasonal waterlogging, a tendency which is further accentuated where seepage takes place from higher ground. Most of the soils are artificially drained, but some wet spots occur, especially on concave slopes. Much of the land carries arable crops or leys; there are some orchards, mainly of plums, near Pitstone, and the remainder is in permanent grass.

Of the three representative profiles recorded below, those from Buckland (Bu 109) and Weston Turville (Bu 111) are of the Halton series, and the third (Bu 106), from Edlesborough, conforms to the Burwell series.

In Halton profiles the A horizon is typically a stiff calcareous clay loam containing angular or sub-angular flints and occasional chalk fragments. Under old grass it may be up to 12 in. thick, and the upper few inches are friable and mellow, with a well developed granular structure. On arable land, the ploughed layer is dark grey, plastic, and heavy to work when wet, but breaks down readily under frost, and may appear nearly white when dry. Beneath the surface there is commonly a greyish brown or olive, A/C or (B) horizon of similar texture, with a medium to fine, sub-angular blocky structure. This is followed by a very calcareous, often gravelly, layer, designated C(g), containing angular flint and rounded chalk fragments in a chalky or marly matrix, which rests with a sharp, irregular boundary on grey or greenish marl with few stones. The subsoil horizons vary considerably in thickness, texture and stoniness over short distances. Thus, where the drift is shallow, the Chalk Marl may be encountered at 18 in. or less; elsewhere, as in the Buckland profile (Bu 109), the drift is over four feet thick, and may include discontinuous layers of chalky gravel with a sandy matrix. In most profiles the upper 15 in. are unmottled, but distinct, fine ochreous mottling appears below that depth, and is usually most pronounced immediately above the solid substratum. White deposits of secondary carbonate, most evident in the dry condition, may sometimes be noted in and immediately beneath the gravelly layer, which is occasionally weakly cemented.

The surface horizon of the profile at Weston Turville (Bu 111) is only slightly calcareous, and is followed by a distinct but discontinuous, dense, brown (B) horizon with faint variegated mottling, resembling that of the Tring series. Soils showing a similar tendency to decalcification also occur sporadically near World's End and Terrick, and are associated in each case with terrace-like features at or a little below 400 ft. O.D., suggesting that they incorporate relics of a deposit older than those at lower levels.

The Burwell soils are always very calcareous and, except for the occurrence of subsoil mottling, resemble those of the Wantage series. In the profile described, the A horizon is a silty clay loam with a few small flints, and the subsoil, which is free of stones, is apparently derived from Chalk Marl *in situ*. Commoner variants, developed on gentle foot-slopes along the edge of the Icknield Belt, have less compact, rust-mottled, marly or chalky subsoils containing chalk fragments and occasional flints, resting sharply on the Chalk Marl at depths from two to three feet, and clearly consist of material sludged or washed down-slope. There are usually springs in these localities, and drainage conditions are consequently variable. North-east of Ivinghoe, and south of Aston Clinton, the soils are locally dark brown calcareous loams, and the subsoils appear to consist largely of disintegrated chalk; elsewhere, notably north-east of Marsworth, stiff marly drift rests on glauconitic Upper Greensand beds. Where springs are, or have been, active, the surface horizons are very dark-coloured and rich in organic matter, and the chalky subsoils may include redeposited, tufaceous material.

Descriptions of representative profiles
(*Analytical data in Table* 10, *p.* 159)

PROFILE NO.: Bu 109 (Halton series)

Location: Manor Farm, Buckland (grid ref. SP/895123).
Slope: level.   *Altitude:* 350 ft. O.D.
Land use: permanent grassland.

Horizons:

A   0–6 in.   Very dark greyish brown (2·5 YR 3/2), friable to firm, flinty calcareous clay loam containing small rounded chalk fragments; moderate fine sub-angular blocky and granular structure; abundant fine roots; clear boundary.

(B)   6–15 in.   Grey-brown (2·5 Y 4/2–5/2) firm flinty clay loam with darker colours associated with structural faces and worm channels; moderate medium blocky structure; some widely spaced vertical fissures; stones include fresh shattered flints, ochreous sub-angular flints and rounded chalk fragments; frequent roots; sharp undulating boundary.

C(g)   15–30 in.+   Light brownish grey (2·5 Y 6/2), flinty and chalky, clay loam with distinct, common, very fine ochreous mottlings and occasional darker-coloured channels; stones mainly shattered angular flints and rounded chalk fragments; more friable than above, with weakly developed fine blocky structure; few roots.

PROFILE NO.: Bu 111 (Halton series)

Location: Mill Farm, Weston Turville (grid ref. SP/867100).
Slope: level.   *Altitude:* 375 ft. O.D.
Land use: arable (fallow).

Horizons:

Ap   0–8 in.   Dark greyish brown (2·5 Y 4/2), friable to firm, flinty clay loam containing occasional rounded chalk fragments; flints mainly sub-angular and brown-stained; moderate medium sub-angular blocky and granular structure; frequent roots; sharp, smooth boundary.

(B)(g)   8–15 in.   Olive-brown (2·5 Y 4/4) firm clay loam with many faint, very fine, pale grey and ochreous mottlings; darker colours on structural faces and in channels; flints as above, but no chalk fragments; moderate medium blocky to prismatic structure; numerous small manganiferous concretions; frequent roots; this horizon only intermittently developed; merging boundary.

C1(g)   15–24 in.   Light brownish grey (2·5 Y 6/2), very calcareous, clay loam containing many rounded chalk fragments and small angular flints; much distinct fine ochreous mottling and occasional darker-coloured infillings; weak medium sub-angular blocky structure; more friable than above; numerous small manganiferous concretions; few roots; horizon up to 18 in. thick; clear irregular boundary.

C2ca   24–28 in.   Very pale brown (10 YR 7/3), very calcareous, clay loam to loam, containing numerous small shattered flints and rounded chalk fragments; compact in place, but friable when removed, with moderate fine blocky structure; weakly cemented locally by re-deposited calcium carbonate; this horizon variable in thickness, with sharp, irregular boundary.

C3(g)ca   28 in.+   Light olive-grey (5 Y 6/2), compact, very calcareous, stoneless clay loam with common, faint, fine, light olive-brown mottlings and few prominent dark red spots; blocky to weakly laminated structure; secondary carbonate occurring as incoherent deposits on structural faces and as concretions in old root or worm channels. (Chalk Marl *in situ*.)

PROFILE NO.: Bu 106 (Burwell series)

Location: Sparrowhall Farm, Edlesborough (grid ref. SP/965190).
Slope: nearly level.   *Altitude:* 320 ft. O.D.
Land use: permanent grassland.

Horizons:

A   0–6 in.   Dark greyish brown (2·5 Y 4/2) calcareous friable silty

		clay loam containing a few small sub-angular flints; moderate granular and fine sub-angular blocky structure; plastic when wet; earthworms active; abundant fibrous roots; merging boundary.
A/C	6–12 in.	Greyish brown (2·5 Y 5/2), very calcareous, firm stoneless silty clay with darker colours associated with aggregate faces and worm channels; moderate medium sub-angular blocky structure; frequent roots; clear undulating boundary.
Cg	12–30 in.+	Light grey (5Y Y/2), extremely calcareous, stoneless silty clay with distinct, common, fine, yellowish brown mottling; occasional worm channels with humose infillings; slightly more friable than above when dug out, but very compact in place, with moderate, medium to coarse prismatic structure; few roots.

GUBBLECOTE SERIES

This series, which covers nearly 600 acres of almost flat land around Wilstone and Long Marston, is formed on flint and chalk gravel, spread over the Chalk Marl, Upper Greensand and Gault. Similar soils in Berkshire have been classed as the Grove series (Kay, 1934), but there the gravel consists of chalk and malmstone fragments, with few flints. The surface horizons are of stiff, flinty loam containing appreciable quantities of coarse sand, and are always calcareous, differing in this respect from those of the Weston Turville series on similar materials. Profiles with a substratum of chalky gravel difficult to penetrate with an auger also occur in the Halton and Ford End complexes, but the gravel in the Gubblecote series is thicker and more continuous, and the soils are normally coarser in texture. Much of this land was cultivated in the pre-war period, and the greater part is now under arable crops or leys.

The profiles are characterized by a very dark-coloured sandy clay loam or clay loam A horizon up to 12 in. thick, followed by a greyish brown or yellowish, more or less stony sub-surface horizon which rests on gravel at depths ranging from 15 to 27 in. The gravel layer is rarely more than 4 ft. thick, and may be considerably less. It is largely composed of angular or sub-angular, often brown-stained, flints and small water-worn chalk fragments, and although patches are loose the greater part is bonded by a calcareous matrix of sand and clay in varying proportions.

The drainage of the soils is at best moderate, and may be imperfect: although the surface and sub-surface horizons are fairly permeable, and water moves easily through the gravel layer, downward percolation is impeded by the "solid" substratum, so that the lower part of the profile is periodically or even permanently waterlogged. Rusty mottlings indicative of the former condition occur in the gravel and extend in places into the subsoil, but as much of the land is artificially drained seasonal wetness is presumably less pronounced than formerly, at least in the upper horizons. The drier soils occur mainly south of the Aylesbury Canal, where the gravel is coarsest, and rests on Chalk Marl or Upper Greensand rather than on Gault. As the ground falls gently north-westwards, the drainage tends to deteriorate, and soils of the Weston Turville and Ford End series occur, especially on the western side.

Two representative profiles are described below, one on arable land east of Wilstone, and the other under old grass near College Farm, Gubblecote. In the first profile a very dark greyish brown, flinty A horizon 11 in. thick merges into a very flinty, greyish brown, sub-surface horizon, designated A/(B), which rests on loose gravel at about 19 in. The A horizon has a moderately well developed sub-angular blocky structure and, although containing only 22 per cent clay, is distinctly firm when moist and plastic when wet. At this site the gravel rests on Chalk Marl at about 44 in. and drainage is moderately good. In August 1955, after a dry summer, there was no sign of wetness in any horizon, but the gravel layer becomes waterlogged in winter.

Under old grass the A horizons are friable and richer in organic matter, and have a strong granular structure at the surface, grading below 6 in. into fine sub-angular blocky. In the profile described, the gravel layer is encountered at about 24 in., and the overlying yellowish (B)(g) horizon, which is only slightly stony, is finely and faintly mottled with ochreous colours. The gravel rests on Gault clay, and is permanently wet below about 30 in., so that the drainage of the soil is classed as imperfect.

Descriptions of representative profiles

(Analytical data in Table 10, p. 159)

PROFILE NO.: Ht 56 (Gubblecote series)

Location: Wilstone Great Farm (grid ref. SP/912140).

Slope: nearly level.   *Altitude:* 320 ft. O.D.

Land use: grass-clover ley.

Horizons:

Ap	0–11 in.	Very dark greyish brown (2·5 Y 3/2), friable to firm, flinty sandy clay loam; flints mainly sub-angular; some rounded chalk fragments; moderate, medium and fine sub-angular blocky structure; slightly plastic and sticky when wet; abundant roots; clear smooth boundary.
A/(B)	11–19 in.	Greyish brown (10 YR 5/2), firm, very flinty, sandy clay loam with numerous rounded chalk fragments and dark-coloured infillings: frequent roots; clear irregular boundary.
C1(g)	19–27 in.	Loose gravel of sub-angular ochreous flints and rounded chalk fragments with a light yellowish brown sandy chalky matrix; some faint fine ochreous mottling, becoming more pronounced with depth; occasional ferruginous nodules; few roots; clear irregular boundary.
C2gca	27–44 in.	Light olive-grey (5 Y 6/2), very calcareous, gravelly clay loam with many prominent, fine, brownish yellow to strong brown (10 YR–7·5 YR 5/8) mottles; clear irregular boundary.
C3g	44 in.+	Light grey (5 Y 7/2), very calcareous silty clay with distinct, common, fine, strong brown (7·5 YR 5/8) mottles. (Chalk Marl *in situ*.)

PROFILE NO.: Ht 72 (Gubblecote series)

Location: College Farm, Gubblecote (grid ref. SP/904149).
Slope: nearly level.   *Altitude:* 300 ft. O.D.
Land use: permanent grassland.

Horizons:

A1	0–6 in.	Very dark greyish brown (10 YR 3/2), very friable, calcareous clay loam containing occasional small sub-angular flints and rounded chalk fragments; strong granular structure; abundant fine roots; earthworms active; merging boundary.
A2	6–13 in.	Dark greyish brown (10 YR 4/2), friable, calcareous, loam to clay loam with occasional stones as above; moderate fine sub-angular blocky structure, with granular infillings; frequent roots; clear irregular boundary.
(B)(g)	13–24 in.	Light yellowish brown (2·5 Y 5/4–6/4) friable calcareous loam, stony as above, with few, faint, fine, yellowish brown mottlings and darker colours on structural faces and in channels; moderate, fine to medium blocky structure; slightly plastic when wet; clear irregular boundary.
Cg	24–48 in.+	Chalky and flinty gravel with coarse sandy matrix; wet and prominently mottled yellowish brown below 30 in.

HARWELL COMPLEX
(*Harwell and Ardington Series*)

The soils included in the Harwell complex, covering about 1,400 acres, are formed on the beds of fine sandy, micaceous and glauconitic marl and malmstone which lie between the Lower Chalk and the Gault, together constituting the Upper Greensand of this locality. As indicated in Chapter I, the beds are nowhere more than about 35 ft. thick, and are often obscured by spreads of flinty and chalky drift. The associated soils do not, therefore, occur as a continuous belt, but as more or less elongated patches alternating with Halton, Gubblecote and Ford End soils. The profiles are characterized by dark grey surface horizons and stiff, olive-grey or greenish subsoils; drainage is normally moderate or imperfect, and although the soils are mainly non-calcareous at the surface, and contain appreciable amounts of silt and fine sand, they present no great contrast in consistency or morphology with those on adjoining formations. The upper horizons often contain flints, and occasionally chalk fragments or quartzose pebbles, indicating that they are developed partly in thin drift. Most of the land was under grass in pre-war years and, although the greater part has since been ploughed, grass is still the predominant crop.

In Berkshire, where the Upper Greensand is 80–100 ft. thick and outcrops as a broad platform at the foot of the Downs, Kay (1934) distinguished two sedentary soil series with free or moderate drainage. The Harwell series, which is the most extensive, consists of non-calcareous, fine sandy loams and loams developed on interbedded strata of malmstone and grey, micaceous, sandy marl. Between these beds and the Lower Chalk, and often covered by chalky drift, are 16 to 25 ft. of green sand and sandy marl, composed of quartz and glauconite with variable amounts of clayey and calcareous matter, and giving rise where exposed to stiff greenish-coloured soils of the Ardington series. The Harwell complex includes soils of both series but, as the much attenuated Upper Green-sand in the Vale of Aylesbury is more argillaceous than further west, textures are generally finer, and imperfectly drained variants, resembling the Hendred series of Kay (1934), are of frequent occurrence.

The soils conforming to the Harwell series are exemplified below by profile Bu 42, described on rising ground under ley near Bushey Leys, Ellesborough. A dark greyish brown loamy A horizon, containing over 70 per cent of silt and very fine sand, is succeeded by a finer-textured olive (B)(g) horizon, showing a well marked prismatic structure on drying. This merges below 17 in. into olive-grey, faintly mottled, silty clay loam with irregular layers of earthy weathering malmstone. The soft substrata become less plastic, appreciably micaceous and distinctly laminated with depth, and contain green grains of glauconite. The surface horizon is slightly acid, and the profile is non-calcareous to a depth of 40 in., below which powdery segregations of secondary carbonate are en-countered; commonly, however, the substrata are calcareous at 24 in. or less and the soil is approximately neutral. Owing to the high content of silt and fine sand, the surface of fallow ground is easily flattened by rain, and on drying the soil has a light grey colour, giving it the appearance of chalk-land. Hard rock is occasionally encountered in the subsoil, and fragments may be brought up by the plough, but the stone bands are rarely more than a few inches thick, and are usually well fissured and softened by weathering.

These soils are chiefly confined to elevated or sloping land west and north of Wendover (Plate VIIIa), where the malmstone and associated fine sandy marls are thickest and best represented. Elsewhere, however, the subsoils are only slowly permeable, and percolation is further impeded locally by the underlying Gault, so that, where relief is subdued, drainage is normally imperfect. This imperfectly drained variant is represented by profile Bu 107, described under old grass on nearly level land north of Wellwick Farm, Wendover. Here the upper horizons to a depth of 15 in. contain a few flints, and may have developed in a thin solifluxion layer composed mainly of locally derived material. The profile shows a rust-mottled, silt loam A horizon, merging into a subsoil horizon of olive-grey silty clay with prismatic structure, designated (B)(g), which is leached of carbonates, and becomes plastic and impervious when wet. Although the subsoil is subject to seasonal waterlogging, ochreous mottling is not pronounced, presumably either because the parent material is low in iron, or because the iron-bearing minerals present, principally glauconite, are only slowly decomposed under the prevailing neutral or alkaline conditions.

North-east of Halton, the micaceous beds become progressively thinner, and the overlying soils are mostly imperfectly drained silty clay loams and clay loams, often with traces of flinty or chalky drift in the upper horizons. Rock bands are rare, and the soils are very stiff and, when wet, are plastic, but are distinguished from the adjoining Wicken clays by the more silty and less cal-careous nature of the subsoils, which are appreciably micaceous and often slightly greenish in colour.

The sandy glauconitic strata giving rise to soils of the Ardington series are only a few feet thick and, lying immediately beneath the Lower Chalk, their outcrop is frequently obscured by chalky drift. The associated soils are there-fore of very limited extent, but are easily recognized by the striking green colour of their sub-surface horizons. The largest patch identified is north of

Marsworth, where the surface is sporadically modified by thin drift containing occasional quartzose pebbles. The series also occurs on gentle slopes near Great Seabrook, north-west of Drayton Beauchamp, on Church Farm, Weston Turville, south of World's End, and near Bushey Leys. A representative profile (Bu 102) from near Drayton Beauchamp is described below. The surface horizons are dark grey clay loams or fine sandy clay loams, often with a greenish tinge, which break down to a fine granular structure. Below the surface the soil becomes stiffer and more compact, and passes into green, fine sandy clay loam or fine sandy clay with a characteristic greasy feel. Occasionally, and usually where some weathered drift is present, there is a yellowish or olive-brown sub-surface layer with faint greyish and ochreous mottling; more commonly the horizons merge into one another, there is no distinct brown (B) horizon, and the glauconite in the subsoil appears little weathered. The soil occurs in close association with those of the Halton complex, and is frequently contaminated at the surface by chalky drift; thus, in the profile described, the Ap horizon contains 4·8 per cent calcium carbonate, whereas the sub-surface horizons, designated A/C(g) and C(g) respectively, are only slightly calcareous to a depth of 44 in.

Descriptions of representative profiles
(*Analytical data in Table* 10, *pp.* 159–60)

PROFILE NO.: Bu 42 (Harwell series)

Location: Bushey Leys, Ellesborough (grid ref. SP/830077).

Slope: 1° even.   *Aspect:* south.   *Altitude:* 400 ft. O.D.

Land use: grass-clover ley (third year).

Horizons:

Ap	0–8 in.	Dark greyish brown (2·5 Y 4/2) friable loam containing occasional small angular flints and malmstone fragments, granular to moderate fine sub-angular blocky structure; abundant roots; clear smooth boundary.
(B)(g)	8–17 in.	Pale olive (5 Y 6/3) firm silty clay loam with few prominent ochreous mottles and soft iron-stained malmstone fragments; some infilled worm channels; moderate medium prismatic and blocky structure; frequent roots; merging boundary.
C(g)	17–28 in.+	Olive-grey (5 Y 5/2), firm micaceous silty clay loam with a few faint brownish mottles, and irregular layers of soft weathering malmstone; weak blocky to platy structure; occasional worm channels; few roots; non-calcareous to 40 in.

PROFILE NO.: Bu 107 (Harwell series; imperfectly drained variant)

Location: Wellwick Farm, Wendover (grid ref. SP/848093).

Slope: nearly level.   *Altitude:* 350 ft. O.D.

Land use: permanent grassland.

Horizons:

A(g)	0–5 in.	Dark greyish brown (10 YR 4/2) friable silt loam with fine rusty mottling associated with root channels; occasional small shattered flints and malmstone fragments, strong fine sub-angular blocky and granular structure; earthworms active; abundant roots; clear irregular boundary.

A/(B)(g)   5–15 in.   Greyish brown (2·5 Y 4/2–5/2), firm, coarsely blocky to
                             prismatic, silty clay loam to silty clay with darker colours
                             associated with cleavage faces and infilled worm channels,
                             and faint light olive-brown mottling within aggregates,
                             a few stones as above; frequent roots; clear boundary.

(B)(g)   15–24 in.   Olive-grey (5 Y 5/2) stoneless plastic silty clay with moderate
                             blocky structure; few roots; merging boundary.

C(g)   24–33 in.+   Light olive-grey to pale olive (5 Y 6/2–6/4), faintly mottled,
                             calcareous silty clay loam, becoming laminated; more
                             friable and apparently drier than above; malmstone rock at
                             36 in.

PROFILE NO.: Bu 102 (Ardington series)

Location: Lower Farm, Drayton Beauchamp (grid ref. SP/893128).

Slope: 2° convex.   *Aspect:* north-west.   *Altitude:* 345 ft. O.D.

Land use: arable (fallow).

Horizons:

Ap   0–6 in.   Very dark greyish brown (2·5 Y 3/2), firm, slightly calcareous,
                             clay loam containing occasional small angular flints and
                             rounded chalk fragments; cloddy structure, breaking easily
                             to fine sub-angular blocky and granular when partly dry;
                             clear smooth boundary.

A/C(g)   6–15 in.   Dull grey-green firm stoneless clay loam with olive-grey
                             (5 Y 4/2) cleavage faces and very faint fine yellowish brown
                             mottling within aggregates; moderate medium sub-angular
                             blocky structure; some infilled worm channels; few roots;
                             merging boundary.

C(g)   15–30 in.+   Dull green firm stoneless fine sandy clay loam with distinct
                             fine yellowish brown mottling and greyer cleavage faces;
                             moderate medium prismatic to blocky structure; few roots;
                             becoming calcareous at 44 in.

WICKEN SERIES

The Wicken soils are dark-coloured clays and clay loams with very stiff, olive-coloured subsoils overlying pale grey, calcareous Gault clay. First recognized as a series in Cambridgeshire (Soil Survey of Great Britain, 1951), they are among the most extensive soils in the Vale of Aylesbury, occupying some 7,000 acres on this sheet. The largest areas lie between Cheddington and Wingrave, and around Long Marston, Puttenham, and Aston Clinton, where the Gault is comparatively drift-free. Most of this land is gently undulating, but towards the north-west the relief becomes more pronounced, culminating around Wingrave in moderately steep slopes which locally exceed 10°. South of the Tring–Aylesbury road, the Gault outcrop is largely obscured by Chalky Gravel Head, and Wicken soils are accordingly confined to limited areas, mainly on slopes, where the drift is thin or absent.

Except locally on convex slopes, the soils have formed in a clayey superficial layer, apparently re-worked by solifluxion or frost action, which rests on little-disturbed Gault at depths ranging from a few inches to 2 ft. or more. The re-worked layer usually contains scattered flints, accompanied in places by small chalk fragments and, north of Long Marston, by occasional quartzose pebbles; its lower boundary is often irregular, and may be marked by lenses or pockets of gravelly or sandy material. Generally, however, the profiles consist throughout of tenacious clay, thus differing from those of the Weston Turville and Rowsham series, which are characterized by subsoils of uniformly coarser texture. They are typically calcareous throughout, but the calcium-carbonate content rarely exceeds 10 per cent at the surface, and in some places, particularly under old pasture, the top-soil may be slightly acid.

During and before the 19th century, these heavy soils were extensively cultivated, with wheat and beans as the principal crops, but by the 1930's the greater part had been laid down to grass. Large acreages were ploughed up during the 1939–45 war, and about half the area mapped is now under arable crops or leys. Despite their fine texture, the drainage of the soils is typically imperfect rather than poor; surface waterlogging rarely persists for very long, except where poaching has occurred, and is further reduced on much of the land by either pipe or mole-drainage.

Seasonal changes in the moisture content of these soils have been studied on a profile basis by Nicholson (1935) at Cambridge. As the profile dries out in summer, the clay shrinks and cracks, and the moisture content is reduced below its winter level to depths as great as 70–80 in., so creating a reservoir that in drought years may absorb 11 in. of rain before the drains begin to run. Nor is the network of fissures completely obliterated by re-expansion of the soil mass, so that, following a drought, the permeability of the subsoil may be materially enhanced for a while.

Typical profiles show three main horizons, A, (B)(g) and Cg, separated by clear or merging boundaries. The A and (B)(g) horizons are normally developed in the re-worked layer, and are subject to marked seasonal changes in moisture content. They are much less calcareous than the Cg horizon, which represents the uppermost, slightly weathered zone of the Gault, and remains moist and plastic throughout the year. This layer usually contains between 20 and 40 per cent calcium carbonate, part of which is present as small rounded concretions and incoherent deposits of secondary origin; where the Gault merges into the Upper Greensand, it is distinctly silty and micaceous, and often very calcareous, whereas to the west and north, as lower beds are encountered, it tends to become less calcareous, stiffer, and darker in colour, but this variation is not consistently reflected in the overlying soil horizons, the morphology of which depends on the constitution of the re-worked layer.

The A horizon is very dark grey to dark greyish brown, and is generally of clay texture, clay loams being confined to limited areas where the re-worked layer is appreciably modified by sandy drift. Under grass the A horizon is often between 12 and 15 in. thick, and is usually divisible into two sub-horizons differing in structure and organic-matter content. At the surface is a layer a few inches thick, with over 10 per cent of organic matter and a strong granular structure. Below this is a stiffer sub-surface horizon, designated A2, with a coarser, predominantly blocky structure, and a lower content or organic matter, much of which is concentrated on structural faces and in channels. This horizon results partly from the activity of earthworms and decay of roots *in situ*, and partly from the incorporation of humose material which has fallen or been washed into fissures, where it is squeezed and plastered on to structural faces when the peds expand in the wet season. On arable land, the tenacious clods formed by cultivation in the wet condition break down into very hard angular blocks on drying out, but alternate wetting and drying, especially when accompanied by frost, produces a thin, finely blocky, superficial layer that acts as a mulch to shield the underlying soil from further loss of moisture by direct evaporation.

The (B)g horizon, usually about 12 in. thick, has an olive-grey to light olive-brown colour, and is divided by fissures into prismatic and blocky aggregates with smooth, grey, more or less humus-stained faces, and faint, fine, yellowish brown mottling internally. In the underlying Cg horizon, the vertical fissures are more widely spaced, and the large prisms so formed tend to shear between the weight of the soil above and the comparatively incompressible material below, forming wedge-shaped or pyramidal aggregates (Clarke, 1957). The upper part, at about 24–36 in., is light olive-grey or light grey, with distinct yellowish brown mottling; at greater depths the clay becomes more uniformly grey, less plastic, and often apparently drier, and the structure massive or weakly laminated.

Three representative profiles are described below, on arable land, under a short-term ley, and under old grass respectively. In the first two profiles (Bu 39 and Ht 58), both of which are of the dominant clay type, the occurrence of a re-worked layer is only evidenced in the field by the presence of occasional flints, and in both the soil is calcareous to the surface. In any particular locality, the most calcareous soils are generally associated with slopes and knolls where erosion and run-off have been active, and drift influence is accordingly slight. On such sites, notably around Wingrave, the (B)(g) horizons are only very faintly mottled, indicating that drainage is moderately good. Locally, however, the soil is kept moist by seepage from higher ground.

The third profile (Bu 90) has a non-calcareous, clay loam A horizon, and represents a soil, transitional to the Weston Turville series, in which the re-worked layer contains much sand and discontinuous inclusions of chalky, sandy clay. Soils of a similar kind occur sporadically on gentle slopes and tend to be more strongly mottled than those which are calcareous to the surface. On flat, low-lying land and concave slopes with poor natural drainage, they are included in the Challow complex, and north of the Thistle Brook, where the modifying drift contains little or no chalk, they often appear as intergrades to the Rowsham series.

Descriptions of representative profiles
(Analytical data in Table 10, p. 160)

PROFILE NO.: Bu 39 (Wicken series)

Location: Westend Farm, Cheddington (grid ref. SP/905169).

Slope: c. 1°.   *Aspect:* south-east.   *Altitude:* 290 ft. O.D.

Land use: arable (wheat stubble).

Horizons:

A1p	0–8 in.	Very dark greyish brown (2·5 Y 3/2), friable to firm, slightly calcareous clay containing occasional small angular and sub-angular flints and quartzite pebbles; cloddy structure, breaking down easily to fine blocky and granular aggregates when partly dry; abundant roots; clear boundary.

A2(g)   8–13 in.   Dark greyish brown (2·5 Y 4/2), very firm, blocky, slightly calcareous clay with darker colours associated with structural faces; fine ochreous mottling within aggregates; stones as above; frequent roots; clear boundary.

(B)(g)   13–23 in.   Light olive-brown (2·5 Y 5/4), very firm, calcareous clay with moderate medium blocky to prismatic structure; stones as above; greyer colours on cleavage faces and faint, fine, greyish and ochreous mottling internally; some worm channels; frequent roots; clear undulating boundary.

Cgca   23–47 in.+   Light olive-grey (5 Y 6/2–6/3), very firm, stoneless calcareous clay with distinct strong brown mottling; blocky to prismatic structure, becoming more massive with depth; occasional worm channels; secondary calcium carbonate; few roots.

PROFILE NO.: Ht 58 (Wicken series)

Location: Potash Farm, Puttenham (grid ref. SP/888146).
Slope: 2° convex.   *Aspect:* south-east.   *Altitude:* 290 ft. O.D.
Land use: grass-clover ley.

Horizons:

Ap   0–5 in.   Very dark grey (5 Y 3/1), very firm, clay containing occasional small sub-angular flints; cloddy structure, breaking down fairly easily to fine to medium blocks and granules with organic coatings; numerous fissures; abundant roots; added chalk; clear irregular boundary with many infilled channels.

(B)(g)   5–16 in.   Olive (5 Y 4/3), very firm clay with olive-grey cleavage faces and very faint, very fine, greyish and ochreous internal mottling; occasional flints as above; moderate, medium to coarse prismatic and blocky structure; some worm channels; frequent roots; slightly calcareous; clear smooth boundary.

C1gca   16–30 in.   Light grey (5 Y 7/2), very firm, stoneless calcareous clay with somewhat darker-coloured cleavage faces and faint to distinct, yellowish brown internal mottling; coarse prismatic structure; secondary carbonate deposits; occasional worm channels; roots rare; merging boundary.

C2gca   30–40 in.+   Grey (5 Y 6/1), firm to plastic, stoneless calcareous clay with distinct fine brownish yellow (10 YR 6/8) mottling; becoming massive, with few, widely spaced vertical cleavages; some secondary carbonate concretions; roots rare.

PROFILE NO.: Bu 90 (Wicken series)

Location: County Farm, Stoke Mandeville (grid ref. SP/842118).
Slope: c. 1°.   *Aspect:* north-east.   *Altitude:* 310 ft. O.D.
Land use: permanent grassland.

Horizons:

A1   0–4 in.   Very dark greyish brown (2·5 Y 3/2) friable clay loam containing occasional small flints; moderate granular to very fine blocky structure; abundant fine roots; added chalk; merging boundary.

A2(g)   4–10 in.   Dark greyish brown (2·5 Y 4/2) and olive-brown (2·5 Y 4/4), faintly calcareous, firm clay loam, slightly stony as above; the darker colours associated with aggregate faces and channels; moderate, medium to coarse blocky and prismatic structure; frequent fine roots; clear undulating boundary.

(B)(g)   10–20 in.   Olive-grey (5 Y 4/2), very firm, slightly calcareous clay containing occasional flints and rounded chalk fragments, faintly mottled with olive-brown; moderate prismatic structure; frequent roots; horizon 7 to 14 in. thick, with clear, irregular, boundary.

Cgca   20–36 in.+   Grey (5 Y 6/1), stoneless, very firm, calcareous clay, distinctly mottled with light olive-brown (2·5 Y 5/6) and becoming darker with depth; moderate prismatic structure; secondary carbonate concretions and powdery deposits below 30 in.; occasional roots. (At one end of pit, the upper part of this horizon is replaced by a pocket of olive (5 Y 4/3), sandy clay loam to sandy clay, prominently mottled with strong brown and yellowish brown, and containing small rounded chalk fragments and sub-angular flints, which extends in places to 36 in.)

CHALLOW COMPLEX

(*Challow and Weston Turville Series*)

The dominant soils in this complex are heavy clays and clay loams conforming to the Challow series of Kay (1934). The soils are closely allied to the Wicken series, but have developed under poorer drainage conditions, as evidenced by more pronounced subsoil gleying and other effects of wetness. They occur in flat low-lying parts of the sub-edge plain, and on footslopes subject to seepage from higher ground. The area mapped amounts to about 2,200 acres, a considerable proportion of which is located in three large patches north of Aston Clinton. Other tracts lie north of Ivinghoe, and further west between Kimble and Stoke Mandeville.

In each locality the soils are formed mainly in clayey drift derived chiefly from the underlying Gault, but the re-worked layer tends to be thicker and more heterogeneous than in the Wicken areas and several ill-defined variants can be distinguished, depending on the nature and origin of the incorporated materials. The surface soils are often devoid of carbonates, but are rarely more than slightly acid, and the subsoils are usually calcareous at 18 in. or less. When the upper horizons are non-calcareous, the profile tends to resemble that of the Denchworth series, and where the two units adjoin, for example west of Bierton, the boundary between them is difficult to define exactly.

Between Bierton and Puttenham, and south-west of Stoke Mandeville, the subsoils include discontinuous layers of chalky gravel and sandy clay, so that profiles conforming to the Weston Turville series may occur sporadically in association with the predominant, clayey soils; locally, on flat low-lying ground, the pattern is further diversified by strips of dark-coloured, calcareous, alluvial soils of the Ford End complex, associated with present or former streams.

These are mapped separately as far as possible, but some of the Challow soils may have received alluvial additions when flooding was more extensive than it is today. A similar pattern occurs north of Ivinghoe, but here the soils contain occasional quartzose pebbles, as well as flints and patches of chalky gravel.

In the patch north-east of Cheddington and again near Marstongate and south of Wingrave, the foreign material in the drift appears to have come mainly from the north. Little chalk is present, and the profiles tend to resemble those of the Denchworth or Rowsham series. Another variant, having affinities with the Hendred series of Kay (1934), occurs on land adjoining the Harwell complex in Kimble and Ellesborough parishes (Plate VIIIa), and west of World's End. The soils thereabouts are partly developed in Head or colluvium containing materials of Upper Greensand origin, and are therefore appreciably micaceous, and silty in texture.

Despite poor natural drainage, much of the land was formerly used for arable cultivation, as witnessed by the widespread occurrence of ridge-and-furrow. In the thirties, however, it was mainly under grass and, although a moderate acreage has been cultivated during and since the war, grass remains the predominant crop. Actual drainage conditions vary considerably from place to place, depending on the effectiveness of ditches and field drainage systems in removing excess surface water. Thus, in the flat area west of Ivinghoe Aston, where new, straight watercourses were excavated in the 19th century, the land is drained by pipes into deep ditches, and much of it used for arable cultivation (Plate VIIb). On similar land between Bierton and Puttenham, where drainage has been neglected, the soil remains waterlogged for several months in most years, and the grass fields are poor and weedy, with rushes, sedges, meadowsweet, buttercups and tufted hair-grass as common constituents of the swards.

A profile (Bu 67) from the latter area, with Gault clay at 40 in., is described below. The A horizon consists of very dark grey to greyish brown, non-calcareous, humose clay, and shows abundant rusty mottling along root channels, a feature rare in the Wicken series, but characteristic of poorly drained grassland soils. In the upper 4 in., which contains about 15 per cent organic matter, the structure is moderately granular, but below this it becomes coarser and more blocky, with humus mainly concentrated on aggregate surfaces. Beneath the A horizon is a coarsely blocky to prismatic, faintly calcareous, (B)g horizon with light grey, shiny cleavage faces, which merges downwards into grey and yellowish brown, mottled, calcareous clay containing inclusions of chalky gravel in an ochreous, sandy clay matrix. The subsoil horizons contain few roots, and are more prominently mottled than in Wicken profiles; the clay is very hard when dry, and large cracks develop during droughts, but for most of the year it remains extremely tenacious and sticky.

The second profile described (Bu 47), also under permanent grass, is located on a foot-slope site north-west of Terrick, and may be regarded as transitional to the Hendred series (Kay, 1934). This soil is influenced by micaceous, silty material of Upper Greensand origin, and is affected by irregular seepage from springs which break out at the base of the malmstone outcrop, and give rise to rushy patches. In the profile recorded, the re-worked layer is about 30 in. thick, and contains occasional malmstone fragments, as well as small flints. Apart from a marked zone of secondary carbonate deposition at 30–33 in. the soil is only slightly calcareous, and is slightly acid at the surface. The A horizon is a very dark brown, humose, silty clay with rusty mottling, and is distinctly more friable than in the preceding profile, but below 18 in. the subsoil consists of very plastic clay, which for most of the year is wet and slimy, and offers little resistance to the auger.

Descriptions of representative profiles
(*Analytical data in Table* 10, *p.* 161)

PROFILE NO.: Bu 67 (Challow series)

Location: north of College Farm, Aston Clinton (grid ref. SP/871147).
Slope: level.   *Altitude:* 275 ft. O.D.
Land use: permanent grassland.

Horizons:

A1g	0–8 in.	Very dark grey to greyish brown (2·5 Y 3/1–3/2), humose clay with distinct fine, yellowish red mottling associated with roots; occasional small angular flints, structure coarsely granular in upper 4 in. passing to medium to coarse blocky below; organic matter apparently concentrated on aggregate surfaces; very hard when dry; abundant roots; merging boundary.
A2g	8–12 in.	Dark grey (2·5 Y 4/0), coarsely blocky to prismatic, very firm clay with much distinct light olive-brown mottling; organic matter concentrated on cleavage faces and in channels; frequent roots; clear smooth boundary.
(B)g	12–24 in.	Olive-grey, coarsely blocky to prismatic, very firm clay with grey (2·5 Y 5/0) cleavage faces and much light olive-brown mottling internally; occasional flints as above; few roots; merging boundary.
C1gca	24–40 in.	Grey (5 Y 5/1–6/0) stoneless calcareous plastic clay with distinct fine yellowish brown (10 YR 5/8) mottling and discontinuous gravelly inclusions of small rounded chalk fragments and sub-angular flints in an ochreous sandy clay loam to sandy clay matrix; structure becoming more massive, with only occasional vertical and oblique fissures; secondary carbonate concretions, mainly below 36 in., roots rare.
C2gca	40 in.+	Grey stoneless clay with much secondary carbonate as concretions and incoherent deposits. (Gault *in situ*.)

PROFILE NO.: Bu 47 (Challow series)

Location: Grove Farm, Ellesborough (grid ref. SP/835086).
Slope: 2–3° even.   *Aspect:* north-west.   *Altitude:* 340 ft. O.D.
Land use: permanent grassland with rushy patches.

Horizons:

Ag	0–7 in.	Very dark brown (7·5 YR 2/2), friable to firm, silty clay with much distinct fine yellowish red mottling associated with root channels and structure faces; occasional small sub-angular flints and malmstone fragments; moderate, granular to fine sub-angular blocky structure; earthworms present; abundant roots; clear smooth boundary.

A/(B)(g)   7–18 in.   Greyish brown (2·5 Y 5/2) firm blocky silty clay with darker colours associated with cleavage faces; a few stones as above; frequent roots; merging boundary.

(B)g   18–30 in.   Olive-grey (5 Y 5/2–6/2), coarsely blocky, plastic clay with faint yellowish brown (10 YR 5/8) mottling within peds, becoming prominent at base; stones as above; few roots; clear boundary.

C1gca   30–33 in.   Light olive-grey plastic clay with a little faint ochreous mottling and secondary carbonate as rounded concretions and tubular deposits in root channels; sharp smooth boundary.

C2g   33–40 in.+   Olive-grey (5 Y 5/2), slightly calcareous, stoneless plastic clay with distinct fine yellowish brown mottling; becoming massive.

DENCHWORTH SERIES

Some 2,500 acres north and east of Aylesbury are occupied by clayey gley soils grouped with the Denchworth series. Their most characteristic feature, distinguishing them from soils of the Wicken series, is the occurrence of a thick, non-calcareous, sub-surface horizon, which normally shows pronounced yellowish mottling, resting on dark grey, calcareous clay at depths of 2 to 3 ft. The surface horizons may be slightly to moderately acid in reaction, and drainage, though varying to some extent with relief, is typically poor. The widespread occurrence of ridge-and-furrow indicates that these tenacious soils were once extensively cultivated; by the 1930's, however, almost all the land had been laid down to grass, much of which was poor and weedy. During or since the war most of it has carried arable crops and about one-quarter is now in cultivation, the remainder being chiefly under grass of variable quality.

The series was first defined in Berkshire by Kay (1934), who mapped it on both Kimmeridge and Gault clays, and later work has shown that soils of similar morphology and constitution are extensively developed on Oxford and Lower Lias clays, those on the latter formation having been mapped as the Charlton Bank series (Avery, 1955). In each formation, the rocks underlying the soils are chiefly grey or bluish, more or less shaly, marine clays, containing significant amounts of organic matter and finely divided iron sulphide, and are generally less calcareous than those giving rise to the Wicken and related soils. It is clear, however, that the extent to which the soils are devoid of calcium carbonate depends partly on factors other than the original carbonate content of the rocks, including the incidence of erosion and run-off, the persistence of older weathered horizons, and the occurrence of thin superficial deposits containing extraneous materials.

Where developed under similar topographic conditions, the decalcified and acid soils are more strongly gleyed than those which have remained neutral or alkaline, and also show a tendency to textural differentiation, so that the A horizons of Denchworth soils are commonly more loamy than those of the Wicken series. As a rule, however, the texture profile is only pronounced where the upper horizons are modified by sandy or silty drift, the presence of which facilitates water movement, and provides sufficient of the coarser fractions to form a coarser-textured A horizon when the clay content is depleted by eluviation.

In the Aylesbury district, Denchworth soils are primarily associated with the Kimmeridge Clay outcrop, but they also occur south of Wingrave and near Broughton on clay mapped as Gault by the Geological Survey, and similar soils may be encountered locally in the Challow complex. As with the Wicken and Challow soils, the upper horizons commonly appear to have formed in a disturbed or re-worked layer overlying the solid substratum. A few sub-angular flints and quartzose pebbles are usually present, and the A horizons may be loamy, but the subsoils consist predominantly of tenacious clay, with only occasional gravelly or sandy inclusions.

In typical profiles under grass, the A horizon is 9–12 in. thick, and very dark greyish brown to dark grey in colour, with rusty mottling along root channels. It usually has a granular structure at the surface, passing at 4–6 in. into medium to coarse blocky, but both structure and consistency vary to some extent with the texture, which may range from loam to clay.

Below the A horizon is a non-calcareous clay subsoil, designated (B)g, which has a coarse blocky to prismatic structure, and is extremely plastic and sticky in the wet condition. In the upper part the cleavage faces often have humose coatings, but below 15–18 in. they are olive-grey or grey, and have a shiny, polished appearance, with ripple-like undulations (slickensides) produced by the sliding of one surface over another when irregular swelling of the clay aggregates takes place. The interiors of the peds exhibit prominent yellowish brown to reddish yellow mottles, and occasional root channels are outlined in light grey. At depths below 18–24 in., in what is normally the most persistently moist zone of the profile, mottling with yellowish colours becomes finer and less pronounced, and cleavage faces are commonly oriented at oblique angles, producing coarse, wedge-shaped or pyramidal units. This horizon, which may be slightly calcareous, merges into less weathered and more massive grey clay, with fine brown mottling and secondary deposits of calcium carbonate, which becomes darker in colour, less plastic, and often shaly with depth. Powdery or coarsely crystalline gypsum also occurs at varying depths below 30 in., the zone of maximum accumulation generally lying a little below that of calcium carbonate. The gypsum results from reaction of calcium carbonate with sulphuric acid produced by the oxidation of finely divided iron sulphide in the original deposits.

Two profiles, both under permanent grass, are recorded below. In the first (Bu 76), described under very old pasture near Hulcott, the A horizon is of clay texture, and the upper 6 in., containing approximately 20 per cent organic matter, has a moderately acid reaction. Both here and south of Wingrave, the Denchworth soils occupy flat to gently sloping ground at about 275 ft. O.D. and are fairly uniform in morphology, with surface textures ranging from clay loam to clay. Although much of the land has been artificially drained, many fields remain waterlogged for considerable periods, and the subsoil retains its tenacious, pasty consistency for much of the year. In addition to the prevalence of seasonal waterlogging, the soils are more liable to cap and set into hard intractable lumps than those of the Wicken series, so that arable cultivation presents considerable difficulties in all but the most favourable seasons.

The second profile (Bu 85), from near Grendonhill Farm, Bierton, has a loamy A horizon which is distinctly more friable and lower in organic matter. Soils of this type are common in the north-west of the area, where the profiles are much influenced by loamy or gravelly drift, more or less incorporated with the underlying Kimmeridge Clay to form a re-worked layer which varies considerably in texture and thickness over short distances, and often appears to extend over flat and sloping ground alike. Soils with both surface and sub-surface horizons of clay loam or coarser texture are grouped as far as possible with the Rowsham complex, but owing to the complexity of the pattern the boundaries on the map are inevitably simplified, so that limited areas of these deeper, loamy soils may be found in the Denchworth series.

Soils like that described, in which a thin loamy horizon overlies yellow-mottled clay, are waterlogged in winter, but tend to dry out markedly in summer. Where they are under pasture, the surface horizon assumes a fine, powdery structure after dry weather, and on cultivated land it readily caps after rain and sets hard.

Another variant has a less clearly differentiated profile, consisting mainly of grey or dark grey clay, with only faint mottling. Soils of this kind occur chiefly on convex slopes and resemble those of the Wicken series, but are generally non-calcareous to at least 18 in.

Descriptions of representative profiles
(*Analytical data in Table* 10, *p.* 161)

PROFILE NO.: Bu 76 (Denchworth series)

Location: Manor Farm, Hulcott (grid ref. SP/855163).

Slope: 1–2° (ridge and furrow micro-relief; profile on ridge).   *Aspect:* east.
        Altitude: 275 ft. O.D.

Land use: permanent grassland.

Horizons:

A1g	0–5 in.	Very dark greyish brown (10 YR 3/2) firm humose clay with much fine yellowish red mottling associated with roots; strong granular structure; peds very hard when dry, with dark grey highly organic coatings; earthworms present; abundant roots; clear boundary.
A2g	5–12 in.	Dark grey (2·5 Y 3/1), very firm, coarsely blocky clay with darker colours associated with structural faces and in-filled channels; much, faint to distinct yellowish brown mottling internally; occasional small flints; frequent roots; clear irregular boundary.
(B)g	12–21 in.	Grey-brown (2·5 Y 4/2–5/2), light grey and reddish yellow (7·5 YR 6/8), prominently mottled, very firm clay with weak coarse blocky to prismatic structure; cleavage faces and channels mainly dark greyish brown; light grey associated with root channels; occasional flints and quartzose pebbles; very plastic when wet; few roots; merging boundary.

Clg 21–36 in. Olive-grey plastic clay with much fine, distinct, light grey and yellowish brown mottling; weak coarse blocky to prismatic (pyramidal) structure with smooth wavy faces inclined at irregular angles; few roots; merging boundary.

C2gca 36–48 in.+ Grey (5 Y 6/1), massive, stoneless, slightly micaceous clay with distinct fine brown mottling; containing secondary carbonate as rounded concretions and incoherent powdery deposits; becoming darker in colour, tougher, faintly laminated and apparently drier with depth.

PROFILE NO.: Bu 85 (Denchworth series)

Location: Grendonhill Farm, Bierton (grid ref. SP/831170).

Slope: 1–2°, slightly concave. *Aspect:* south. *Altitude:* 275 ft. O.D.

Land use: permanent grassland.

Horizons:

Ag 0–6 in. Dark greyish brown (2·5 Y 4/2) friable loam with distinct fine ochreous mottling associated with roots; a few small sub-angular flints and quartzose pebbles; moderate, granular to fine sub-angular blocky structure; abundant roots; earthworms active; clear smooth boundary.

A/(B)g 6–12 in. Greyish brown (2·5 Y 5/2) firm clay loam with distinct fine ochreous mottling and moderate, medium blocky to prismatic structure; darker colours associated with cleavage faces and worm channels; a few stones as above; frequent roots; merging boundary.

(B)g 12–20 in. Olive-grey (on cleavage faces) to olive (5 Y 4/3), very firm and plastic clay with distinct, fine, yellowish brown to strong brown mottling; stones as above; moderate medium prismatic structure; occasional manganiferous concretions; frequent roots; merging boundary.

Clg 20–30 in. Olive-grey stoneless plastic clay with mottling rather less distinct than above, and prismatic structure less well developed; merging boundary.

C2(g)ca 30–48 in.+ Dark grey very firm calcareous clay with deposits of secondary calcium carbonate and gypsum.

BIERTON COMPLEX
(*Bierton Series*)

This complex, covering about 700 acres, includes a range of loamy soils derived from the sandy and pebbly basal strata of the Portland Beds, and from the underlying fine sandy clay (Hartwell Clay) constituting the upper part of the Kimmeridge Clay formation in the Aylesbury district. The main area of occurrence is around Bierton and Aylesbury, where the soils occupy flat and gently sloping land in association with those of the Aylesbury series. Apart from occasional flints and quartzose pebbles in the upper horizons, there is little drift of extraneous origin in this locality, but, owing to the limited thickness and variability of the beds, the profiles are usually composite, and some of the soils on sloping land appear to have developed in thin, locally-derived Head deposits overlying Hartwell Clay. A belt of generally similar soils, containing scattered limestone fragments and lydite pebbles, encircles the Gault-capped Portlandian outlier at Groveway Farm. Here the slopes are steeper, and the beds have clearly been much disturbed, the broken nature of much of the ground suggesting that landslips have occurred.

The soils are affected in varying degrees by local, perched water-tables held up by the clay. Depending on relief and the thickness of pervious material above the clay, drainage conditions range from free to poor, but imperfectly drained profiles predominate, and well drained soils are of very limited extent. Nearly all the land was under grass in pre-war years, and a major proportion is in permanent grass or leys at present.

The most extensive soils, classed as the Bierton series, are imperfectly drained loams and fine sandy clay loams derived from the more or less disturbed and weathered remains of the lowest Portlandian strata, resting on Hartwell Clay at depths of 2 to 4 ft. This series is exemplified by profiles Bu 95 and Bu 94 below, both described under old grass with ridge-and-furrow micro-relief.

In the first profile (Bu 95), the surface horizon is a dark grey, rust-mottled calcareous loam with a well developed granular structure; it contains a few small flints, limestone fragments, and black lydite pebbles, and merges into a stiffer sub-surface horizon, designated (B)(g), which is yellowish brown when crushed, but contains much humose material in worm channels and as coatings on structural faces. Below this, at 17–32 in., is a horizon of brownish yellow, friable loam to fine sandy loam with ochreous mottling and patches of cream-coloured, marly material. The succeeding, brightly mottled, pebbly layer (C1gca) is the Lydite Bed (see Chapter I, p. 6), which rests in turn on Hartwell Clay (C2gca), consisting of grey, micaceous, fine sandy clay with green grains of glauconite. All the horizons above the Hartwell Clay are evidently weathered to some extent; there is much secondary carbonate in the basal layers, and the Lydite Bed is partly cemented by calcareous or redeposited ferruginous mateiial. In July, 1956, when the profile was recorded, the Hartwell Clay and the lower part of the Lydite Bed were waterlogged, and it seems that in wet seasons the level of saturation may rise to within 18 in. of the surface.

The upper horizons of the second profile (Bu 94) appear to have developed in locally-derived Head incorporating disturbed remains of the Portlandian strata. Beneath an A horizon of friable loam, there is a slightly stiffer sub-surface layer with a yellowish brown colour, more or less masked by humus. This is succeeded by a firm, brightly mottled (B)g horizon of clay loam texture, which passes at about 30 in. into olive-grey, glauconitic, fine sandy clay loam to fine sandy clay (Hartwell Clay), with secondary carbonate appearing at 48 in. Drainage is impeded to some extent by the fine-textured (B)g horizon, and a zone of saturation appears at the base of the profile, presumably where water is held up by more impervious Kimmeridge Clay below. Soils of this kind occur near the outer edge of the main area mapped, on either side of the shallow valley south-east of Bierton, and on the slopes around Groveway Farm. Surface textures range from loam to silty clay loam, and drainage is generally imperfect, becoming poor locally in sites receiving seepage from higher ground. To judge from auger borings and occasional sections, the appreciably sandy Hartwell Clay forming the substratum is rarely more than 10 ft. thick. As the underlying dark shaly clays approach the surface, the profile assumes the characteristics of the Denchworth series, the subsoil becoming more plastic and finer in texture.

Adjacent to the Aylesbury series, where the sandy strata between the limestone and the Hartwell Clay are normally thickest and least disturbed, imperfectly drained soils resembling Bu 95 give way locally to a well drained variant typified by profile Bu 65. The A horizon of this soil has a finer texture than lower horizons, and probably incorporates weathered remains of the formerly overlying limestone. Between the site of the profile and the area mapped as Aylesbury series around Bierton Lodge, a trench showed the limestone apparently wedging out down-slope into an impersistent sub-surface layer of marly, weathered material; and further south-east, some 8 ft. below the base of the limestone, the Lydite Bed and underlying Hartwell Clay appeared at the bottom of the trench, with water oozing from near the junction.

Descriptions of representative profiles
(*Analytical data in Table* 10, *pp.* 161–2)

PROFILE NO.: Bu 95 (Bierton series)

Location: Hood's Farm, Bierton (grid ref. SP/839163).
Slope: nearly level, with ridge-and-furrow micro-relief. *Altitude:* 305 ft. O.D.
Land use: permanent grassland.

Horizons:

A(g)	0–5 in.	Dark grey (10 YR 3/1–4/1) friable calcareous loam with distinct fine ochreous mottling associated with roots; occasional small sub-angular flints, limestone fragments and lydite pebbles; strong granular to fine sub-angular blocky structure; abundant roots; clear boundary.
(B)1(g)	5–17 in.	Yellowish brown (10 YR 5/4–5/6) when crushed, firm calcareous loam with darker colours associated with structural faces and infilled worm channels, and faint fine ochreous mottling internally; a few small stones as above; medium to fine sub-angular blocky structure, with some prismatic tendency; frequent roots; clear boundary.
(B)2g	17–32 in.	Brownish yellow (10 YR 6/6–6/8) friable loam and fine sandy loam with patches of soft pale yellowish calcareous material ("race") and distinct yellow and red mottlings; a few very small lydite pebbles; common, small, pin-head sized ferruginous concretions; weak fine blocky structure; frequent worm tracks and roots; clear irregular boundary.
C1gca	32–40 in.	Very pale brown to light yellow, weakly laminated, very calcareous, pebbly, fine sandy loam to fine sandy clay loam with much ochreous and red mottling which becomes dominant towards base; numerous very small lydite pebbles; compact in place and locally cemented by secondary carbonate or ochre, but friable when dug out; occasional worm channels; few roots; sharp smooth boundary.
C2gca	40–45 in.+	Grey plastic fine sandy clay with distinct brown mottling, and much secondary carbonate (Hartwell Clay *in situ*); wet, with water seeping in (July, 1956).

PROFILE NO.: Bu 94 (Bierton series)

Location: Burcott Lodge Farm, Bierton (grid ref. SP/840150).

Slope: c. 1°, with ridge-and-furrow micro-relief. *Aspect:* north. *Altitude:* 275 ft. O.D.

Land use: permanent grassland.

Horizons:

A	0–6 in.	Very dark greyish brown (10 YR 3/2) friable loam containing occasional small sub-angular flints and lydite pebbles; moderate granular structure; abundant fine roots; clear smooth boundary.
A/(B)(g)	6–12 in.	Dark greyish brown and yellowish brown, friable to firm, loam to silty clay loam with faint ochreous mottling; a few small stones as above; darker colours associated with infilled worm channels and structural faces; fine sub-angular blocky structure with some prismatic tendency; frequent roots; merging boundary.
(B)g	12–30 in.	Grey-brown (10 YR 5/2) and strong brown (7·5 YR 5/8), distinctly mottled, firm blocky clay loam with a few small lydite pebbles; paler colours on cleavage faces and ochreous mottling within aggregates; occasional worm channels; few roots; merging boundary.
Cgca	30–36 in.+	Olive to olive-grey (5 Y 5/2–5/3), plastic fine sandy clay loam with a greenish tinge due to glauconite, and much distinct fine ochreous mottling; few roots; becomes darker and greyer below 48 in., and contains deposits of secondary carbonate; water seeping in at 60 in. (June, 1956).

PROFILE NO.: Bu 65 (unnamed variant on Portland Sand)

Location: Bierton Lodge, Aylesbury (grid ref. SP/83147).

Slope: c. 1°. *Aspect:* south-east. *Altitude:* 290 ft. O.D.

Land use: permanent grassland.

Horizons:

A	0–5 in.	Dark greyish brown (10 YR 4/2) calcareous friable fine sandy clay loam containing occasional small black lydite pebbles and soft limestone fragments; moderate fine sub-angular blocky and granular structure; abundant roots; clear smooth boundary.
A/(B)	5–10 in.	Yellowish brown (10 YR 5/6) calcareous friable fine sandy loam with few stones; darker colours associated with structural faces and worm channels; weak granular and sub-angular blocky structure; frequent roots; merging boundary.
(B)	10–22 in.	Brownish yellow (10 YR 6/6–6/8) stoneless friable fine sandy loam with weak sub-angular blocky structure; occasional in-filled worm channels; few roots; merging boundary.
(B)/Cca	22–30 in.+	Yellowish brown (10 YR 5/8) soft friable loamy fine sand with distinct fine ochreous mottling and pale yellowish calcareous deposits ("race").

WESTON TURVILLE SERIES

This series, second in extent to the Wicken among those mapped in the Vale, comprises imperfectly drained, sandy clay loams and clay loams formed on Chalky Gravel Head, which rests for the most part on Gault clay. Covering about 3,500 acres, it is most widespread around Weston Turville and Stoke Mandeville, and also appears near Wilstone and Marstongate, and north-west of Ivinghoe. In the last-mentioned localities, and in a large area north of Weston Turville, the soils occupy tracts of low-lying land with scarcely perceptible gradients, and merge laterally into alluvial soils of the Ford End complex. Westward, about Stoke Mandeville, where slightly higher-lying spreads of gravelly drift have been dissected by stream action, isolated patches of similar soil occur on gentle slopes and terrace-like features, extending in places on to the Upper Greensand, and bordered by the Wicken and Harwell series. Comparable soils in the Vale of the White Horse, where the gravel layers consist largely of chalk and malmstone fragments, were classed as the Steventon series by Kay (1934).

In the 19th century, these comparatively easy-working soils seem to have been devoted largely to arable cultivation, and much of the type area north of Weston Turville remained under the plough during the 1930's (Temple, 1929). At least half the area mapped is now in arable crops or leys, the proportion under tillage being distinctly higher than on the neighbouring clayey soils.

Typical profiles have a very dark greyish brown A horizon 6–9 in. thick, followed by a stiff, dark yellowish or olive-brown (B)(g) horizon of similar or finer texture, with fine ochreous and greyish mottling increasing in intensity with depth. Rust-stained, chalky gravel is normally encountered at depths from 12 to 30 in., but the overlying horizons contain little or no chalk, and may be acid, differing in this respect from those of the Gubblecote series on similar materials.

The surface horizon contains variable amounts of angular and sub-angular flints, accompanied in the areas north of Long Marston and Ivinghoe by occasional quartzose pebbles. Often it is only slightly stony, but it may be very stony locally when the gravel lies at 15 in. or less. Despite its considerable sand content, which may amount to 50 per cent, the soil is distinctly plastic when wet; it is easier to work than the Wicken clay, and breaks down to give softer and more crumbly aggregates, but the structure so produced is notably less stable. The surface readily caps after rain and, on fallow ground, undergoes superficial resorting as shown by the appearance of sandy coatings on exposed clods and sedimentation of fine material in minor depressions and furrow bottoms. Under old grassland, a fine, soft, granular structure develops in the upper 4–6 in., and rusty mottling often occurs along root channels, especially where the soil has become acid.

The sub-surface horizons vary considerably in thickness and stone content and in the extent to which the dominant brownish colour is modified by gleying, but are normally distinctly more friable than the associated clayey soils, breaking down fairly easily when partly dry into fine and medium, sub-angular blocky aggregates. Textures range from sandy clay loam to clay, the former occurring chiefly in profiles transitional to the Wicken series, in which the succeeding gravelly layer is thin or only intermittently developed.

The gravelly layer is typically composed of sub-angular, brown-stained flints and small chalk pebbles in an appreciably sandy matrix, and varies in thickness from a few inches to 4 ft. or more, often within short distances. The thickest deposits appear to occupy hollows or troughs in the surface of the underlying clay and often contain little fine material, but as a rule the matrix is of sandy loam or finer texture, and may be chalky or marly, so that the material as a whole locally resembles Coombe-Rock. Towards the lowest altitudinal limits of each spread of drift, the flints in the deposit often tend to become smaller and less numerous, and the gravel is replaced locally by layers of calcareous sandy material with few stones. This occurs south and east of Aylesbury, and in the northern part of the Ivinghoe tract.

Drainage is impeded by the clay substratum, so that the overlying horizons are subject to periodic or permanent waterlogging. On flat land especially, surface wetness may also result from the relative impermeability of the immediate subsoil. Differences in the depth and thickness of this layer, coupled with minor variations in level, give rise to frequent variations in hydrologic conditions, the morphological effects of which are partly obscured by artificial drainage. In most instances the subsoils are distinctly mottled with greyish and ochreous colours below 12–15 in., but locally, and chiefly on slightly elevated or sloping ground, the sub-surface horizon is uniformly brown or yellowish brown, indicating that drainage is moderately good. Elsewhere, usually on flat low-lying land or in slight depressions, the A horizon is darker and richer in organic matter, and the sub-surface horizons show such pronounced gleying that an over-all brownish colour is no longer evident. This phase of the series, which appears to have developed under conditions of poor drainage, occurs on the low ground north of the Tring–Aylesbury road, and in a strip extending in a north-north-easterly direction from Westend Farm, Weston Turville. In the latter instance, however, seasonal wetness is no more pronounced than on much of the adjoining land, suggesting that drainage has been improved recently.

Much of the old arable land on this and related soils was laid up in ridge-and-furrow in order to alleviate the effects of winter wetness. The micro-relief thereby produced is often clearly reflected in profile morphology, the soils on the ridge-tops being moderately well drained, and those in the adjacent furrows conforming to the poorly drained phase.

The first two profiles recorded below, both described under first-year ley, are located between Weston Turville and the Tring–Aylesbury road. Similar, slightly calcareous, surface and sub-surface horizons occur in each profile, and the soils are both moderately flinty, but whereas in Bu 113 the underlying gravel extends to at least 42 in., in Bu 100 it is only about 6 in. thick and at 25 in. rests sharply on re-worked Gault containing occasional flints and chalk fragments. At the latter site, however, the lower boundary of the gravel is known to be very uneven, for two other pits excavated nearby failed to reach clay at 48 in. The intensely gleyed lower part of the gravel layer in the deeper profile appears to be permanently waterlogged, and the upper part, through which the water-table fluctuates, is weakly cemented in places by prominent ochreous deposits.

Towards the western and northern margins of the Weston Turville spread, and in each of the other areas mapped, the soils are commonly less flinty, and the gravel layer is thinner or lies at greater depths. This variant is exemplified by profile Bu 63, described under old grass on flat land adjacent to the Wendover–Aylesbury road. Here the soil is a moderately acid clay loam containing few stones in the upper 12 in.; chalky gravel is encountered at about 24 in., and the subsoil above it is more gleyed than the sub-surface horizons of the two preceding profiles.

Descriptions of representative profiles

(Analytical data in Table 10, p. 162)

PROFILE NO.: Bu 113 (Weston Turville series)

Location: Mill Farm, Weston Turville (grid ref. SP/855118).

Slope: nearly level.   *Altitude:* 305 ft. O.D.

Land use: grass-clover ley (first year).

Horizons:

Ap	0–8 in.	Very dark greyish brown (2·5 Y 3/2), friable to firm, flinty sandy clay loam with moderate fine sub-angular blocky and granular structure; flints mainly small and sub-angular; occasional chalk fragments; abundant roots; sharp smooth boundary.
(B)(g)	8–13 in.	Olive-brown (2·5 Y 4/4) firm flinty sandy clay loam with distinct, fine, ochreous and grey mottling and darker colours associated with structure faces and infilled worm channels; moderate, fine to medium sub-angular blocky structure; frequent roots; clear undulating boundary.
C1gca	13–23 in.	Light olive-brown (2·5 Y 5/6 when mixed) firm gravelly sandy clay loam with increasingly prominent, fine, ochreous and grey mottling. Stones include sub-angular flints and very small rounded chalk fragments; some powdery deposits of secondary carbonate; occasional worm channels; few roots; clear undulating boundary.
C2g	23–42 in.+	Loose wet sandy gravel of sub-angular flints and rounded chalk fragments, weakly cemented in places near upper limit by prominent ochreous deposits; becoming paler in colour, more chalky and stickier below; ground-water at 27 in. (October, 1956).

PROFILE NO.: Bu 100 (Weston Turville series)

Location: County Farm, Weston Turville (grid ref. SP/852119).

Slope: nearly level.   *Altitude:* 300 ft. O.D.

Land use: grass-clover ley (first year).

Horizons:

Ap	0–6 in.	Very dark greyish brown (2·5 Y 3/2), friable to firm, flinty sandy clay loam; flints mainly sub-angular; weak fine sub-angular blocky and granular structure; frequent roots; sharp smooth boundary.

(B)(g)   6–19 in.   Olive-brown (2·5 Y 4/3) firm flinty sandy clay loam with dark grey-brown associated with structural faces and channels, and faint ochreous and greyish mottling internally; moderate medium prismatic structure, breaking to fine blocky; few roots; clear irregular boundary.

C1g   19–25 in.   Friable to loose, calcareous gravel of sub-rounded chalk pebbles <½ in. and sub-angular flints <4 in., with a sandy loam matrix prominently mottled with grey and ochreous colours; few roots; this horizon variable in thickness and degree of expression, with inclusions of grey clay; sharp irregular boundary.

C2gca   25–33 in.+   Olive-grey (5 Y 5/2) calcareous plastic clay with distinct fine light olive-brown mottling, containing some chalk fragments and occasional flints to at least 48 in.

PROFILE NO.: Bu 63 (Weston Turville series)

Location: County Farm, Stoke Mandeville (grid ref. SP/840116).

Slope: nearly level.   *Altitude:* 320 ft. O.D.

Land use: permanent grassland.

Horizons:

A   0–4 in.   Very dark greyish brown (10 YR 3/2) friable clay loam, containing occasional small sub-angular flints; moderate granular structure; abundant roots; earthworms active; merging boundary.

A/(B)(g)   4–12 in.   Dark brown (10 YR 4/3) firm clay loam with some faint ochreous mottling and darker colours associated with cleavage faces and worm channels; a few flints as above; moderate, medium to fine sub-angular blocky structure; frequent roots; merging boundary.

(B)g   12–24 in.   Greyish brown (10 YR 5/2–5/3) to brown, firm clay loam with distinct fine ochreous mottling; becoming increasingly flinty; moderate, medium to fine sub-angular blocky structure; roots rare; merging boundary.

Cg   24–36 in.+   Greyish brown (2·5 Y 5/2) calcareous gravelly sandy clay loam with much prominent ochreous mottling, becoming coarser in texture and more gravelly with depth; gravel of sub-rounded chalk pebbles <½ in. and sub-angular flints <1 in.

ROWSHAM COMPLEX
(*Rowsham Series*)

In the undulating clay-land north and north-east of Aylesbury, the dominant Denchworth and Wicken series are interspersed with more or less stony, generally non-calcareous soils with distinctly loamy surface and sub-surface horizons developed in superficial deposits of variable origin. These soils, occurring on plateau and terrace remnants and in lower slope positions, are grouped as the Rowsham complex, and cover about 1,300 acres. As the clay substrata are everywhere impervious, drainage is predominantly imperfect or poor, and much of the land is in ridge-and-furrow. Prior to 1939, it was almost entirely under grass and, although a considerable acreage has since been cultivated, grass remains the predominant crop.

At Wingrave the drift includes fluvio-glacial gravel and boulder clay, and is generally over 6 ft. thick. Thin weathered remnants of what may once have been a continuous sheet of glacial drift also occur on the hill-tops farther west, but the more widespread deposits on lower ground appear for the most part to have been re-arranged by solifluxion or stream-action, and locally incorporate materials derived from nearby Portlandian outcrops. Imperfectly and poorly drained soils formed in the latter deposits are classed as the Rowsham series. The soils on the higher-lying drifts include several distinct variants of limited extent, but their classification as named series has been deferred, pending surveys in the country farther north.

Soils of the Rowsham series have a surface horizon of loam, sandy clay loam or clay loam with scattered sub-angular flints and quartzose pebbles, followed by a stiffer mottled subsoil, containing appreciable amounts of sand, which breaks down when partly dry into medium and fine, sub-angular blocky aggregates. They are normally acid at the surface, and the profiles show a distinct tendency to textural differentiation. Where drainage is imperfect the upper part of the subsoil may be brown or yellowish brown, with only faint mottling, but fine greyish and ochreous mottlings become more pronounced with depth, and are generally prominent below 15 in. The clay substratum is encountered at depths ranging from 18 to 36 in., and is overlain in places by a coarser-textured and more gravelly layer subject to waterlogging, but continuous layers of chalky gravel such as occur in the Weston Turville series are rarely to be found. Elsewhere the subsoil is distinctly sandy, but contains few stones, and may have a reddish tinge.

These soils are typically developed on either side of Thistle Brook, and often extend on to adjoining slopes, grading into the Denchworth series as the drift becomes thinner and more clayey. Isolated patches of similar soil, containing variable quantities of sand and stones, are mapped on the lower slopes north of Groveway Farm, and in tributary valleys south-east and west of Wingrave. A poorly drained profile (Bu 91) under old grass, with Kimmeridge Clay at 28 in., is recorded below from Dunsham Farm, Aylesbury. The soil is only a few feet above the adjacent alluvium, and receives seepage from the higher ground to the east. Elsewhere the subsoils are commonly browner in colour and gleying is less pronounced, at least in the upper 12 in.

On foot-slopes north and west of Bierton, the soils appear to have formed in Head containing much material sludged from the neighbouring Portlandian outcrop and are affected locally by seepage from springs arising at its base. The underlying Kimmeridge Clay is generally encountered at 2 to 3 ft., the lower boundary of the drift being marked in places by a thin layer of calcareous gravel containing small limestone fragments and lydite pebbles. Above the junction the subsoils consist predominantly of yellowish brown clay loam to fine sandy clay, more or less mottled with greyish and ochreous colours. This variant is typified by profile Bu 89, described under grass on a relatively well drained site protected from down-slope seepage by a cut-off ditch. Similar profiles have been noted on foot-slopes below the Groveway Farm outlier, although the drift in that locality generally contains a higher proportion of foreign stones.

On the high ground in and west of Wingrave village, there are limited areas of stony loam and sandy loam soil overlying non-calcareous, flinty and quartzose gravel, typified by profile Bu 103. The gravel appears to rest on Gault at variable depths, and is subject to waterlogging, but where it is more than 2 ft. thick the drainage of the soil is locally moderately good, and the profiles show clear affinities with those of the St. Albans series. In the example described, a brown, very friable, stony, sub-surface horizon of sandy loam to sandy clay loam overlies about 3 ft. of sandy gravel, which rests in turn on grey clay, probably weathered Gault *in situ*. The gravel layer is prominently mottled throughout with grey and yellowish red, and in places has a clayey matrix, the clay being concentrated in discrete skins coating stones and sand grains.

Elsewhere on the Wingrave plateau, and on the outlying hills farther west, the subsoil horizons are finer in texture, and appear to consist of more or less weathered or disturbed boulder clay.

In profile Bu 99, west of Wingrave, slightly weathered Boulder Clay containing small, sub-rounded, chalk fragments is encountered at 33 in. beneath a loamy superficial layer. More commonly, however, the drift is no more than about 3 ft. thick, and is often decalcified throughout, the subsoil consisting of stony clay or sandy clay with grey, yellow and reddish mottling. Similar profiles, containing a little chalk at the base, have also been identified locally at lower levels, notably on the flat-topped hill north of Bierton (grid ref. SP/842171), where thin drift, shown as Boulder Clay by the Geological Survey, rests on Hartwell Clay.

Descriptions of representative profiles
(*Analytical data in Table* 10, *pp.* 162–3)

PROFILE NO.: Bu 91 (Rowsham series)

Location: Dunsham Farm, Aylesbury (grid ref. SP/823157).

Slope: c. 1° even.   *Aspect:* west.   *Altitude:* 245 ft. O.D.

Land use: permanent grassland.

Horizons:

A	0–5 in.	Very dark brown (7·5 YR 3/1) friable loam with a few small quartzose and lydite pebbles and sub-angular flints; moderate granular to fine sub-angular blocky structure; abundant fine roots; clear smooth boundary.
A/(B)(g)	5–11 in.	Dark greyish brown to brown (10 YR 4/2–4/3), firm, coarsely blocky clay loam with much distinct fine ochreous mottling; darker colours associated with fissures and worm channels; occasional stones as above; some vertical fissures; frequent roots; merging boundary.
(B)g	11–28 in.	Grey and brown mottled, firm to plastic, slightly stony clay loam to clay with weak blocky structure; greyish brown (2·5 Y 5/2) on cleavage faces and much distinct ochreous mottling internally; some fine manganiferous concretions; few roots; sharp irregular boundary marked in places by a thin layer of calcareous gravel.

Cgca   28–36 in.+   Dark grey (2·5 Y 4/0), very firm, faintly laminated, stoneless clay with fine light olive-brown mottling; deposits of secondary carbonate and gypsum; (Kimmeridge Clay *in situ*).

PROFILE NO.: Bu 89 (Rowsham series)

Location: Dunsham Farm, Aylesbury (grid ref. SP/829152).

Slope: 1°.   *Aspect:* west.   *Altitude:* 260 ft. O.D.

Land use: permanent grassland.

Horizons:

A   0–4 in.   Very dark greyish brown (10 YR 3/2), friable to firm loam containing a few very small sub-angular flints and lydite pebbles; strong granular structure; abundant fine roots; earthworms active; clear smooth boundary.

A/(B)   4–10 in.   Dark brown (10 YR 4/3) firm clay loam containing some very small flints, limestone fragments and occasional lydite pebbles; darker colours associated with cleavage faces and worm channels; moderate medium to fine sub-angular blocky structure, with widely spaced vertical cracks and granular infillings, frequent roots; merging boundary.

(B)(g)   10–24 in.   Dark yellowish brown (10 YR 4/4) firm clay loam with faint fine ochreous mottling and darker greyer colours on cleavage faces; stones as above; moderate medium prismatic structure, breaking easily to medium sub-angular blocky; roots less frequent; sharp irregular boundary marked in places by a trace of sandy, calcareous gravel.

Cgca   24–30 in.+   Olive-grey (5 Y 4/2), stoneless, very firm to plastic, calcareous clay with distinct light olive-brown mottling; secondary carbonate occurring as small concretions and incoherent, powdery deposits; few roots; (Kimmeridge Clay *in situ*).

PROFILE NO.: Bu 103 (unnamed variant on fluvio-glacial gravel)

Location: Parsonage Farm, Wingrave (grid ref. SP/863193).

Slope: nearly level.   *Altitude:* 420 ft. O.D.

Land use: permanent grassland.

Horizons:

A   0–6 in.   Dark greyish brown (10 YR 4/2) friable sandy loam with occasional stones, mainly sub-angular flints and quartzose pebbles; bleached sand grains; moderate granular structure; abundant fine roots; added chalk, merging boundary.

(B)   6–24 in.   Dark brown (10 YR 4/2–4/4) friable gravelly, sandy loam to sandy clay loam with numerous infilled worm channels; stones include sub-angular flints and fragments of vein quartz, quartzite and sandstone; weak, granular to fine sub-angular blocky structure; abundant roots; clear irregular boundary.

C1g	24–60 in.	Loose sandy gravel, prominently mottled with colours ranging from grey to yellowish red (5 YR 5/8); stones as above; becoming more clayey with depth; a few roots and worm channels.
C2	60 in.+	Passing to dark grey non-calcareous clay, probably weathered Gault *in situ*.

PROFILE NO.: Bu 99 (unnamed variant on Chalky Boulder Clay)

Location: Floyds Farm, Wingrave (grid ref. SP/873193).

Slope: nearly level.   *Altitude:* 430 ft. O.D.

Land use: shelter belt (horse chestnut) with rough un-grazed grass.

Horizons:

A	0–6 in.	Very dark greyish brown (10 YR 3/2), friable to firm, slightly stony sandy clay loam with occasional small sub-angular flints and quartzite pebbles; strong granular structure; abundant fibrous and woody roots; clear smooth boundary.
A/(B)(g)	6–18 in.	Dark brown (10 YR 4/3) firm sandy clay loam with some faint ochreous mottling and darker colours associated with structural faces and worm channels; stones as above; moderate medium blocky to prismatic structure; frequent roots; merging lower boundary.
(B)g	18–33 in.	Yellowish brown (10 YR 5/4), firm, slightly stony, clay loam with distinct fine reddish yellow mottling and greying on cleavage faces; moderate medium prismatic structure; a few manganiferous concretions; some worm channels; frequent roots; clear irregular boundary.
Cgca	33–40 in.+	Grey and brown, prominently mottled, slightly stony, firm calcareous clay loam to clay containing rounded chalk fragments, sub-angular-flints and quartzose pebbles; extends to at least 75 in.

FORD END COMPLEX
(*Ford End and Mead Series*)

The Ford End complex, covering about 2,400 acres, consists of calcareous gley soils associated with scarp-foot springs and with the numerous small streams draining the sub-edge plain. It is most extensive around Ivinghoe Aston, Long Marston and Aston Clinton, and other smaller patches and strips appear on low-lying ground in widely scattered localities from Kimble and Stoke Mandeville north-eastwards to Ivinghoe.

The deposits giving rise to the soils spread over Lower Chalk, Upper Greensand and Gault, and vary from 18 in. to 4 ft. or more in thickness. They often contain fragments of gastropod shells, and generally appear to have been laid down in water, although near the scarp-foot springs they extend in places on to appreciable slopes, suggesting that they accumulated in part as mud-flows when seepage was more active than at present. Some of the soils in such areas are now fairly well drained, and most of the lower land, which was formerly subject to floods, has been rendered drier by ditching and locally by diverting streams (e.g. the Whistle Brook) to more direct courses. In many places, however, a zone of permanent saturation occurs within 3 ft. of the surface, and the subsoils are normally waterlogged for part of the year. The wetter areas rarely show any sign of ridge-and-furrow and were probably utilized as summer pasture or for hay in pre-enclosure days. Nearly all the land was under grass during the 1930's, but arable cultivation is now fairly widespread, especially where drainage is relatively good.

The most extensive soils, classed as the Ford End series, are characterized by dark-coloured A horizons of loam or clay loam texture, overlying very calcareous, rust-mottled subsoil layers (designated Cg) with layers of fine chalky gravel. They occur around Ivinghoe Aston and Aston Clinton, adjoining the Mill Brook at Kimble, and in other localities where the parent deposits have been laid down by streams issuing from the Lower Chalk. The profiles often resemble those of the Halton series, but the surface and sub-surface horizons are normally more friable and less stony, and the gravel layers commonly encountered at the base consist largely of water-worn chalk fragments with only few small flints. As the deposits descend to lower and flatter land, more Gault-derived material is incorporated, and the soils tend to become finer in texture and less calcareous, and eventually grade into the Mead series, which is characterized by a sub-surface horizon of grey plastic clay. In a few places, notably near Apsley and north-east of Weston Turville, the alluvium consists partly of grey, fine sandy or silty clay loam derived largely from Upper Greensand rocks. Another variant, north-west of Long Marston, and north of the Tring–Aylesbury road, is appreciably sandy and less calcareous, and appears to represent a poorly drained phase of the Weston Turville series which has received alluvial additions.

The soils that have remained under old grass have friable granular surface horizons rich in well decomposed organic matter, and on the wettest sites, where the organic-matter content may exceed 20 per cent, the upper 6 in. often have a mellow or spongy consistency, with finer, more crumb-like aggregates than the layer below. When such soils are first ploughed, they are almost black when wet, and tend to give puffy seed-beds composed of small granules which, once dry, are slow to re-wet.

Of the three grassland profiles recorded below, those from Ivinghoe Aston and Wilstone are typical Ford End soils, whereas the third, described on low ground between Bierton and Puttenham, represents a poorly drained phase having affinities with the Weston Turville series.

The Ivinghoe Aston soil (Bu 30) is very calcareous throughout, and has a friable, loamy surface horizon, passing at about 10 in. into light olive-grey, slightly rust-mottled, chalky silty clay loam with fine to medium sub-angular blocky structure. Below this is a layer of rust-stained chalky gravel, resting at 27 in. on silty glauconitic marl. Owing to the low-lying situation, and the presence of impervious Gault at no great depth, the marl contains a permanent water-table which rises into the gravel layer during winter and spring. In the Wilstone profile (Ht 70), the A horizon is finer in texture, and the layer of sandy chalk gravel at the base extends to a depth of 5 ft., where it rests on Gault.

Although both profiles are affected by a fluctuating water-table, the surface and sub-surface horizons are rarely waterlogged. Drainage conditions are variable, however, and are poor or very poor locally, as in small areas south-west of World's End and around Wilstone reservoir. The subsoil horizons are also variable in thickness and constitution, consisting in some places largely of disintegrated chalk or marl, and in others of more sandy or clayey materials.

In profile Bu 97, the surface consists of very dark grey, slightly calcareous, humose clay loam with rusty mottling along root channels and occasional conspicuous coarse sand grains. Below this is a grey and ochreous mottled horizon of silty clay loam texture, containing shell fragments and appreciable amounts of humus, followed by a layer of rust-stained chalky gravel, which rests on Gault at 30 in. The sub-surface horizon remains moist and plastic for most of the year, and the lower part of the gravel layer is permanently waterlogged.

Descriptions of representative profiles
(*Analytical data in Table* 10, *p.* 163)

PROFILE NO.: Bu 30 (Ford End series)

Location: Grove Farm, Ivinghoe Aston (grid ref. SP/945178).
Slope: level.   *Altitude:* 310 ft. O.D.
Land use: permanent grassland.

Horizons:

A	0–10 in.	Very dark greyish brown (10 YR 3/2–4/2) friable calcareous loam with occasional small flints and chalk fragments; moderate granular structure; some small gastropod shells; abundant roots; clear smooth boundary.
C1(g)	10–17 in.	Light olive-grey (5 Y 6/2), friable, very calcareous, silty clay loam with few faint fine ochreous mottlings; some small chalk pebbles; moderate fine to medium sub-angular blocky structure; worm channels; secondary carbonate deposits on structure faces; frequent roots; clear smooth boundary.
C2gca	17–27 in.	Light grey (2·5 Y 7/2), very calcareous, very friable gravelly clay loam to sandy clay loam with much distinct fine ochreous mottling; gravel of small chalk pebbles; weak fine sub-angular blocky structure; secondary carbonate concretions; few roots; clear smooth boundary.
C3g	27–36 in.+	Light grey silty marl with a greenish tinge and few faint fine ochreous mottles; wet.

PROFILE NO.: Ht 70 (Ford End series)

Location: Church Farm, Wilstone (grid ref. SP/901140).
Slope: level.   *Altitude:* 300 ft. O.D.
Land use: permanent grassland.

Horizons:

A	0–6 in.	Very dark brown (10 YR 2/2) friable humose calcareous clay loam with strong granular structure; occasional small sub-angular flints; abundant roots; clear smooth boundary.

A/C1(g)   6–16 in.   Greyish brown (2·5 Y 5/2) friable calcareous clay loam with darker colours associated with structural faces and worm channels, and few, faint to distinct, brownish yellow mottles; a few small sub-angular flints and chalk pebbles; moderate medium sub-angular blocky structure with granular infillings; some small gastropod shells; frequent roots; merging boundary.

C2g   16–26 in.   Grey-brown (2·5 Y 5/2) to light grey, very calcareous, structureless gravelly loam with distinct yellowish brown (10 YR 5/8) mottling; gravel mainly of chalk pebbles $< \frac{1}{4}$ in., with some small sub-angular flints; few roots; clear irregular boundary.

C3gca   26–60 in.   Fine white chalk gravel with some sub-angular flints in a fine sandy matrix consisting largely of disintegrated chalk; prominently mottled yellowish brown and weakly cemented in places by secondary carbonate; ground-water at 50 in. (July, 1956).

C4   60 in.+   Dark grey (5 Y 4/1) calcareous clay (Gault *in situ*).

PROFILE NO.: Bu 97 (Ford End series)

Location: midway between Bierton and Puttenham (grid ref. SP/860149).

Slope: level.   *Altitude:* 245 ft. O.D.

Land use: permanent grassland.

Horizons:

Ag   0–6 in.   Very dark grey (2·5 Y 3/1), stoneless, friable to firm, humose clay loam with very fine distinct rusty mottling along root channels; occasional coarse sand grains; strong granular structure; abundant fine roots; earthworms active; merging boundary.

A/C1g   6–19 in.   Greyish brown (2·5 Y 5/2) firm calcareous silty clay loam with distinct, fine, light grey and brownish yellow mottling; dark grey humose material associated with structural faces and channels; occasional very small sub-angular flints; weak coarse blocky and prismatic structure; very sticky and plastic when wet; shell fragments present; frequent fine roots; sharp irregular boundary.

C2g   19–30 in.   Loose wet gravel of chalk pebbles and very small ($< \frac{1}{2}$ in.) angular and sub-angular flint fragments in a loamy sand to sandy clay loam matrix, prominently mottled with yellowish brown, strong brown and grey; weakly cemented in places by ferruginous deposits; few roots; sharp irregular boundary.

C3gca   30–40 in.+   Light grey (5 Y 7/2), very calcareous clay, with fine, distinct, pale olive and olive-yellow (2·5 Y 6/6) mottling; a little gravel in upper few inches; occasional fine roots, and some large dead woody roots (probably Gault *in situ*).

MEAD SERIES

The soils of the Mead series have formed under conditions of poor or very poor drainage in fine-textured flood deposits laid down by the Thistle Brook and its tributaries. About 900 acres are delimited, and other small ill-defined areas are included in the Ford End complex.

This low-lying land was formerly subject to periodic flooding, and the Thistle Brook still overflows occasionally (Plate III). Drainage has been somewhat improved during and since the 1939–45 war by clearing streams and ditches but, owing to the lack of fall and the relatively impervious sub-surface horizons, the soils are difficult to drain satisfactorily and are commonly waterlogged for most of the year. There is some arable cultivation near Puttenham, but the wetter areas are almost entirely under grass, which is mainly of indifferent quality. Tufted hair-grass, meadow-sweet, and various species of sedge are common, and patches of rushes occur locally.

The alluvium in which the soils are formed is largely derived from Gault or Kimmeridge Clay, and is predominantly of silty clay or clay texture. In the flood-plain of the Thistle Brook it is sometimes over 3 ft. thick, and may rest directly on the Kimmeridge Clay, but north-west of Puttenham it is generally thinner and more silty, and usually overlies layers of chalky gravel or of finely divided calcareous material resembling lake marl. A substratum of well-humified peat or "muck" also occurs locally, notably on the west side of the "island" north-west of Folly Farm. Fragmented gastropod shells are generally present and serve in some places to distinguish the soils from those of the Challow or Denchworth series, which they may otherwise resemble.

In typical profiles under old grass, the A horizon consists of humose clay or silty clay with a well developed granular structure, and is usually slightly calcareous. Because of its high organic-matter content, amounting in places to 20 per cent or more, the soil is mellow and easily crushed in the moist condition, but when thoroughly dried out it separates into hard black granules which are slow to re-wet. At 5–7 in. it passes into a very plastic sub-surface horizon, which assumes a coarse blocky to prismatic structure on drying, and in which the predominantly grey colour of the mineral material is more or less masked by incorporated humus. Where the clayey alluvium is more than 15 in. thick, the subsoil consists of grey, structureless, plastic clay with varying amounts of yellow mottling.

Two profiles of the series are described, the second (Bu 108) being located north of College Farm, Drayton Beauchamp, in an area mapped as Ford End complex. In profile Bu 87, sited in the flood-plain of the Thistle Brook near Grendonhill Farm, the sub-surface horizon contains numerous shells and is clearly of alluvial origin. Below 12 in., however, the clay is only slightly calcareous and probably represents weathered Kimmeridge Clay *in situ*. In profile Bu 108 a compact layer of white, extremely calcareous material with yellow mottling extends from 16 to 46 in. and is underlain by wet chalky gravel, which rests in turn on Gault at 64 in.

Another profile, 150 yards to the east, adjacent to the mapped boundary of the Challow complex, was clayey throughout, and showed no trace of the white, calcareous layer. Gault was encountered at 48 in. and a fragment of pottery, thought to be of the 12th century, was found at 36 in., suggesting that the overlying clay had accumulated since medieval times.

Descriptions of representative profiles
(*Analytical data in Table* 10, *p.* 163)

PROFILE NO.: Bu 87 (Mead series)

Location: Grendonhill Farm, Bierton (grid ref. SP/826172).

Slope: level. *Altitude:* 245 ft. O.D.

Land use: permanent grassland.

Horizons:

A	0–3 in.	Very dark greyish brown (2·5 Y 3/2) stoneless friable humose clay with moderate granular structure; abundant roots; slightly calcareous; clear smooth boundary.
A/C1g	3–12 in.	Dark greyish brown (2·5 Y 4/2–5/2), very plastic, stoneless calcareous clay with distinct fine strong brown (7·5 YR 5/8) mottling; moderate coarse prismatic to blocky structure; numerous shell fragments; frequent roots; clear smooth boundary.
C2g	12–24 in.+	Grey (5 Y 6/1), wet, stoneless and plastic clay with distinct, fine, strong brown to reddish yellow mottling; coarse prismatic to massive structure; few roots; becoming darker in colour with depth, and containing secondary gypsum between 24 and 36 in. (probably Kimmeridge Clay *in situ*).

PROFILE NO.: Bu 108 (Mead series)

Location: North of College Farm, Aston Clinton (grid ref. SP/867145).

Slope: level. *Altitude:* 270 ft. O.D.

Land use: permanent grassland with *Agrostis* spp., *Festuca rubra, Carex flacca, Ranunculus repens* and *Filipendula almaria*; wild white clover (*Trifolium repens*) present locally.

A1	0–5 in.	Very dark brown (10 YR 2/2), friable to firm, humose clay with occasional small flints; strong granular structure; aggregates hard when dry; abundant roots; clear smooth boundary.
A2g	5–16 in.	Dark grey (5 Y 4/1) to olive (5 Y 4/3), very plastic, stoneless, coarsely blocky clay with darker colours associated with cleavage faces and channels and increasingly distinct fine ochreous mottling within aggregates; a few gastropod shells; frequent roots; clear smooth boundary.
C1g	16–46 in.	White (5 Y 8/2), extremely calcareous, stoneless silty clay loam to silty clay with prominent fine olive-yellow (2·5 Y 6/6) mottling; compact, but less plastic than above; weak coarse blocky structure; occasional infilled channels; few roots.
C2g	46–64 in.	Wet gravel, consisting of small chalk pebbles in a sandy to clayey matrix.
C3g	64 in.+	Pale grey calcareous clay with brown mottlings (Gault *in situ*).

CHAPTER V

Discussion of Analytical Data

Routine analytical data were obtained on samples from 158 profiles examined during the course of the survey. Results of mechanical analyses and determinations of organic carbon, nitrogen, calcium carbonate and pH relating to the 70 profiles recorded in Chapters III and IV are given in Tables 9 and 10 respectively (pp. 153–63). In addition, estimates of exchangeable cations, potassium-supplying power, total and citric-soluble phosphorous, free iron oxide, and clay-mineral composition, were obtained for selected profiles, including some not in Tables 9 and 10, and are presented in Tables 11–16 (pp. 164–75). Unless otherwise stated, all percentages are based on the oven-dry weight of samples passing a 2-mm. sieve, and this should be borne in mind when interpreting the results, since some of the soil horizons, notably in the Berkhamsted, St. Albans, Winchester and Charity series, contain over 50 per cent by weight of stones.

The analytical methods used are summarized at the end of this chapter.

PARTICLE-SIZE DISTRIBUTION

Determinations of particle-size distribution (mechanical analyses) were made on all samples, other than those composed largely of gravel or fragmentary chalk. For surface horizons, and in some profiles for lower horizons also, the results include percentages of clay (e.s.d. $<2\mu$), U.S.D.A. silt (e.s.d. 2–50μ), fine sand (50–200μ) and coarse sand (200–$2,000\mu$). The figures for clay and silt were obtained by the pipette method, following treatment with hydrogen peroxide to remove organic matter, and dispersion with Calgon (sodium hexametaphosphate), and those for the sand fractions by the use of appropriate B.S. sieves. For other samples from sub-surface horizons, percentages of clay and silt only are quoted; these were obtained by the hydrometer method, without removal of organic matter. Using Calgon, satisfactory dispersion of calcareous soils can usually be achieved without acid pre-treatment, providing the organic-matter content is low. The latter procedure was therefore omitted, so that particles of calcium carbonate are included in appropriate size-grades, allowing the particle-size distribution of calcareous and non-calcareous soils to be expressed on a uniform basis.

The results were used primarily to check field assessments of texture (see Chapter II, p. 44), those for surface horizons being recalculated for this purpose as percentages of the total inorganic fraction. In profiles from the Chilterns, the field determinations generally agreed well with the percentages of clay and silt obtained by mechanical analysis, but in the Vale the clay content of the soils was often over-estimated. Wherever such discrepancies appeared, the textural class names in the profile descriptions are those derived from mechanical analyses, and reference is made in the accounts of the mapping units to the notably stiff and plastic consistency of the soils concerned.

141

Besides providing a quantitative basis for textural classification, mechanical analyses supplement field observations regarding the origin and uniformity of the soil-forming materials, and aid the designation of horizons. In identifying horizons of differing origin, emphasis is placed on the relative proportions of the sand and silt fractions, as these, together with stones, constitute the immobile "skeleton" of the soil; whereas vertical changes in clay content may arise through translocation, weathering, or residual accumulation resulting from solution of calcareous particles, as well as from original variations.

Textural characteristics of the soil series and other variants are discussed in the preceding chapters, and only certain general trends revealed by the results will be noted here. Among the most striking is the occurrence of high silt contents in the upper horizons of profiles on Plateau Drift (Batcombe and Berkhamsted series), Clay-with-flints (Winchester series) and High-level Gravels (St. Albans series), and in soils derived from Coombe Deposits (Charity and Coombe series), suggesting that the horizons concerned are partly derived from loess. The soils on Chalk Marl (Wantage and Burwell series) and on Upper Greensand rocks (Harwell series) are also rich in silt, but the drift-derived soils of the Vale (e.g. Gubblecote, Weston Turville and Rowsham series) contain very much more sand, relative to silt, than those on the Chilterns, so that sandy clay loam and clay loam textures are far commoner than silt loam and silty clay loam.

CARBON AND NITROGEN

All samples from surface horizons and some from lower horizons were analysed for organic carbon, and in certain of these total nitrogen was also determined. For cultivated soils, and for uncultivated soils in which the organic matter is well humified (C:N ratio near 10), an approximate measure of the organic-matter content is obtainable by multiplying the organic-carbon figure by 1·72.

In profiles under semi-natural beech and oak woods on the Chilterns, the amount and distribution of organic matter vary in accordance with the type of soil formation. The A horizons of rendzinas and brown calcareous soils, as represented by Bu 20 (Icknield series) and Bu 101 (Coombe series), contain 6–8 per cent organic carbon; whereas brown earths (*sols lessivés*) with acid mull, including Bu 14 (Batcombe series), Bu 16 and Bu 54 (Winchester series), and Bu 55 (Charity series), have thinner A horizons containing 4–6 per cent organic carbon, indicating a smaller accumulation of incorporated humus. Where the forest-floor layers are of mor type, as in Bu 13 (Batcombe series), Ht 47 (Berkhamsted series) and Bu 56 (Charity series), the carbon figures fall from high values in the F and H layers to less than 2 per cent at 1–2 in. below the surface of the mineral soil. In profile Ht 69 (Southampton series), which is strongly podzolized, a sharp decrease below the surface is followed by a rise in the Bh horizon.

Under old grass, as under woodland, brown earths lacking a reserve of added lime are commonly low in organic matter (e.g. Ht 29, Berkhamsted series), compared with calcareous soils in which the organic-carbon content of the A horizon is generally at least 5 per cent, and may rise to over 10 per cent (e.g. Bu 8, Icknield series). The finer-textured gley soils of the Vale also usually contain between 5 and 10 per cent organic carbon in the A horizon: over 10 per cent was recorded in the Mead soils (Bu 87 and Bu 108) and less than 5 per cent in loamy soils of the Denchworth series (Bu 85) and Rowsham complex (Bu 89).

The organic-matter content of arable soils is largely dependent on previous cropping and manuring. In this survey, the profiles sampled on regularly cultivated land were mainly in fields carrying leys of varying duration, and only a few were under arable crops. The Ap horizons generally contain between 2 and 4 per cent organic carbon, but much lower values, down to 1 per cent, may be obtained on land which has carried a succession of cereal crops without addition of organic manure.

The C/N ratio in a soil horizon depends primarily on the degree of decomposition of the organic residues it contains. Compared with soil organic matter, plant residues, particularly woody and fibrous tissues, normally have a very high C/N ratio, because during their decomposition much carbon is mineralized as carbon dioxide, while nitrogen accumulates in relatively resistant humus. In cultivated top-soils containing little undecomposed material the ratio is generally about 10, and values of 10–15 are found in A horizons of mull type under grass or woodland. Incomplete or inefficient break-down of plant residues, as in mor layers, is revealed by a higher C/N ratio of 15–25 or more, indicating a slow rate of mineralization and a retarded release of inorganic nitrogen to plants.

In arable and mull soils, the ratio normally decreases with depth, partly as a result of the accumulation in sub-surface horizons of ammonium ions strongly held by clay minerals (Bremner, 1959). In podzolized soils, by contrast, the C/N ratio remains high in Ea and B horizons, as a result of the formation and downward migration of humose substances low in nitrogen.

CALCIUM CARBONATE

Amounts of carbon dioxide evolved from calcareous samples on treatment with acid were determined volumetrically, and the results expressed as percentages of calcium carbonate.* The amounts recorded range up to 80 per cent in soils of the Icknield series, but owing to the ease with which small chalk fragments are crushed when preparing the samples for analysis, the figures for these and other chalky soils undoubtedly include calcium carbonate present as "stones", as well as in the "fine earth".

Of 35 originally acid soils sampled on agricultural land in the Chilterns, 19 contained added chalk, amounting in a few instances to more than 5 per cent (e.g. Bu 79, Charity series). Although the chalk content is usually highest at the surface, small amounts commonly occur in sub-surface horizons, and locally, as in profile Ht 43 (Winchester series), the residues of former dressings appear concentrated in a layer at the base of the A horizon, a feature which Darwin (1881) noted on the North Downs and attributed to burial of the original surface by worm casts while the land was under pasture.

---

* None of the calcareous rocks in the area contain significant amounts of magnesium carbonate.

SOIL REACTION (pH)

The pH of 1:2·5 soil suspensions was determined electrometrically in water and in M/100 calcium chloride solution. The values obtained by the latter procedure are up to one pH unit lower than in aqueous suspensions, and are believed to correspond more closely to the effective pH of the solution in immediate contact with the soil particles (Russell, 1961). They are also more reproducible and less affected by seasonal fluctuations in the concentration of the soil solution.

Ranges in pH characteristic of particular soils or soil horizons have already been referred to in the preceding chapters, using the following scale:

	pH (in water)
Strongly acid	< 4·5
Moderately acid	4·5–5·5
Slightly acid	5·5–6·5
Neutral	6·5–7·5
Alkaline	> 7·5

Soils containing appreciable amounts of chalk are normally neutral or alkaline (pH 7·0–8·5). The brown earths and podzolized soils on the Chilterns are moderately or strongly acid under semi-natural conditions, but the pH values of the cultivated soils vary widely, depending on the presence or otherwise of added lime. Certain of the gley soils in the Vale (e.g. Denchworth series, Weston Turville series, Rowsham series) may also be moderately acid at the surface, although all become alkaline at depth.

EXCHANGEABLE CATIONS AND PERCENTAGE SATURATION

Determinations of exchangeable cations were made only on samples from non-calcareous horizons, the results being expressed in milli-equivalents per 100 gms. soil (Table 11). In addition to the exchangeable metallic cations (exchangeable bases), calcium, magnesium, potassium and sodium, which were determined in neutral normal ammonium acetate leachates, amounts of "exchangeable hydrogen" were estimated in samples from selected profiles by equilibration with ammonia solution using a modification of Mados' (1943) method.

The sum of exchangeable metallic cations and exchangeable hydrogen gives a measure of the cation-exchange capacity of the soil, and the "percentage base-saturation" shows the proportion of the exchange capacity utilized by the metallic cations. It is now recognized that the increase in hydrogen-ion concentration (pH) resulting from equilibration of an acid soil with a salt solution may be due chiefly to hydrolysis of adsorbed aluminium or hydroxy-aluminium ions rather than to direct release of hydrogen ions. The amount of titratable acidity developed varies with the pH and composition of the solution in which it is measured, so that both exchangeable hydrogen and cation-exchange capacity values must be regarded as conventional, the figures obtained depending on the methods used for their determination.

The capacity of a soil to retain cations in exchangeable form depends on the amount and kind of both organic and inorganic constituents, the contribution of the inorganic material residing mainly in the clay fraction. As the organic component of the exchange complex usually has a higher exchange capacity, weight for weight, then the inorganic component, the total capacity of the soil commonly decreases below the surface, but may increase if the clay content increases. Among the soils studied, the calculated cation-exchange capacity varies from 5 to over 50 m.e./100 gms., the lowest values being obtained in the Ea horizons of sandy podzolized soils (Southampton series) and the highest in either humose surface horizons or extremely clay-rich subsoil horizons.

The percentage base-saturation ranges from over 90 in certain neutral or slightly acid horizons to as little as 1 in a podzol of the Southampton series (Bu 80). For soil materials of similar composition a rough proportionality exists between percentage base-saturation and pH, but there is no general relationship between the two values, mainly because the various organic and clay-mineral components of the exchange complex differ considerably in the ease with which they release hydrogen ions and other cations into solution. Thus, pH values in calcium chloride solution between 4·0 and 4·5 are associated with percentage saturation values ranging from 5 to 70, and similar variations have been noted elsewhere (Deckers and Vanstallen, 1955). In the more base-rich soils, calcium generally accounts for over 90 per cent of the exchangeable metallic cations, but the proportion of magnesium tends to rise as the percentage saturation decreases, and exceeds that of calcium in one profile (Bu 13).

In brown earths (*sols lessivés*) of the Batcombe (Bu 14), Winchester (Bu 16, Bu 54) and Charity (Bu 55) series under semi-natural beechwoods, both percentage saturation and amounts of individual metallic cations are at a minimum in Eb and/or upper Bt horizons, the higher values at the surface being attributable to accumulation of calcium and other mineral elements derived from the leaf-fall. The acid gley soil (Ht 66) of the Cowcroft series shows a similar trend and, together with the Batcombe and Berkhamsted (Ht 47) soils, has a distinctly lower base status in corresponding horizons than those of the Winchester and Charity series. Comparison of the results for Batcombe and Charity profiles with mull (Bu 14, Bu 55) and mor (Bu 13, Bu 56) humus forms respectively reveals no very significant differences, indicating that the development of these contrasting forest-floor types is unlikely to have been governed by original variations in the base status of the mineral soils. The ratio exch.Ca:exch.Mg approaches or exceeds unity in the lower horizons of the Batcombe profile, whereas in the more calcium-rich Winchester and Charity soils it is higher throughout, with minimum values between 4 and 7 in the Eb or upper Bt horizons.

Percentage saturation is very low (< 10) in all the mineral horizons of the two podzols (Southampton series) examined. but is not significantly lower than in the uncultivated Batcombe and Berkhamsted soils at similar depths. The superficial H layers have a very high exchange capacity, and their exchangeable-cation content is consequently much higher than in the sub-surface horizons. In profile Ht 69, particularly, the high proportion of potassium is noteworthy, and is probably related to the presence of bracken, the accumulated residues of which may be comparatively rich in potash.

The cultivated soils on the Chiltern Plateau which lack a reserve of added chalk, including Bu 57 and Ht 60 (Batcombe series), Ht 29 (Berkhamsted series), Ht 48 (St. Albans series) and Ht 53 (Cowcroft series), commonly have a high (10–20 m.e./100 gms.) content of exchangeable calcium, presumably derived in part from former dressings; and in the two profiles (Bu 57 and Ht 29) for which estimates are recorded the percentage saturation ranges from 60 to 85.

The majority of the Vale soils sampled are calcareous throughout, and in those with non-calcareous upper horizons the percentage saturation does not fall below 60, the lowest values recorded being for the two Denchworth profiles (Bu 76 and Bu 85). As most of the soils are well supplied with both clay and organic matter, they generally have a high cation-exchange capacity, and contain high or very high amounts of exchangeable calcium, ranging from 10 to over 40 m.e./100 gms.

POTASSIUM

The results in Table 11 show that under semi-natural woodland conditions the brown earths (*sols lessivés*) and podzolized soils contain very low (< 0·2 m.e./100 gms.) amounts of exchangeable potassium in the sub-surface horizons, rising to higher values in the superficial humose layers. Thus, where F and H layers were sampled, as in profiles Bu 56 (Charity series), Bu 80 and Ht 69 (Southampton series), moderate to high amounts, up to 1–2 m.e./100 gms., are recorded; and in acid mull A horizons, as in profiles Bu 14 (Batcombe series), Bu 16 and Bu 54 (Winchester series), and Bu 55 (Charity series), the contents range from 0·25 to 0·35 m.e./100 gms. The two podzols sampled (Bu 80 and Ht 69) have very low amounts in all the mineral horizons, but in profiles Bu 13 (Batcombe series) and Ht 47 (Berkhamsted series) showing superficial podzolization, the levels rise in the clayey Bt horizons to low or moderate values (0·2–0·45 m.e./100 gms.).

The values for arable and grassland soils are of limited significance in characterizing soil series, as they are largely dependent on previous management. The results obtained were supplemented by analysing the results of some 700 determinations of readily-soluble potassium (Truog method) made for advisory purposes in Hertfordshire by Mr. H. W. Gardner (1960). These indicated predominantly low levels in soils of the Batcombe, Berkhamsted, Winchester, Charity and Coombe series, whereas among the Vale soils those of the Wicken series were on average moderately supplied and those of the Ford End complex contained low amounts.

From the results of numerous field and pot experiments, it is clear that many soils contain reserves of non-exchangeable potassium which become available to crops as exchangeable and water-soluble potassium are depleted. Recent work by Arnold (1960) indicates that, in many English soils derived from sedimentary rocks, the reserve of available but non-exchangeable potassium is chiefly located in micaceous clay minerals, and that, to a first approximation, the amounts released may be correlated with the total quantity of potassium present as a constituent of fine clay (e.s.d. < 0·3µ). In soils derived from Upper Greensand rocks, however, weathering of silt-sized grains of glauconite contributes significant amounts of potassium to crops.

Amounts of non-exchangeable potassium released to ryegrass on continuous cropping in the greenhouse by 11 soils from this area which had not received heavy dressings of potassic fertilizers are listed in Table 12 (p. 168). Also included for comparison are two soils of the Batcombe series from the Broadbalk field (continuous wheat since 1843) at Rothamsted Experimental Station, one from plot 11 (N, P, no K), and the other from plot 13 (N, P, K). The potassium reserves in the soil from Broadbalk plot 11 and in the Icknield soil were soon exhausted, but the Wicken, Halton and Harwell soils continued to supply potassium to ryegrass satisfactorily for 15–18 months, and released larger amounts of potassium than the continuously fertilized Broadbalk soil, in which the available reserve probably consists largely of accumulated fertilizer residues held in vermiculite-type materials.

The finding of Arnold (1958), that a hydrogen-saturated cation-exchange resin will extract potassium from soils in amounts approximating to those removed by grass growing in pots, affords a possible method for estimating the potassium-supplying power of soils. Amounts of potassium extracted by hydrogen-saturated "Amberlite 1R-120" from 24 surface soils representative of 17 soil series in the area are given in Table 13 (p. 169), together with contents of exchangeable potassium. Judging by these results the brown earths (*sols lessivés*), especially the Batcombe and Berkhamsted soils, are generally poor suppliers of potassium, yielding less than 25 mgm./100 gms. H-resin extractable K. The two Icknield soils studied also released small amounts of potassium, whereas the Wantage and Halton soils were good suppliers, a result which may partly explain their higher fertility. Apart from Bu 63 (Weston Turville series), the Vale soils examined appear to have a moderate or high potassium status, the glauconitic Ardington and Harwell soils giving outstandingly high values.

PHOSPHORUS

Determinations of total phosphorus (by perchloric acid digestion), and of phosphorus soluble in 1 per cent citric acid, were carried out on samples from 16 selected profiles, and the results are given in Table 14 (p. 170), expressed as mgm.P_2O_5 per 100 gms. soil. Soils containing more than 10 per cent chalk were not included.

Five of the profiles, representative of the Batcombe, Berkhamsted, Southampton, Winchester and Charity series respectively, are under semi-natural woodland. The remainder are arable or grassland profiles, the phosphorus content of which will depend in varying degrees on past fertilizer practice. Since residues of phosphatic fertilizers are rapidly converted to sparingly soluble forms, they are mainly retained in the surface horizons, where they may constitute a considerable proportion of the total amount of phosphorus present.

In the uncultivated Batcombe, Berkhamsted and Southampton profiles, the total-phosphorus content is highest in the humose surface horizons and falls to low (50–100 mgm./100 gms.) or very low (< 50 mgm./100 gms.) values in the sub-surface and subsoil horizons. The proportion of the total that is citric soluble is also highest at the surface, the subsoil horizons all containing very low (< 5 mgm./100 gms.) amounts of readily-soluble phosphate. In the Winchester (Bu 54), and particularly in the Charity profile (Bu 55), both total and citric-soluble phosphorus are higher, except at the surface, than in the Batcombe and Berkhamsted. The high values in the lowest (Bt 2) horizon of the Winchester, and in the Bt horizon of the Charity, is consistent with the presence of collophane, an apatite-like mineral of organic origin, identified in the fine sand fractions of these horizons by Avery *et al.* (1959).

The cultivated Batcombe, Berkhamsted, Winchester and Charity profiles each contain moderate or high amounts of both total and citric-soluble phosphorus in the surface horizons, indicating the presence of fertilizer residues; and the figures for the subsoil horizons, particularly in the Batcombe (Bu 57), are also generally higher than in the corresponding semi-natural profiles.

Many of the Vale soils are derived more or less directly from the Upper Greensand, Gault and Portland Beds, which contain nodular deposits of impure calcium phosphate. Such deposits are localized, however, and although unusually high amounts of phosphorus occur in certain of the profiles examined, samples of surface soil taken for advisory purposes show wide variations in readily-soluble phosphorus content.

Of the two Harwell profiles studied, one (Bu 35) is high in phosphorus throughout, whereas the other (Bu 42) contains low amounts in surface and subsurface horizons, and roughly four times as much at 28–36 in. (C1 horizon), of which a remarkably high proportion is soluble in citric acid.

The total-phosphorus content of the Wicken profiles (Bu 39 and Ht 58) ranges from moderate to very high in the horizons analysed, and the citric-soluble phosphorus figures are high throughout. The average content of readily-soluble phosphorus (Truog method) in 17 surface soils of this series from Puttenham and Tring Rural parishes was also high (Gardner, 1960), but several samples contained low amounts. The Denchworth soil analysed (Bu 76) is high in phosphorus at the surface, but both total and citric-soluble figures fall to low values in the (B)g horizon.

In the Weston Turville profile (Bu 63), the total-phosphorus content is moderate, and decreases only slightly with depth, whereas the citric-soluble phosphorus values show a marked increase. Results on soils taken for advisory purposes show that soils of this series are often high in readily-soluble phosphorus, as are those of the related Gubblecote series.

The Mead profile (Bu 68), referred to on page 139, is high in phosphorus throughout, and at 30–36 in. contains nearly 0·6 per cent P_2O_5, about half of which is citric-soluble. Unusually high concentrations of readily-soluble phosphorus are commonly associated with old settlement sites, and as a fragment of pottery was found in this horizon it very probably represents an occupation surface buried by recent flood deposits.

FREE IRON OXIDE

Samples from woodland profiles of the Charity, Batcombe and Southampton series were analysed for "free iron oxide" by Deb's (1950) method to assess the extent to which differential eluviation of iron had occurred. The results for successive horizons are given in Table 15 (p. 172), together with the corresponding percentages of clay, and free iron oxide/clay ratios.

The Charity profile (Bu 55) and the Batcombe profile (Bu 14) are brown earths (*sols lessivés*) under acid mull, the latter with subsoil gleying, and neither shows any morphological evidence of podzolization. In both the free iron oxide content increases with depth, but the free Fe_2O_3:clay ratio decreases in passing from the Eb to the Bt horizons, suggesting that, relative to the clay, there is a slight accumulation of readily soluble Fe_2O_3 in the A and Eb horizons, and that iron has been translocated to the Bt horizon as a constituent of the clay fraction.

Profile Bu 13 (Batcombe series) has a mor humus layer succeeded by the very thin Ea horizon of a "micro-podzol", below which the horizons are analagous to those of Bu 14. In Bu 80 (Southampton series) there are well defined Ea and Bfe horizons, separated in places by a weakly developed Bh horizon, and followed by a clay Bt(g) horizon as in the Batcombe series.

The Ea horizons of these podzolized soils contain less than half as much free Fe_2O_3 as the A and Eb horizons of the first two profiles, and the free Fe_2O_3:clay ratios indicate that differential eluviation of iron has occurred, leading to a relative accumulation in the Bfe horizon of the Southampton soil.

CLAY MINERALOGY

Clay separates (e.s.d. $< 1\cdot4\mu$) from selected profiles were examined by X-ray diffraction techniques. The predominant alumino-silicate clay minerals were identified at group level, and semi-quantitative estimates of the amounts present were made by visual comparison of line intensities on photographs of glycerol-treated and 300°C-heated specimens. The resulting data (Table 16, p. 173) show the approximate proportions in which the listed mineral groups occur, but do not indicate absolute amounts, as no allowance is made for the presence of accessory minerals or amorphous material.

Minerals of the kaolin and mica (including glauconite) groups together constitute a significant proportion of nearly all the soil clays examined, and are accompanied by varying and often preponderant amounts of expanding minerals of the vermiculite and montmorillonite groups, with basic structures similar to that of mica. Chlorite was detected in small amounts only in 3 profiles.

Accessory minerals, occurring for the most part in trace amounts, include quartz, calcite, goethite, lepidocrocite, feldspar and cristobalite. Of these, quartz is generally present, calcite is found principally in the clays of the Icknield, Wantage, Aylesbury, Halton and Wicken soils, whereas feldspar and cristobalite were only occasionally identified, the latter notably in the Harwell soil. Goethite and/or lepidocrocite were detected in most of the samples from weathered (oxidized or rust-mottled) surface and sub-surface horizons, but little of either was found in the predominantly greyish Harwell, Wantage and Wicken profiles. After heating at 540°C., the clays containing identifiable crystalline iron oxides gave broad reflections due to haematite, which in some were stronger than would be expected from the amounts of goethite and/or lepidocrocite in the unheated clays, suggesting the initial presence of hydrated iron oxide amorphous to X-ray diffraction.

In soils derived from sedimentary rocks, the clay minerals may originate; (1) by direct inheritance from the parent material, notably on clays and shales; (2) by complete or partial alteration of minerals of similar structure; or (3) by synthesis from dissolved or amorphous products of weathering. Partial alteration is probably most important in minerals with a basic mica structure. Whereas micaceous clay minerals may undergo complete decomposition, particularly in very acid soils, there is abundant evidence (Rich and Thomas, 1960) that they may also undergo progressive alteration to vermiculite and/or montmorillonite group minerals by processes involving replacement of inter-layer K+ ions by other and more hydrated ions, reduction in negative charge, and lattice-expansion, the effects of which may be reflected in cation-exchange and swelling properties. Kaolin-group minerals are less liable to alteration, but may form in soils either by synthesis, or by desilicification of montmorillonite.

The clay fractions of the brown earths (*sols lessivés*) on Plateau Drift consist principally of kaolin, mica and vermiculite-group minerals and, except in Bu 57 (Batcombe series), montmorillonite occurs only as a minor constituent in the lower (Bt) horizons. In the Winchester series, however, the Clay-with-flint subsoils are rich in montmorillonite throughout, with kaolin and mica subsidiary, and it is only in the thin A and Eb horizons of the uncultivated, uneroded profile (Bu 54) that there is a marked decrease, accompanied by a sharp rise in the proportion of vermiculite. Although the relative amounts are again variable, a similar trend is apparent in the Charity profiles, vermiculite decreasing with depth in the Bt horizons as the content of montmorillonite increases.

The significance of these results in relation to the origin and development of the Chiltern soils has been discussed by Avery et al. (1959), with particular reference to profiles Bu 14 (Batcombe), Bu 54 (Winchester) and Bu 55 (Charity). As noted previously, mechanical and mineralogical analyses confirm that both Batcombe and Winchester profiles are composite in origin, and that their upper horizons may be partly derived from loess, so that changes in clay-mineral content with depth may reflect differences in parent material. Apart from loess, the chief formations contributing to the soils are presumably Reading Beds and Upper Chalk. The non-calcareous residue of the Upper Chalk consists almost entirely of montmorillonite and mica, and clays from the Reading Beds show a predominance of the same minerals, together with variable but generally low amounts of kaolin. It is clear, therefore, that the clay-mineral constitution of the soil and drift materials affords no satisfactory evidence of their origin, especially as they have evidently undergone considerable weathering, which probably accounts for their relatively high kaolin content. The high montmorillonite content of the Clay-with-flints *sensu stricto* (Winchester subsoils), as compared with the Plateau Drift (Batcombe and Berkhamsted subsoils), is noteworthy, and may arise from differential weathering; alternatively, since montmorillonite is likely to predominate in the finest particle-size grades, selective translocation of fine clay may have resulted in its accumulation adjacent to the Chalk.

Another feature of note is the common occurrence in these soils of a dioctahedral, vermiculite-group mineral (Brown, 1954) which expands to give a basal reflection at about 14Å on glycerol treatment, but collapses and reinforces the 10Å mica reflection on heating. This mineral, which is scarce or absent in the related solid formations, is relatively most abundant in the most base-deficient horizons of the uncultivated profiles, and is thought to result from alteration of micaceous minerals under acid conditions. According to Tamura (1958) and Sawhney (1958), its formation normally involves partial decomposition of the lattice and transference to inter-layer positions of hydrated aluminium, magnesium, and possibly ferric ions, a process which may lead eventually to a chlorite-like structure.

In the chalky Icknield and Wantage soils, and in practically all the profiles from the Vale, montmorillonite is the dominant clay mineral, accompanied by varying proportions of mica-group minerals and generally limited amounts of kaolin. As clays separated from the subjacent rocks, including the Chalk, Upper Greensand, Gault and Kimmeridge Clay, consist chiefly of mica and montmorillonite (Perrin, 1956, 1957; Brown and Farrow, 1960), it is probable that the clay minerals in the soils are largely inherited either directly or through locally derived drifts. There is, however, evidence that, on the Gault and Kimmeridge clays particularly, the soil horizons are richer in montmorillonite than the unweathered rocks. This suggests that the change from the semi-fissile sediments to the more plastic subsoil clays has been accompanied by alteration of mica to montmorillonite, involving hydration and expansion of the mineral lattice and release of non-exchangeable inter-layer potassium. The high content of montmorillonite in the clay fractions of many of the Vale soils (e.g. Halton, Harwell, Gubblecote and Weston Turville series) probably accounts for their notably high plasticity and moisture-retaining capacity, as compared with other soils of similar clay content, and may explain the discrepancies which appeared between field determinations of texture and the results of mechanical analyses (see p. 141).

Cristobalite, a form of silica stable at high temperatures, is present in the clay fraction of the Harwell soil, and may account for the high silica/alumina ratios of 5–6 found in clays from the same series by Kay (1934), and for Way's finding (McConnell, 1902) that the malmstone is characterized by a high content of alkali-soluble silica. The mineral is known to occur, together with montmorillonite, in bentonitic muds derived from volcanic ash, but recently its presence in certain sedimentary rocks has been attributed to crystallization from amorphous silica at normal temperatures and pressures (Konta, 1955).

SUMMARY OF ANALYTICAL METHODS

1. Particle-size distribution: clay (e.s.d. $< 2\mu$) and silt (e.s.d. 2–50μ) were determined, (a) by the pipette method after treatment with H_2O_2 and dispersion with Calgon (sodium hexametaphosphate), or (b) by a modification of the hydrometer method (Bouyoucos, 1951), using Calgon as the dispersing agent. Appropriate B.S. sieves were used to separate the coarser fractions.

2. Organic carbon: a wet digestion method was used in accordance with the recommendations of Tinsley (1950).

3. Nitrogen: a Kjeldahl digestion was followed by steam distillation using a Hoskins apparatus. The ammonia liberated is adsorbed in boric acid solution and titrated with 0·01N. HCl.

4. Calcium carbonate: a calcimeter described by Bascomb (1961) was used.

5. pH measurements were made on 1:2·5 suspensions of soil in water and in M/100 CaCl₂, using a glass electrode assembly.

6. Exchangeable cations were determined in a neutral normal ammonium acetate leachate, after evaporation to dryness and treatment with nitric acid and H_2O_2 to remove organic matter. Magnesium was determined spectrographically using the porous cup technique, calcium by a versenate backtitration procedure, and sodium and potassium using an EEL flame photometer.

7. Exchangeable hydrogen: a modification of the method of Mados (1943) was used. 10 gms. of soil are shaken with 100 ml. 0·2 $N.NH_4OH$ for 2 hours. Formaldehyde is added, followed by $BaCl_2$ solution. The supernatent liquid is titrated with N/10 NaOH, adding 2 ml. in excess, and then backtitrated with N/10 HCl.

8. Total phosphorus: phosphorus extracted by digestion with perchloric and nitric acids, was determined by the colorimetric molybdo-vanadate method of Kitson and Mellon (1944).

9. Citric-soluble phosphorus was determined by the same method in a 1 per cent citric acid extract.

10. Free iron oxides were extracted by Deb's (1950) method and iron determined colorimetrically in the extract, using thioglycollic acid.

TABLE 9

Analytical Data: Soils of the Chiltern Plateau and the Icknield Belt

Soil Series	Profile No.	Horizon	Depth in.	Sand 200μ–2 mm. %	Sand 50–200μ %	Silt 2–50μ %	Clay (<2μ) %	Carbon %	Nitrogen %	C/N Ratio	CaCO₃ %	pH H₂O 1:2.5	pH M/100 CaCl₂
Batcombe (pp. 64–68)	Bu 14	A	0–1½	3	18	58	13	4·5	0·38	12	—	4·4	3·9
		Eb	1½–8	2	22	57	17	1·5			—	4·5	4·1
		Eb/Bt	9–15	1	18	51	29				—	4·5	4·1
		Bt1(g)	16–29	1	13	32	54				—	4·7	4·1
		Bt2(g)	36–60	8	19	15	58				—	5·0	4·0
		Bt/C(g)	78–90	2	4	6	88				—	4·7	4·0
	Bu 13	F/H	0–1					30	0·77	39	—	4·1	3·5
		A/Ea	1–6	5	8	63	19	2·8	0·08	35	—	4·0	3·5
		Eb1	6–13	5	6	61	17	1·8			—	4·2	3·7
		Eb2(g)	13–23	2	6	63	21	0·2			—	4·4	4·1
		Bt1(g)	24–36	4	6	52	38				—	4·3	3·9
		Bt2g				22	67				—	4·2	4·0
	Bu 57	Ap	1–6	5	13	58	21	2·2	0·19	12	—	7·1	6·6
		Eb1	7–15			56	23	0·82	0·10	8·2	—	6·9	6·4
		Eb2(g)	18–24			56	24					6·8	6·2
		Bt(g)	24–30			18	65					6·7	6·2
	Bu 58	Ap	1–6	7	14	54	23	2·4	0·23	10	—	7·0	6·7
		Bt(g)	10–15			42	45	0·62	0·08	7·7	—	7·5	6·9
	Ht 60	Ap	1–4	10	8	54	24	2·9			0·2	6·8	6·8
		Eb	7–12			57	24				0·1	7·1	7·1
		Bt1(g)	23–30			23	54				0·1	7·2	7·0
		Bt2(g)	36–41			51	34				0·1	7·2	7·0
	Ht 61	Ap	2–5	12	8	52	23	2·4			—	6·5	6·1
		Eb	9–12			47	24				1·8	7·3	7·0
		Bt1(g)	14–18			16	66				0·9	7·4	7·0
		Bt2(g)	*36–40			2	30				0·1	7·4	7·1

* Sandy inclusion.

TABLE 9 (continued)

Soil Series	Profile No.	Horizon	Depth in.	Sand 200µ–2 mm. %	Sand 50–200µ %	Silt 2–50µ %	Clay (<2µ) %	Carbon %	Nitrogen %	C/N Ratio	CaCO₃ %	pH H₂O 1:2·5	pH M/100 CaCl₂
Berkhamsted (pp. 70–72)	Ht 47	A/Ea	1–2	14	20	38	7	8·7	0·40	22	—	3·7	3·2
		Eb	5–8			49	13	0·51			—	4·5	4·0
		Eb/Bt	14–18			42	32				—	4·6	3·9
		Bt1(g)	20–25			22	61				—	5·0	4·7
		Bt2g	30–33			22	58				—	5·4	5·0
	Ht 44	Ap	1–6	23	17	44	14	3·3	0·23	14	0·6	7·6	7·2
		Eb	6–14			50	16				0·4	7·9	7·4
		Bt(g)	30–40			39	44				—	7·2	6·9
	Ht 29	A	1–6	25	13	41	13	3·6	0·22	16	—	5·5	5·1
		A/Eb	6–12			23	17	1·8	0·15	12	—	5·0	4·5
		Eb1	12–21			18	17				—	5·0	4·4
		Eb/Bt1(g)	21–30			1	11				—	4·9	4·6
		Bt2g	30–38			1	51					5·8	5·4
St. Albans (p. 74)	Ht 48	Ap	0–6	36	17	35	11	1·9			—	6·0	5·5
		Eb	9–13			16	9				—	6·2	5·7
		Eb/Bt	20–24			2	7				—	5·7	5·1
		Bt	32–35			1	29				—	5·9	5·5
Southampton (pp. 72 & 75)	Bu 80	H	1–6	12	36	45	7	35	1·70	21	—	4·0	3·2
		Ea/Bh	9–16	10	35	41	14	3·1				4·4	3·6
		Bfe	18–30	10	27	7	56	0·98				4·4	3·9
		Bt(g)									—	4·3	3·9
	Ht 69	H	3–11	67	9	20	4	47	1·94	24	—	3·8	2·7
		Ea	14–17			4	9	1·2	0·04	30	—	4·1	3·3
		Bh	18–27			2	7	2·5			—	3·9	3·1
		Bfe	36–40			2	11	0·41			—	4·3	3·8
		Eb/Bt									—	4·4	3·9

TABLE 9 (*continued*)

Soil Series	Profile No.	Horizon	Depth in.	Sand 200μ–2 mm. %	Sand 50–200μ %	Silt 2–50μ %	Clay (<2μ) %	Carbon %	Nitrogen %	C/N Ratio	$CaCO_3$ %	pH H_2O 1:2.5	pH $M/100$ $CaCl_2$
Cowcroft (pp. 77–78)	Ht 66	H/A	2–6	25	12	44	11	16·5	1·01	16	—	4·1	3·5
		Ebg	8–17			6	54	2·4			—	4·1	3·6
		Bt1g	20–27			6	48				—	4·4	3·9
		Bt2g	37–42			21	69				—	4·8	4·0
		Cg									—	5·3	4·2
	Ht 53	Ap	1–5	9	17	43	28	4·1				6·2	6·0
		Bt1(g)	8–13			38	44					6·6	5·9
		Bt2g	15–24			27	54					6·2	6·0
Bursledon (p. 78)	Ht 67	Ap	0–8	6	49	28	13	2·0			0·8	7·2	7·1
		Eb	9–15			22	16				0·3	7·2	7·1
		Bt/C(g)	25–30			19	22				0·3	6·8	6·3
Winchester (pp. 81–84)	Bu 16	A	0–2½	13	21	42	23	5·9	0·42	14	—	4·7	4·4
		Eb	2½–7	15	19	51	15	3·7	0·24	15	—	5·3	4·9
		Bt	7–15	4	6	10	79				—	5·3	4·8
	Bu 54	A	0–2½	11	28	37	14	6·0	0·45	13	—	4·8	4·4
		Eb	2½–7	15	32	35	15	2·9	0·22	13	—	4·5	4·0
		Bt1	7–12	10	20	9	60				—	4·3	3·9
			12–26	8	22	6	64				—	4·6	4·2
		Bt2	26–37	2	5	6	87				—	5·0	4·5
			37–43	1	4	4	92				—	6·4	6·1
	Bu 71	Ap	0–6	7	8	50	35	1·9			1·3	7·5	7·2
		Bt	9–23			21	70				1·2	7·3	7·1
		Bt/C	23–33			31	56				39	7·4	7·2

TABLE 9 (continued)

Soil Series	Profile No.	Horizon	Depth in.	Sand 200μ–2 mm %	Sand 50–200μ %	Silt 2–50μ %	Clay (<2μ) %	Carbon %	Nitrogen %	C/N Ratio	CaCO$_3$ %	pH H$_2$O 1:2·5	pH M/100 CaCl$_2$
Winchester—continued	Bu 70	A	0–7	13	15	38	31	4·7	0·45	10	1·3	7·2	7·0
		Eb	10–14	12	16	47	23	0·86	0·09	9·1	0·6	7·6	7·0
		Bt	14–24			16	70				0·5	7·5	7·1
			26–30			11	73				0·4	7·3	7·0
	Ht 43	Ap	0–6	17	5	37	31	4·6			tr.	7·4	7·3
		Eb	6–11			39	27				3·6	8·0	7·8
		Bt	13–20*			44	30				0·2	7·8	7·5
			13–24			16	70				0·2	7·7	7·2
			20–36			14	70				0·2	8·2	7·9
Charity (pp. 86–88)	Bu 55	A	0–3	5	17	55	14	5·3	0·35	15	—	4·6	4·0
		Eb	3–11	5	21	58	12	1·6	0·18	8·9	—	4·5	3·8
		Eb/Bt	11–17	5	23	50	21				—	5·0	4·2
		Bt	17–27	3	15	38	43				—	5·3	4·7
			27–33	3	15	36	46					5·8	5·4
		C	33–39†	4	16	42	38				33	8·1	7·5
	Bu 56	H	4–10	9	16	54	15	31	1·5	21	—	4·5	3·6
		Eb	17–24	7	13	33	44	0·85			—	4·7	4·0
		Bt1	24–32	8	20	29	43				—	5·0	4·4
		Bt2	35–40	5	13	27	54				—	5·4	4·8
												5·5	5·2
	Bu 79	Ap	0–5	9	13	56	15	2·3	0·21	11	5·2	7·7	7·2
		Eb	5–21			54	19	0·61	0·09	6·8	0·5	7·7	7·1
		Eb/Bt	21–36			43	28				0·7	7·6	7·1
		Bt	36–54			30	53				2·5	7·4	7·0
		C	54–96			41	42				64	8·0	7·2

* Loamy inclusion.   † Particle-size distribution on a carbonate-free basis.

TABLE 9 (*continued*)

Soil Series	Profile No.	Horizon	Depth in.	Sand 200μ–2 mm. %	Sand 50–200μ %	Silt 2–50μ %	Clay (<2μ) %	Carbon %	Nitrogen %	C/N Ratio	CaCO₃ %	pH H₂O 1:2.5	pH M/100 CaCl₂
Nettleden (p. 88)	Ht 63	Ap	0–8	11	8	55	24	3·1			—	6·7	6·6
		(B)	11–20			55	20				0·2	7·1	6·8
		C1(g)	36–40			28	16				tr.	7·0	6·8
Icknield (pp. 91–92)	Bu 20	A	0–4	6	9	43	33	8·1	0·71	11	70	7·9	7·6
	Bu 7	A	0–7	10	9	42	23	9·4	0·92	10	58	7·7	7·6
	Bu 8	A	0–7	5	6	40	36	14·0	1·04	14	13	7·5	7·3
	Bu 115	Ap	1–5	16	17	41	20	2·9			63	8·3	7·7
	Bu 81	Ap	0–8	20	20	47	16	2·1	0·23	9·1	79	8·0	7·6
		C	9–15			51	23	1·0	0·14	7·1	81	8·1	7·8
Wantage (pp. 94–95)	Bu 26	Ap	1–4	6	5	51	36	2·6	0·28	9·3	33	7·4	7·2
		A/C	14–17			41	50				50	7·5	7·4
	Bu 27	Ap	1–4	6	7	57	30	2·1	0·24	8·8	59	7·7	7·6
		A/C	9–12			48	40	0·80	0·11	7·1	68	7·8	7·8
	Ht 71	A	1–4	7	8	41	33	5·3			21	8·1	7·6
		A/C	7–11			42	31				31	8·2	7·8
Coombe (pp. 98–99)	Bu 101	A	0–3	5	12	41	29	6·2	0·42	15	17	7·8	7·5
		(B)	7–10			53	27				23	8·0	7·6
		C	16–21			46	34				60	8·2	7·7
	Bu 74	Ap	1–6	10	8	48	23	3·8	0·33	11	22	7·6	7·2
		(B)	8–14			49	22	1·7	0·20	8·5	32	7·7	7·4
		C1	20–26			53	26				74	7·8	8·2

TABLE 9 (*continued*)

Soil Series	Profile No.	Horizon	Depth in.	Sand 200μ–2 mm. %	Sand 50–200μ %	Silt 2–50μ %	Clay (<2μ) %	Carbon %	Nitrogen %	C/N Ratio	CaCO₃ %	pH H₂O 1:2.5	pH M/100 CaCl₂
Coombe—*continued*													
	Bu 50	Ap	0–6	6	16	49	29	2·0			38	8·5	7·8
		(B)	6–22			41	36	1·1			30	8·6	7·9
		A¹	22–29			42	38	1·6			3·2	8·4	7·8
		(B)¹	29–36			45	37	0·7			26	8·4	7·9
Wallop (pp. 99–100)													
	Bu 17	A	0–5	9	12	32	38	5·1	0·41	13	0·3	5·6	5·1
		(B)	5–11	4	5	15	73	1·6	0·14	11	—	6·6	6·6
	Ht 36	A	1–4	15	10	30	38	6·2	0·61	10	15	7·6	7·5
		A/(B)	4–7			42	44	3·1	0·29	11	21	7·8	7·6
		(B)	11–15			45	44				15	7·9	7·7
Tring (p. 101)													
	Ht 114	Ap	1–7	11	9	49	29	3·2			1·0	7·7	7·3
		(B)(g)	8–16			43	41				0·2	7·7	7·3
		(B)/C(g)	18–23			45	33				21	8·2	7·6
		C1(g)	28–34			44	24				40	8·2	7·7
Gade (p. 103)													
	Ht 51	A	2–6			67	10	3·4	0·32	10·7	—	5·8	5·0
			10–14			68	11	2·8	0·23	12	—	5·8	5·0
		A/C(g)	18–22			54	27				—	5·8	5·1
		C1g	28–36			32	26					6·5	6·1
		C2g	38–43			46	18				12	8·0	7·5

TABLE 10

Analytical Data: Soils of the Aylesbury Vale

Soil Series	Profile No.	Horizon	Depth in.	Sand 200μ–2 mm. %	Sand 50–200μ %	Silt 2–50μ %	Clay (<2μ) %	Carbon %	Nitrogen %	C/N Ratio	CaCO₃ %	pH H₂O 1:2·5	pH M/100 CaCl₂
Aylesbury (p. 105)	Bu 114	Ap	1–5	13	24	33	28	3·0	0·31	9·3	27	8·3	7·5
		(B)/C	9–15	11	23	38	24				49	8·5	7·7
Halton (pp. 107–8)	Bu 109	A	1–4	14	9	36	31	3·4	0·32	11	17	8·4	7·8
		(B)	9–13			37	32	0·91	0·08	11	21	8·4	7·9
		C(g)	20–24			40	29				58	8·6	8·0
	Bu 111	Ap	1–4	15	17	35	33	1·9			5·0	8·4	7·6
		(B)(g)	9–13			26	35				1·2	8·3	7·4
		C1g	16–20			32	30				32	8·7	7·9
		C3(g)ca	28–32			45	26				64	8·8	7·9
Burwell (p. 108)	Bu 106	A	1–5	7	7	44	35	2·3			29	8·3	7·7
		A/C	7–12			42	41				35	7·9	7·7
		Cg	20–24			47	43				60	8·3	7·8
Gubblecote (pp. 110–11)	Ht 56	Ap	0–6	30	17	29	22	3·1	0·26	11	18	7·5	7·2
		C2gca	30–36			36	32				54	7·9	7·3
		C3g	44–48			45	48				45	8·0	7·2
	Ht 72	A1	1–4	15	8	33	33	6·8	0·63	11	11	7·6	7·3
		A2	7–12			40	26	3·3	0·37	8·9	18	8·0	7·6
		(B)(g)	16–20			37	25				40	8·5	7·9
Harwell (p. 113)	Bu 42	Ap	3–5	3	31	42	19	2·0	0·19	10	—	5·9	5·4
		(B)(g)	12–14			44	38	0·58	0·09	6·4	—	6·4	5·8
		C(g)	28–36			44	37				—	6·9	6·2
			40–44			47	26				7·1	7·8	7·3

TABLE 10 (continued)

Soil Series	Profile No.	Horizon	Depth in.	Sand 200μ–2 mm. %	Sand 50–200μ %	Silt 2–50μ %	Clay (<2μ) %	Carbon %	Nitrogen %	C/N Ratio	CaCO₃ %	pH H₂O 1:2·5	pH M/100 CaCl₂
Harwell (imperfectly drained variant) (p. 113)	Bu 107	A(g)	1–4	6	11	49	22	5·2			—	5·9	5·7
		A/(B)(g)	8–13			42	40				—	6·1	5·7
		(B)(g)	16–20			38	54				0·3	7·5	7·3
		C(g)	33–37			57	38				29	8·4	7·9
Ardington (p. 114)	Bu 102	Ap	1–4	7	27	28	31	2·4			4·8	7·0	6·7
		A/C(g)	9–13			31	30				0·3	7·0	6·5
		C(g)	30–34			29	20				0·2	7·0	6·7
Wicken (pp. 116–117)	Bu 39	A1p	2–6	3	2	37	56	3·3	0·31	11	2·5	7·7	7·2
		A2(g)	9–12			36	59	2·0	0·20	10	3·0	7·8	7·3
		(B)(g)	18–21			33	62				9·7	7·8	7·4
		Cgca	30–34			34	64				40	7·8	7·2
	Ht 58	Ap	1–5	9	4	34	48	3·1	0·30	10	1·7	7·7	7·5
		(B)(g)	9–14	5	4	39	42	0·88	0·10	8·8	2·5	7·8	7·7
		C1gca	20–28			35	48				32	8·1	7·7
		C2gca	36–40			26	58				25	8·3	7·6
	Bu 90	A1	1–4	18	8	23	34	6·8	0·50	14	—	6·2	6·0
		A2(g)	5–9	23	9	24	45				1·2	7·4	7·1
		(B)(g)	16–20	3	3	19	75				18	8·0	7·7
		Cgca	20–24	3		17	76				25	8·3	7·8
			28–32*	64		11	15				21	8·4	7·9
			32–36			21	76				30	8·2	7·8

* Sandy inclusion.

TABLE 10 (*continued*)

Soil Series	Profile No.	Horizon	Depth in.	Sand 200μ–2 mm %	Sand 50–200μ %	Silt 2–50μ %	Clay (<2μ) %	Carbon %	Nitrogen %	C/N Ratio	CaCO₃ %	pH H₂O 1:2.5	pH M/100 CaCl₂
Challow (p. 120)	Bu 67	A1g	1–4	8	4	28	45	8·2	0·69	12	—	6·5	6·1
			4–8	11	5	28	40	7·2	0·58	12		6·5	6·1
		A2g	8–12			25	64				tr.	6·7	6·5
		(B)g	12–24			29	42				0·4	7·8	7·4
		C1gca	24–30			21	73				11	7·8	7·3
		C2gca	43–47			32	65				26	7·8	7·3
	Bu 47	Ag	2–5	4	5	37	42	5·7			tr.	6·1	5·9
		A/(B)g	10–16			44	41				0·2	7·0	6·7
		(B)g	22–28			36	52				30	7·5	7·1
		C1gca	31–33			31	65				0·9	7·7	7·1
		C2g	40–44			36	64					7·6	7·2
Denchworth (pp. 123–4)	Bu 76	A1g	1–5	6	3	27	39	10·0	1·06	9·4	—	5·1	4·7
		A2g	6–11			32	51	2·3	0·23	10	0·3	6·3	5·6
		(B)g	15–21			29	60				0·5	7·0	6·4
		C1g	24–32			27	56				11·2	7·2	6·8
		C2gca	40–46			40	53					7·8	7·4
	Bu 85	Ag	1–5	12	14	43	22	2·9				6·0	5·8
		A/(B)g	7–11			40	38					6·7	6·6
		(B)g	14–18			43	46					7·4	7·1
		C1g	24–28			28	53					7·6	7·4
		C2(g)ca	42–46			31	59				4·8	8·2	7·8
			48–52			26	48				8·5	7·6	7·6
Bierton (p. 126)	Bu 95	A(g)	1–4	13	28	35	17	6·0			16	7·4	7·2
		(B)1(g)	7–16			35	22				26	8·1	7·6
		(B)2g	19–28			49	10				61	8·4	7·8

TABLE 10 (*continued*)

Soil Series	Profile No.	Horizon	Depth in.	Sand 200µ-2 mm. %	Sand 50–200µ %	Silt 2–50µ %	Clay (<2µ) %	Carbon %	Nitrogen %	C/N Ratio	CaCO₃ %	pH H₂O 1:2·5	pH M/100 CaCl₂
Bierton (p. 127)	Bu 94	A	1–4	13	27	33	17	6·7			—	6·9	6·9
		A/(B)(g)	8–11			34	24				2·2	7·4	7·3
		(B)g	16–20			30	30				0·2	7·3	7·2
		Cgca	36–40			26	28				0·6	8·2	7·6
Unnamed variant on Portland Sand (p. 127)	Bu 65	A	1–4	6	33	23	19	6·2	0·51	12	6·9	7·8	7·3
		A/(B)	7–10			29	17	1·5	0·15	10	10·1	8·0	7·6
		(B)	16–20			31	16				21	8·4	7·8
		(B)/Cca	24–30			31	12				23	8·4	7·8
Weston Turville (pp. 130–31)	Bu 113	Ap	1–4	34	13	23	24	2·3			0·5	7·7	6·9
		(B)(g)	9–12			23	28				0·4	8·2	7·6
	Bu 100	Ap	1–5	29	18	25	25	2·4	0·21	11	0·3	7·0	6·9
		(B)(g)	9–14			25	28	0·85	0·08	11	tr.	6·5	6·5
		C2gca	33–37			33	55				9·5	7·9	7·6
	Bu 63	A	1–4	23	14	25	30	5·6	0·39	14	—	5·4	4·8
		A/(B)(g)	8–11	26	12	27	29	1·6	0·16	10	—	6·0	5·7
		(B)g	17–21	25	18	25	29					6·6	6·5
		Cg	25–29			21	28				11	8·1	7·6
Rowsham (pp. 133–4)	Bu 91	A	1–4	20	18	35	22	5·4	0·44	12	—	6·0	5·2
		A/(B)(g)	6–10			38	37	3·0	0·34	8·8	—	6·7	6·1
		(B)g	15–20			36	43				0·4	7·8	7·3
		Cgca	36–40			34	62				16	8·1	7·9
	Bu 89	A	1–4	15	26	27	23	3·8	0·38	10	1·4	7·0	5·2
		A/(B)	5–9			33	28	1·7	0·19	8·9	4·2	7·4	6·1
		(B)(g)	14–18			35	37				2·6	7·7	7·3
		Cgca	30–34			27	52				15	8·1	7·9

TABLE 10 (continued)

Soil Series	Profile No.	Horizon	Depth in.	Sand 200μ–2 mm %	Sand 50–200μ %	Silt 2–50μ %	Clay (<2μ) %	Carbon %	Nitrogen %	C/N Ratio	CaCO₃ %	pH H₂O 1:2.5	pH M/100 CaCl₂
Unnamed variant on fluvio-glacial gravel (p. 134)	Bu 103	A (B)	1–5 11–20	49	11	15 16	17 20	3·9			0·3 —	7·2 6·5	6·8 5·8
Unnamed variant on Chalky Boulder Clay (p. 135)	Bu 99	A A/(B)(g) (B)g Cgca	1–4 9–14 24–30 33–39	33	17	23 19 18 25	20 25 36 30	4·9			— 0·3 2·3 20	6·3 7·0 7·8 8·0	6·1 6·9 7·5 7·7
Ford End (pp. 137–8)	Bu 30	A C1(g) C2gca C3g	3–6 12–15 21–24 33–36	9	12	44 46 46 48	23 36 32 26	6·5 1·4	0·68 0·18	9·6 7·6	25 43 44 20	7·7 8·0 8·1 8·1	7·5 7·7 7·6 7·6
	Ht 70	A A/C1(g) C2g C3gca	1–5 9–15 17–21 36–40	14	9	32 30 31 23	31 29 24 12	8·3			12·4 27 52 95	7·7 8·2 8·3 8·5	7·4 7·7 7·8 7·9
	Bu 97	Ag A/C1g C2g C3gca	1–4 12–18 23–27 36–40	21	10	26 42 13 30	35 38 14 68	7·8 0·98			0·5 14·5 35 53	7·2 8·0 8·0 8·0	7·0 7·7 7·7 7·6
Mead (p. 140)	Bu 87	A A/C1g C2g	1–3 6–9 20–24	1	1	25 37 20	56 45 71	10·7 2·6	1·10 0·32	9·7 8·1	2·3 20 0·4	7·1 8·1 8·2	7·1 7·6 7·7
	Bu 108	A1 A2g C1g	1–4 8–12 18–24	2	1	13 21 50	66 68 40	10·0			0·2 0·7 76	7·2 7·4 8·2	7·1 7·6 7·7

TABLE 11

Exchangeable Cations and Percentage Base-saturation

Soil Series	Profile No.	Horizon	Depth in.	Exchangeable cations (m.e./100 gms.)					Cation Exchange Capacity (m.e./100 gms.)	Percentage Saturation
				Ca	Mg	K	Na	H		
Batcombe (pp. 64–68)	Bu 14	A	0–1½	1·7	0·4	0·35	tr.	20·2	22·7	11
		Eb	1½–8	0·5	0·1	0·10	tr.	10·9	11·6	6
		Eb/Bt	9–15	0·3	tr.	0·10	tr.	10·5	11·0	5
		Bt1(g)	16–29	1·5	0·6	0·15	tr.	17·1	19·4	12
		Bt2(g)	36–60	5·2	4·2	0·20	0·3	9·8	19·6	50
		Bt/C(g)	78–90	10·7	6·9	0·40				
	Bu 13	Eb1	1–6	0·5	0·1	0·25	0·2	11·1	12·1	8
		Eb2(g)	6–13	0·7	0·1	0·10	0·1	8·2	9·7	11
		Bt1(g)	13–23	0·5	0·5	0·35	0·2	15·6	17·2	9
		Bt2g	24–36	1·2	2·7	0·30	0·2	17·1	21·5	20
	Bu 57	Ap	1–6	14·1	0·9	0·15	0·1	4·5	19·7	77
		Eb1	7–15	10·9	0·4	0·10	0·1	3·8	15·3	75
		Eb2(g)	18–24	8·8	0·2	0·10	0·1	4·7	13·9	66
		Bt(g)	24–30	28	0·5	0·35	0·2	5·5	35	83
	Ht 60	Ap	1–4	21	0·5	0·20	0·1			
		Eb	7–12	20	0·6	0·20	0·1			
		Bt1(g)	23–30	28	1·1	0·35	0·1			
		Bt2(g)	36–41	25	0·6	0·45	0·1			
Berkhamsted (pp. 70–72)	Ht 47	A/Ea	1–2	1·0	1·0	0·15	tr.	21·6	22·8	5
		Eb	5–8	0·2	tr.	0·05	tr.	11·9	12·2	2
		Eb/Bt	14–18	0·2	0·1	0·10	tr.	11·5	11·9	3
		Bt1(g)	20–25	12·3	0·7	0·20	0·1	6·4	19·7	67
		Bt2g	30–33	13·0	0·5	0·20	0·1	6·1	19·9	69

TABLE 11 (continued)

Soil Series	Profile No.	Horizon	Depth in.	Exchangeable cations (m.e./100 gms.)					Cation Exchange Capacity (m.e./100 gms.)	Percentage Saturation
				Ca	Mg	K	Na	H		
Berkhamsted—continued	Ht 29	A	1–6	11·1	0·2	0·10	tr.	2·0	13·4	85
		A/Eb	6–12	6·5	0·1	0·10	tr.	2·9	9·6	70
		Eb	12–21	4·7	0·1	0·10	tr.	2·8	7·7	64
		Eb/Bt1(g)	21–30	2·6	0·1	0·10	tr.			
		Bt2g	30–38	1·6	0·1	0·10	tr.			
St. Albans (p. 74)	Ht 48	Ap	0–6	7·4	0·3	0·40	0·1			
		Eb	9–13	4·3	0·1	0·20	0·8			
		Eb/Bt	20–24	1·9	0·1	0·10	0·05			
		Bt	32–35	8·6	0·5	0·35	0·2			
Southampton (pp. 72 and 75)	Bu 80	H	1–6	4·5	0·5	0·45	0·3	4·7	5·0	6
		Ea/Bh	9–16	0·2	tr.	tr.	tr.	5·5	6·1	6
		Bfe	18–30	0·4	tr.	0·05	0·1	17·0	17·2	1
		Bt(g)		0·1	tr.	tr.	tr.			
	Ht 69	H	3–11	4·9	2·1	1·1	0·6	5·2	5·6	7
		Ea	14–17	0·3	tr.	tr.	tr.	27	28	2
		Bh	18–27	0·4	0·1	tr.	tr.	8·0	8·3	4
		Bfe	36–40	0·2	0·1	tr.	tr.	5·6	6·0	7
		Eb/Bt		0·2	0·1	0·05	tr.			
Cowcroft (pp. 77–8)	Ht 66	H/A	2–6	6·7	0·8	0·55	0·2	11·7	12·3	5
		Ebg	8–17	0·5	tr.	tr.	tr.	15·8	16·8	6
		Bt1g	20–27	0·8	0·1	0·05	tr.	12·2	15·3	20
		Bt2g	37–42	2·4	0·5	0·15	tr.	10·3	22	54
		Cg		9·5	2·2	0·25	0·3			
	Ht 53	Ap	1–5	22	1·1	0·30	0·1			
		Bt1(g)	8–13	34	1·6	0·40	0·2			
		Bt2g	15–24	35	1·4	0·25	0·3			

TABLE 11 (continued)

Soil Series	Profile No.	Horizon	Depth in.	Exchangeable cations (m.e./100 gms.)					Cation Exchange Capacity (m.e./100 gms.)	Percentage Saturation
				Ca	Mg	K	Na	H		
Winchester (pp. 81–2)	Bu 16	A	0–2½	6·4	1·0	0·30	0·2	16·1	24	33
		Eb	2½–7	2·3	0·4	0·15	0·2	12·8	15·8	19
		Bt	7–15	30	0·2	0·40	0·4	10·0	41	76
	Bu 54	A	0–2½	6·6	0·6	0·25	0·1	17·7	25	30
		Eb	2½–7	1·8	0·2	0·10	0·1	14·3	16·5	13
		Bt1	7–12	10·4	2·7	0·25	0·2	16·5	30	45
			12–26	20	4·2	0·35	0·4	11·3	36	69
		Bt2	26–37	28	3·6	0·45	0·4	9·2	42	78
			37–43	45	2·7	0·45	0·3	3·7	52	93
Charity (pp. 86–87)	Bu 55	A	0–3	5·3	0·7	0·25	0·3	17·4	24	27
		Eb	3–11	1·4	0·2	0·10	tr.	9·4	11·1	15
		Eb/Bt	11–17	3·8	0·5	0·10	0·1	8·4	12·9	35
		Bt	17–27	22	1·3	0·25	0·2	10·0	33	71
			27–33	25	0·8	0·35	0·2	8·4	35	76
	Bu 56	H	4–10	14·1	1·5	1·2	1·1	8·2	9·1	10
		Eb	17–24	0·7	0·1	0·10	tr.	8·8	23	62
		Bt	24–32	12·0	2·2	0·20	0·1	5·8	26	78
				18·0	2·0	0·30	0·3			
Wallop (p. 99)	Bu 17	A	0–5	36	4·1	0·25	tr.	13·8	54	74
		(B)	5–11	15·0	2·1	0·30	0·4			
Harwell (p. 113)	Bu 42	Ap	3–5	17·2	0·8	0·85	0·3	3·8	23	83
		(B)(g)	12–14	27	1·3	0·55	0·6	2·1	31	93
		C(g)	28–36	32	1·1	0·35	0·7	0·9	35	97
Wicken (p. 117)	Bu 90	A1	1–4	34	2·1	0·30	0·4			

TABLE 11 (continued)

Soil Series	Profile No.	Horizon	Depth in.	Exchangeable cations (m.e./100 gms.)					Cation Exchange Capacity (m.e./100 gms.)	Percentage Saturation
				Ca	Mg	K	Na	H		
Challow (p. 120)	Bu 67	A1g	1–4	47	0·3	0·50	0·7			
			4–8	45	0·3	0·70	0·6			
		A2g	8–12	43	0·3	0·45	0·6			
Denchworth (pp. 123–4)	Bu 76	A1g	1–5	26	3·4	4·5	0·3	23·0	58	60
		A2g	6–11	29	0·4	0·90	0·3	5·6	37	85
		(B)g	15–21	31	0·5	0·65	0·3			
	Bu 85	Ag	1–5	10·9	1·8	0·20	0·1	8·1	21·1	62
		A/(B)g	7–11	14·4	2·6	0·20	0·2	4·6	22·0	79
Bierton (p. 127)	Bu 94	A	1–4	43	3·0	0·35	0·3	8·2	55	85
Weston Turville (p. 131)	Bu 63	A	1–4	28	1·0	0·25	0·2	8·8	38	76
		A/(B)(g)	8–11	30	1·1	0·20	0·1	3·1	34	91
Rowsham (p. 133)	Bu 91	A	1–4	25	1·7	0·20	0·3	10·3	37	73
		A/(B)(g)	6–10	30	1·3	0·20	0·2	4·9	37	86

TABLE 12

Amounts of Non-exchangeable Potassium released to Ryegrass

Soil Series	Mgm. K released per 100 gms. soil
Batcombe (Broadbalk plot 11, no K)..	2
Icknield	8
Tring	27
Weston Turville	34
Aylesbury	41
Wantage	45
Batcombe (Broadbalk plot 13, K-fertilized)	57
Harwell	70
Halton	75
Wicken (average of 4 samples) ..	83

TABLE 13

Exchangeable and H-resin Extractable Potassium* in Surface Soils

Soil Series	Profile No.	Potassium (mgm./100 gms. soil)	
		Exchangeable	H-resin extractable
Icknield	Bu 60	8·0	10
Icknield	Bu 115	7·0	12
Berkhamsted ..	Ht 29	6·0	12
Batcombe	Ht 49	6·0	14
Batcombe	Ht 61	7·0	14
Berkhamsted ..	Ht 44	7·5	16
Weston Turville ..	Bu 63	7·5	18
Winchester	Ht 62	14·5	22
Winchester	Ht 40	11·5	25
Charity	Bu 79	7·0	25
Ford End	Bu 32	22	26
Nettleden	Bu 83	13·0	28
Wallop	Ht 39	11·5	28
Denchworth ..	Bu 85	11·0	30
Weston Turville ..	Bu 113	10·0	36
Wicken	Bu 90	16·0	38
Coombe	Bu 74	13·0	42
Mead	Bu 108	17·5	42
Denchworth ..	Bu 93	30	62
Halton	Bu 109	17·0	66
Wicken	Ht 58	31	68
Harwell	Bu 45	68	94
Wantage	Bu 26	44	96
Ardington	Bu 102	42	114

* Potassium-supplying power as indicated by H-resin extractable K (mgm./100 gms.).

Low   <25
Medium   25–50
High   > 50

TABLE 14

Total and Citric-soluble P_2O_5 in selected Profiles

Woodland Soils

Soil Series	Profile No.	Depth in.	P_2O_5 (mgm./100 gms.)	
			Total	Citric-soluble
Batcombe	Bu 13	F/H	179	n.d.
		0–1	19	10·8
		1–6	49	9·3
		6–13	22	3·5
		13–23	22	2·7
		24–36	91	4·1
Berkhamsted	Ht 47	1–2	78	12
		5–8	41	4·7
		14–18	54	2·7
		20–25	54	2·7
		30–33	36	4·1
Winchester	Bu 54	0–2	170	20
		3–7	110	12
		7–12	94	2·7
		12–26	138	3·5
		26–37	138	2·7
		37–43	262	34
Charity	Bu 55	0–3	154	24
		3–11	122	11·5
		11–17	154	18
		11–17	314	18
		27–33	244	n.d.

Arable and Grassland Soils

Soil Series	Profile No.	Depth in.	P_2O_5 (mgm./100 gms.)	
			Total	Citric-soluble
Batcombe	Bu 57	1–6	227	41
		7–15	147	11
		18–24	123	18
		24–30	199	15
Berkhamsted	Ht 29	1–6	150	29
		6–12	102	10·8
		12–21	130	12·1
		21–30	46	8·2
		30–38	99	4·7
Winchester	Bu 70	0–7	234	26
		10–14	134	10·1
		14–24	194	8·2
		26–30	178	8·2
Charity	Bu 79	0–5	162	28
		6–21	130	19
		21–36	114	9·3
		36–54	162	22
Harwell	Bu 42	3–5	59	7·4
		12–14	32	4·1
		28–36	188	114

TABLE 14 (*continued*)

Woodland Soils

Southampton	Bu 80	H	94	n.d.
		1–6	14	2·7
		8–16	14	1·4
		18–30	37	0·7

Arable and Grassland Soils

Weston Turville	Bu 63	1–4	154	14·7
		8–11	143	18
		17–21	138	45
Mead	Bu 68	1–6	298	37
		7–12	282	103
		16–20	274	142
		30–36	586	297

Arable and Grassland Soils

Harwell	Bu 35	1–3	220	49
		8–11	224	59
		16–20	296	103
Wicken	Bu 39	2–6	145	36
		9–12	235	22
		18–21	307	33
	Ht 58	1–5	405	55
		9–14	149	36
Denchworth	Bu 76	1–5	210	32
		6–11	130	11·5
		15–21	65	3·5
		24–32	78	7·4

TABLE 15

Free Iron Oxide in Brown Earths (Sols lessivés) and Podzolized Soils

Type of Soil Formation	Soil Series and Profile No.	Horizon	Free Fe_2O_3 %	Clay %	Free Fe_2O_3/ clay
Sol lessive	Charity (Bu 55)	A	1·7	14	0·12
		Eb	1·6	12	0·13
		Eb/Bt	2·0	21	0·10
		Bt1	3·3	43	0·08
		Bt2	3·3	46	0·07
Gleyed *sol lessive*	Batcombe (Bu 14)	A	2·0	13	0·15
		Eb	2·3	17	0·14
		Eb/Bt	2·9	29	0·10
		Bt1(g)	4·7	54	0·09
		Bt2(g)	5·1	58	0·09
Gleyed *sol lessive* (slightly podzolized)	Batcombe (Bu 13)	A/Ea	0·72	19	0·04
		Eb1	1·7	17	0·10
		Eb2(g)	2·0	21	0·09
		Bt1(g)	3·7	38	0·10
		Bt2(g)	5·1	67	0·08
Humus-iron podzol	Southampton (Bu 80)	Ea/Bh	0·69	7	0·10
		Bfe	2·1	14	0·15
		Bt(g)	4·9	56	0·09

TABLE 16

Mineralogical Composition of Clay Separates (e.s.d. <1·4μ)

Soil Series	Profile No.	Horizon	Depth in.	Kaolin	Mica	Vermiculite	Montmorillonite	Chlorite
Batcombe	Bu 14	A	0–1½	**	*	**	—	tr.
		Eb	1½–8	**	*	***	—	tr.
		Eb/Bt	9–15	**	*	***	—	tr.
		Bt1(g)	16–29	***	**	**	—	—
		Bt2(g)	36–60	**	**	*	—	—
		Bt/C(g)	78–90	**	**	*	*	—
	Bu 57	Ap	1–6	*	**	**	*	tr.
		Eb1	7–15	**	***	***	*	*
		Eb2(g)	18–24	**	***	*	*	*
		Bt(g)	24–30	**	*	**	**	—
Berkhamsted	Ht 47	A/Ea	1–2	***	***	*	—	—
		Eb	5–8	***	***	***	—	—
		Eb/Bt	14–18	***	***	*	tr.	—
		Bt1(g)	20–25	**	**	**	tr.	—
		Bt2g	30–33	**	**	**	tr.	—
St. Albans	Ht 48	Ap	0–6	***	***	tr.	—	—
		Eb	9–13	**	***	tr.	—	—
		Eb/Bt	20–24	*	**	*	—	—
		Bt	32–35	*	**	**	—	—
Southampton	Bu 80	Ea/Bh	1–6	***	*	*	—	—
		Bfe	9–16	***	*	***	—	—
		Bt(g)	18–30	*	*	***	—	—
Winchester	Bu 54	A	0–2½	***	tr.	***	tr.	—
		Eb	2½–7	***	tr.	***	tr.	—
		Bt1	7–12	***	*	tr.	***	—
			12–26	*	*	—	***	—
		Bt2	26–37	*	*	—	***	—
			37–43	*	*	—	***	—

*** = dominant (> 50%)   * = little (5–25%)
** = moderate (25–50%)   tr. = trace (0–5%)
† Non-calcareous residues, prepared by treatment with acetic acid–ammonium acetate mixture at pH 3.

TABLE 16 (continued)

Soil Series	Profile No.	Horizon	Depth in.	Kaolin	Mica	Vermiculite	Montmorillonite	Chlorite
Winchester—continued	Ht 40	Ap	1–6	*	*	*	***	—
		Bt1	6–15	**	*	tr.	***	—
		Bt2	15–26	**	*	tr.	***	—
Charity	Bu 55	A	0–3	*	**	**	—	tr.
		Eb	3–11	*	**	***	—	tr.
		EB/Bt	11–17	*	***	***	—	—
		Bt	17–27	*	***	*	—	—
			27–33	*	***	—	*	—
		C	33–39	*	**	—	**	—
Charity	Bu 79	Ap	0–5	**	***	**	*	—
		Eb	5–21	***	***	tr.	***	—
		Eb/Bt	21–36	*	*	tr.	***	—
		Bt	36–54	*	*	tr.	***	—
		C	54–86					—
Icknield	Bu 20	A	0–4	*	**	—	***	—
		C†	18–24	—	**	—	***	—
Wantage	Bu 27	A	1–4	*	***	—	***	—
		C†	16–20	*	***	*	***	—
Aylesbury	Bu 114	A	1–5	*	**	—	**	—
		(B)/C	9–15	*	***	—	**	—
		C†	20–24	tr.		—	**	—
Halton	Bu 28	A	1–4	*	**	—	***	—
		A/C	7–10	tr.	***	—	****	—
		C1(g)ca	14–17	tr.	*	—	***	—
		C2(g)ca	25–28			—	***	—

TABLE 16 (continued)

Soil Series	Profile No.	Horizon	Depth in.	Kaolin	Mica	Vermiculite	Montmorillonite	Chlorite
Harwell	Bu 45	Ap	2–4	tr.	*	—	***	—
		(B)	8–12	—	*	—	***	—
		C	18–24	—	*	tr.	***	—
Wicken	Ht 58	Ap	1–5	*	*	—	***	—
		(B)(g)	9–14	*	*	—	***	—
		C1gca	20–28	*	*	—	***	—
		C2gca	36–40	*	*	—	***	—
Denchworth	Bu 76	A1g	1–5	*	*	tr.	***	—
		A2g	6–11	*	*	tr.	***	—
		(B)g	15–21	*	*	tr.	***	—
		C1g	24–32	*	*	—	***	—
		C2gca	40–46	*	*	—	***	—
Bierton	Bu 95	A(g)	1–4	*	**	—	***	—
		(B)1(g)	7–16	*	**	—	***	—
		(B)2g	19–28	*	***	—	**	—
Weston Turville	Bu 63	A	1–4	*	*	—	***	—
		A/(B)(g)	8–11	*	**	—	***	—
		(B)g	17–21	*	***	—	***	—
		Cg	25–29	*	*	—	***	—

CHAPTER VI

The Soils in Relation to Agriculture and Horticulture

The ability of a piece of land to produce crops, and the returns obtainable from particular cropping and management systems under a given set of economic conditions, are largely determined by physical characteristics of site and soil. Certain characteristics, such as temperature, slope and depth to bed-rock, are virtually uncontrollable in ordinary farming practice, whereas others can be controlled or modified so as to increase the productivity of the soil, or the range of crops that can be grown. Thus, moisture deficiency can sometimes be made good by irrigation, the harmful effects of waterlogging may be alleviated by drainage, and nutrient deficiencies remedied by the use of fertilizers. Where climatic and topographic conditions are favourable to intensive agriculture, low nutrient reserves rarely constitute a serious limitation, but less easily altered soil properties exercise a continuing influence on productivity, and on the types of farming which are most desirable economically.

Apart from nutrient content and soil reaction, the chief characteristics of importance are the thickness, texture, stoniness, structure and permeability of surface and sub-surface horizons, which together determine the volume of soil freely exploitable by roots, and its capacity to store water and nutrients in forms available to plants. Another important quality is the drainage of the soil: where drainage is excessive, both water and nutrients are wasted by rapid leaching or by run-off, whereas seasonal waterlogging restricts rooting and promotes denitrification. Poor drainage may be due to an impermeable subsoil, to the activity of springs, or to the presence of a permanent water-table, and whereas the two latter conditions may ensure an adequate supply of moisture during the growing season, the former will not.

In this area, as indicated in Chapter I (p. 28), evapo-transpiration normally exceeds rainfall from April to July inclusive, the maximum soil-moisture deficit amounting to about 4 in. in an average summer. Most crop plants require an adequate supply of water held at low tensions to maintain maximum dry-matter production, and irrigation experiments (Lowe and Armitage, 1959; Penman, 1962) have shown that yields of grass in particular are adversely affected by deficits of 2 in. or less, the actual limiting deficit depending on the moisture-storage capacity of the soil and on nitrogen supply. Crops such as grass, potatoes and vegetables may therefore be expected to benefit from irrigation in most years, especially where grown on shallow or coarse-textured soils.

Limitations on productivity imposed by physical soil characteristics are generally most pronounced in abnormally dry or wet seasons, and are more important for perennial crops, such as fruit, than for most farm crops. By such practices as alternate husbandry, use of organic manures, judicious cultivations, and artificial drainage, the farmer can modify the structure and moisture regime of the soil so as to reduce the adverse effects of unfavourable seasons. In many instances, however, more permanent features such as texture, slope, stoniness, or depth of soil, set limits to the adaptability of the land, and to the response obtainable from particular cultural treatments or ameliorative measures.

The following sections deal with land-use capability, outstanding management problems and fertilizer requirements, in relation to soil mapping units in the Chilterns and the Vale respectively. Owing to the generally over-riding effects on crop yields of management and seasonal weather conditions, detailed assessment of relationships between soil/site characteristics and crop performance requires special studies that cannot be made in the course of a soil survey. The discussions are therefore incomplete and insufficiently well based, but may prove useful and serve as a stimulus to further work.

SOILS OF THE CHILTERN PLATEAU AND
THE ICKNIELD BELT

Batcombe, Berkhamsted and Winchester Series

These closely related soils, together covering more than half the area, are generally suited to arable cultivation, but their range of use and productive capacity are limited to varying degrees by stoniness, by unfavourable water relations or working qualities, or by unduly sloping or elevated sites.

Besides causing much wear on implements, the presence of numerous flints leads to difficulties in the cultivation and harvesting of root crops, and may cause damage to the hooves of cattle and sheep when grazing kale or young leys. As against these disadvantages, a partial superficial covering of flints shields seedlings and helps to protect the soil from loss of moisture by evaporation. With increasing stoniness, however, the reserves of water and nutrients in a given depth of soil are proportionately reduced and productive capacity accordingly decreased.

Except locally at the edges of ridges, the Batcombe silt loams are less stony than the Berkhamsted and Winchester soils, and are consequently suited to a wider range of crops. Although originally very acid and inherently low in phosphate and potash, their texture and depth are such that they respond well to good management, and above-average yields, particularly of cereals, can be obtained in most seasons where cultivations and manuring are satisfactory. Fruit trees, including apples and cherries, do well if due attention is paid to drainage and nutrient status, and although the fruit ripens later than in lower localities with favourable aspects, the plateau sites have the advantage of relative freedom from spring frosts. Market-garden crops are also grown successfully on the less stony soils, but neither soil nor site conditions are well suited to intensive vegetable production. Most of the soils are naturally fairly well drained, yet retain sufficient moisture to support moderately productive pastures. Pipe-drainage has been carried out in a few places, notably in orchards at Ashley Green, where tree roots were killed by winter waterlogging. Except in the wettest seasons, however, serious waterlogging is very localized, and for normal agricultural crops artificial drainage is rarely justified. "Busting" with a sub-soiler or mole-plough has proved effective in breaking plough-pans and aiding infiltration of rain-water, but subsoil conditions are generally unfavourable to the survival of mole channels.

The pebbly loams and sandy loams of the Berkhamsted series are often excessively stony, and were regarded as less fertile than the Batcombe soils by early agricultural writers, both Ellis (1745) and Arthur Young (1813) referring to the hungry or "cormorantine" nature of the "gravels with blue pebbles". Their poor reputation, which still obtains locally, may be attributed in part to unfavourable moisture conditions, particularly where the soils occur on ridge-margins. Although the subsoils are clayey, causing winter waterlogging in places, the very stony upper horizons have a low moisture-retaining capacity. These horizons readily dry out and set hard in summer, and permanent grass in particular is liable to suffer badly from drought.

Because of the weak natural structure of the upper horizons, both Batcombe and Berkhamsted soils need care in cultivation. Although excellent seed-beds can be obtained when weather conditions are favourable, there is a tendency, most pronounced in soils with a relatively low clay content, for the clods to disintegrate and run together under the impact of rain, causing the formation of a "cap" which, if dry weather follows, sets hard and may delay the emergence of seedlings. On old arable land the sub-surface horizon may also assume a structureless or weakly laminated condition, causing impedance to drainage and root-growth; a similar tendency has been noted beneath leys which have been "poached" by stock.

The Winchester soils are typically very flinty, the surface of fallow ground when washed by rain often appearing to consist more of flints than soil. Where there has been little accelerated erosion, the surface horizons are friable and resemble those of the adjoining Batcombe or Berkhamsted soils in texture and consistency. Generally, however, the surface soils on cultivated land are of stiff clay loam or clay, resting directly on a retentive clay subsoil. These heavy soils are difficult to work in wet seasons, but are less liable to surface capping than the associated loams and silt loams, and are generally better drained, as they normally occupy appreciable slopes with chalk at moderate depths. Their excessive flintiness and fine texture make them ill adapted to potatoes, sugar beet and vegetables, but cereals, especially wheat, give good yields in most seasons when adequately manured, and most kinds of top-fruit can be grown successfully when 2 ft. or more of clay covers the chalk. Where erosion has been severe, however, unweathered clay is brought to the surface by the plough, and satisfactory seed-beds are difficult to obtain. The most flinty and intractable soils are often left in grass, and moderately productive swards may be found where 9 in. or more of flinty loam covers the clay, but on eroded slopes the surface cracks badly and pastures produce very little keep in a dry summer.

The physical condition of both loamy and clayey soils is improved by regular additions or organic manure or by periods under grass (Williams and Cooke, 1961), but the extent to which such improvements affect the growth and yield of arable crops is problematical, and undoubtedly depends on the season and the kind of crop grown. The fact that plots of Batcombe soil at Rothamsted Experimental Station (Broadbalk and Hoosfield) which have received only mineral fertilizers for more than a century continue to give yields of wheat and barley comparable with those obtained on dunged plots suggests that, despite the low equilibrium percentage of organic matter (about 1 per cent) reached in the former, there has been no serious deterioration in fertility. It seems certain, however, that the improved structure and moisture-holding capacity* associated with higher contents of organic matter are often advantageous in dry seasons, especially for spring-sown crops and for vegetables.

Both the working qualities and the structure of the soils are also dependent on their lime status. The effect of added chalk on ease of working was well shown by measurements of plough draft conducted by Russell and Keen (1921) on a Batcombe soil at Rothamsted. Parts of the field being ploughed had been chalked 9 years previously and on these the average draw-bar pull was 1,380 lbs. as compared with 1,562 lbs. on strips which had received no chalk. Besides making the heavier soils more friable, added chalk visibly improves aggregation and reduces the tendency to cap, probably in part through its influence on the organic cycle. Where parts of a field contain reserves of chalk, while others have become acid, it has often been noted (Gardner and Garner, 1953) that the chalked portion appears darker in colour, as well as being more porous. Similarly, where deciduous plantations occupy former agricultural land which had received heavy dressings of chalk, the A horizon tends to resemble the dark-coloured granular mull of rendzinas, in contrast to the weakly aggregated acid mull or mor found in the semi-natural woods.

Prior to 1939, much of the grassland on soils of each series had become very acid, and when commons and old parkland were brought into cultivation the crops showed marked responses to lime and phosphate. Gardner and Garner (1953) quote results of a 32-plot experiment on Harpenden Common (Winchester series; pH originally 4·6), comparing the effects of superphosphate and silicophosphate on potatoes in the presence and absence of added chalk. All plots received a basal dressing of sulphate of ammonia and muriate of potash, and with no chalk or phosphate the average yield was 2·8 tons/acre. Responses to 3 cwt. of ground chalk and to 0·5 cwt. P_2O_5 as superphosphate were 1·2 and 1·8 tons respectively, but where these two dressings were combined the average yield rose to 7·7 tons, thus demonstrating a positive interaction between chalk and phosphate which amounted in this instance to 1·9 tons/acre. As potatoes are normally considered an acid-tolerant crop, the response to liming is itself noteworthy, and the marked effect of the combined treatments indicates that the value of chalk as a dressing may be due in no small measure to its effect on phosphate-availability. The effect of phosphatic impurities in the chalk may also be significant, the strata immediately above the Chalk Rock, which contain phosphatic and glauconitic grains, having been especially prized in the past for marling (Sherlock, 1922).

Both the classical experiments and the modern long-period rotation experiments at Rothamsted Experimental Station are sited on Batcombe soils or on soils transitional between Batcombe and Winchester series, and the results of the experiments afford abundant information on the fertilizer requirements of crops grown under different systems of management. Recent estimates of the dressings

---

* On the Broadbalk field at Rothamsted, the upper 15 in. of soil at field capacity contained water available for plant growth equivalent to 3·0 in. of rainfall on the unmanured plot, and 3·9 in. where it had received annual dressings of farmyard manure (Russell, 1961).

of phosphate and potash needed by arable crops and leys at Rothamsted to maintain soil fertility, and of optimum dressings of nitrogen for cereals grown in various rotations, are given by Cooke (1959).

Much of the old arable land on the Experimental Farm is well supplied with phosphate remaining as residues from former dressings, but the old grassland and acid parts of the newer arable land have much less readily-soluble phosphate, and sensitive crops give moderate responses to phosphatic fertilizers. As the capacity of the soils to supply potash from non-exchangeable reserves is low, and as most crops take up greater quantities of potash than phosphate, regular additions of potash either as fertilizer or in farmyard manure are required to maintain yields, particularly where leys cut for hay or silage are included in the rotation. A recently established experiment (Reference Plots) on a Batcombe soil ploughed from very old grass (pH 5·3 before liming) measures responses to added nitrogen, phosphate, potash and farmyard manure on a 5-course rotation of wheat, kale, barley, clover-grass ley and potatoes. Results to date indicate that while kale and potatoes were the only crops to benefit appreciably from added phosphate, wheat, barley, clover and potatoes gave large responses to potash. In this experiment farmyard manure improved yields of all crops, even when a complete fertilizer was also applied, potatoes, kale and clover responding particularly well. Significant responses to potash by spring barley were obtained by Widdowson et al. (1959) in experiments on Batcombe soil at Bovingdon, and on Berkhamsted soil at Berkhamsted and at Potterscrouch (east of Bedmond). At each site 0·25 cwt. K_2O/acre drilled with the seed gave higher yields than 0·5 cwt. broadcast and worked into the seed-bed.

All crops except clover respond well to fertilizer nitrogen, kale being particularly dependent on nitrogen for high yields. The returns obtained vary considerably in different seasons, however, and are much affected by previous land use and management. From the results of two rotation experiments begun at Rothamsted in 1947, one on old arable land and the other on old grass, Cooke (1959) estimated that winter wheat grown on land ploughed from well managed grass between 5 and 10 years previously needs no nitrogen after a 3-year ley, and about 0·3 cwt./acre in an all-arable rotation. In the experiment on old arable land, wheat gave a good return from as much as 0·9 cwt./acre when grown in arable rotation, and from 0·6 cwt. after ley. For spring barley the corresponding results indicate that 0·6 cwt./acre may be sufficient for maximum yields in an all-arable rotation, and 0·2 cwt. when following a ley.

St. Albans Series

Although of limited extent in the survey area, these well drained, gravelly soils are important agriculturally in the country farther east. Because of their coarse texture, crops and grass tend to suffer from drought, especially where very stony layers lie close to the surface, and yields are commonly lower than on less stony and more moisture-retentive soils nearby. The capacity of the soils to store moisture and nutrients is much improved by additions of farmyard manure, and for optimum productivity it is desirable to maintain the organic-matter content above the level of 1–2 per cent common on old arable land.

The soils are chiefly under arable crops or leys; they are not generally suited to fruit growing, but market-garden crops may be grown successfully where the stone content is not too high and adequate moisture is either supplied by irrigation or conserved by heavy dressings of organic manure. Dressings of lime are required at regular intervals to prevent the development of acidity and, as nitrogen is readily lost by leaching, autumn-sown crops will generally benefit from spring top-dressings. On land where phosphatic fertilizers have been regularly used, the accumulated residues are commonly sufficient to meet the needs of less sensitive crops such as cereals, but responses to potash added either as fertilizers or in farmyard manure may be expected wherever the cropping system makes appreciable demands on the soil.

Charity Complex

These soils are mainly deep, well drained, flinty silt loams which, although liable to cap on the surface, are relatively easy to work and form useful arable land when well managed. Generally, the profiles have a finer-textured subsoil, almost free of stones in places, which helps to conserve moisture in dry seasons. Locally, however, as in certain of the dry-valley bottoms (Nettleden series), gravel occurs below the surface, causing crops and grass to suffer from drought.

Much of the land is used for cereals or for leys, and barley in particular gives good yields, over 2 tons/acre being obtainable under favourable conditions. The soil is well adapted to lucerne, which yields and persists well when the lime status is satisfactory and adequate dressings of phosphate and potash are given. For horticultural crops, especially fruit, the high frequency of spring frosts in the Chiltern valleys constitutes a serious limitation.

The soils were originally acid and may require chalking from time to time as reserves of previous dressings become exhausted. Natural reserves of phosphate and potash are commonly low,* so that their removal in crops needs to be balanced by appropriate fertilizer applications. Much of the arable land is now fairly well supplied with phosphate, but potash is often low; potatoes, clover and lucerne in particular may be expected to respond to potassic fertilizers, and barley gave significant responses in recent experiments at Studham (Widdowson and Cooke, 1959).

Icknield Series and Coombe Complex

The chief factors limiting the agricultural potentialities of these well drained, chalky soils are unfavourable relief, inadequate depth and/or moisture-supplying capacity, and reduced availability of nutrients (e.g. potash and iron) arising from high pH and calcium-carbonate content. These limitations are more pronounced on the Icknield series than on soils of the Coombe complex, which are normally deeper and contain less chalk.

According to Locket (1946) and Croney and Coleman (1954), chalk contains up to 28 per cent of water at field capacity, the amount varying with the hardness and porosity of the rock. Over 80 per cent of the water is held at tensions between pF3 and pF4 and so constitutes a considerable reserve on which plants may draw

---

* Some of the soils in the Tring Gap have a very high content of readily-soluble phosphate, probably as a result of the former use of London stable-manure, which was off-loaded from the Grand Union Canal near Newground Farm (Gardner, 1960).

in rainless periods. It is therefore to be expected that crops and grass withstand drought better on soils of the Icknield series than on those with hard non-porous rock, coarse sand, or compact little-weathered clay at comparable depths. However, much of the water is solid, unfissured chalk may be inaccessible to roots, so that the effective moisture-supplying power of the soils will depend to a significant extent on the thickness of disintegrated or rubbly material below the A horizon. There is also evidence (Bunting and Elston, 1962) that crop performance is frequently limited by nitrogen deficiency rather than by drought, addition of nitrogen enabling plants to make better use of soil moisture reserves (Lowe and Armitage, 1959).

Except on the Icknield series (steepland phase), much of the land is under cereals or leys, and permanent grassland, though dry and healthy for stock, is rarely very productive. The soils are ill suited to potatoes and most vegetable crops, and little fruit is grown, since drought conditions are liable to cause stunting, and "lime-induced" chlorosis is prevalent. The stiffer and finer-textured Wallop soils, bordering the Winchester series on upper slopes and spurs, are more difficult to work than those of the Icknield and Coombe series, and are often very flinty. This land is well suited to wheat, whereas the lighter soils are better adapted to barley, which at present occupies by far the greater acreage. Barley yields up to 2 tons/acre on Coombe soils, and over 30 cwt./acre are obtainable on the Icknield series with adequate manuring, but crops are commonly thin where the soil is particularly shallow or stony. Among the thinnest and poorest soils are those on slopes and knolls where accelerated erosion has occurred, and those associated with outcrops of relatively hard chalk (e.g. Chalk Rock and Melbourn Rock), called "hurlock" by earlier writers (Ellis, 1745). Such excessively drained soils are probably best left in grass, since regular cultivation is liable to cause further erosion and deterioration.

Trefoil (*Medicago lupulina*) and sainfoin were formerly much used on these soils for short and long leys respectively, especially where experience had shown that good crops of red clover were difficult to obtain. Neither is now cultivated to any extent, and sainfoin, although providing valuable crops of hay, is tending to be replaced by lucerne. As a constituent of leys, lucerne is commonly more productive than sainfoin when well managed, and has a wider range of uses. On the thinnest and most chalky soils, however, lucerne leys are difficult to establish and maintain, and sainfoin grown alone for one or two years is likely to be more successful.

The chalky loams and silty clay loams of the Icknield and Coombe series become soft and sticky when wet, but dry out rapidly and readily break down to form a well aerated tilth showing little tendency to cap. On the lightest and most chalky of these soils, autumn-sown corn is liable to damage by "frost-lift", and requires rolling in spring as soon as weather conditions allow. Because of the rapid drainage, and the readiness with which the surface assumes an open, "puffy" structure, spring cultivations need to be kept to a minimum, although thorough consolidation is essential. The traditional method of maintaining the fertility of these soils, and at the same time of achieving the requisite degree of consolidation, was by folding sheep on leys or green crops.* Leys left

---

* According to Russell (1961), the value of compaction may be partly due to the slightly poorer aeration thereby induced. The carbon dioxide content of the soil air is accordingly increased, which helps to reduce the pH of the soil around plant roots, and so to increase the availability of phosphate and some minor elements.

down for several years and grazed by cattle now serve a similar purpose, and the use of herbicides to control weeds like charlock (*Sinapis arvensis*) and poppy (*Papaver rhoeas*) has reduced the need for intensive spring cultivations.

There is now abundant evidence that these chalky soils are capable of producing consistently good yields of cereals, especially barley, providing that cultivations are satisfactory, planting is early, and adequate fertilizers are applied. Phosphate and potash are preferably drilled with the seed, and additional nitrogen applied either in the seed-bed or as a top-dressing later; alternatively, by using a complete fertilizer high in nitrogen, all the fertilizer can be combine-drilled. Many of the soils are well supplied with phosphate, derived either from the Chalk or as residues of former dressings; but others have low reserves and require regular additions of phosphatic fertilizers, especially for the establishment and maintenance of leys. The Icknield soils in particular have low reserves of potash, and cereals may give marked responses to potassic fertilizers on reclaimed downland or after leys cut regularly for hay or silage; normally, however, 0·3 cwt. K_2O drilled with the seed is a sufficient dressing, and recent evidence indicates that negligible responses are likely where regular fertilizer applications have been given. Both cereals and leys are very responsive to nitrogen; Gardner (1958) considers that dressings totalling 0·9 cwt. nitrogen/acre may be justified for spring barley on the basis of experiments in Hertfordshire, and other trials (Gardner, 1959), conducted on Icknield soil at Pitstone Green Farm, have shown that nitrate nitrogen is likely to be more efficient, weight for weight, than ammonia nitrogen, presumably because the latter is subject to loss in the form of gaseous ammonia when added to the surface of these alkaline soils. The traditional belief that sodium chloride is of value for barley on chalky soils was not confirmed in the same series of experiments.

Wantage Series

These stiff marly soils are well adapted to arable cultivation, and have long been regarded as more fertile than those of the Icknield series. In the 18th and 19th centuries, their distinctive character was clearly recognised by Ellis (1745), Priest (1810), and Read (1855), each of whom noted their superior quality, compared with the poorer "white land" nearer the foot of the hills. Thus, Ellis remarks that whereas the "dry lean chalk will bear wheat, rye, peas and vetches very good, if it is rightly dressed . . . , the fat marl, clayey chalk, is the best of all chalks, producing vast crops of grain or clover grass with but little manure".

Their apparent fertility, compared with the Icknield series, is probably due to their more retentive nature, which increases the water-supplying power and minimises loss of nitrogen by leaching, and to their greater capacity for supplying potash from slowly available reserves (see Chapter V, p. 147). They also tend to be fairly well supplied with phosphate, derived presumably from phosphatic seams in the parent chalk. Crops often do best in a dry season, and rarely suffer from drought, except in the few places where compact rock bands lie immediately below plough depth. Cereals, especially wheat, and clover grow particularly well, but the soil is less well suited to roots and grassland needs careful management to remain productive. Scarcely any fruit is grown, and most of the soils are too shallow to be recommended for this purpose; chlorosis due to immobilization of iron is also liable to occur, especially in cultivated orchards.

Tring Series

Deep, medium to fine-textured soils of this series form a stretch of useful flat to gently sloping land in the Tring Gap. They are somewhat too stiff and slow to dry out for intensive cultivation, but are otherwise suited to most crops, and are potentially among the most productive in the area of cereals and leys. Although gravelly layers occur at depth, the immediate subsoil is commonly only slightly stony and is finely fissured yet retentive of moisture, so that crops rarely suffer from drought. Drainage, though generally good, tends to become imperfect on the lower and flatter ground, some of which is drained by pipes and ditches.

Most of the soils contain reserves of chalk, but some are non-calcareous at the surface and may occasionally require chalking. From the limited data available on their phosphate and potash status, it appears that, whereas the soils are not notably deficient in either nutrient, the natural reserves are commonly insufficient to meet the needs of present-day cropping, so that regular additions will normally be required.

Cowcroft Complex

This miscellaneous group of soils is of limited agricultural importance on the Chilterns, although the series represented are widely distributed on Eocene outcrops elsewhere. Apart from the small acreage of easy-working fine sandy loam (Bursledon series), the predominant soils are pebbly loams and clay loams overlying impervious clay, the chief distinguishing feature of which is a general tendency to seasonal wetness, accentuated locally by the occurrence of springs and seepages. Where the surface horizons are relatively coarse-textured, they tend to lie wet in winter, but dry out and become very compact in summer; often, however, both soil texture and hydrologic conditions vary considerably within a field, so that the soils dry out at different rates, causing difficulty in the timing of cultivations.

Because of defective drainage, these soils are less well adapted to arable cultivation than the adjoining Berkhamsted and St. Albans soils, and therefore are often maintained under grass. As they are naturally acid and poorly supplied with both phosphate and potash, optimum productivity of crops and grass is dependent on adequate additions of lime and fertilizers.

Gade Complex

This alluvial land is chiefly utilized for grazing or for hay, the irregular occurrence of defective drainage conditions and the uneven surface often making it ill-suited to arable cultivation. Some of the soils have a sub-surface horizon of coarse gravel and are liable to dry out excessively in summer, whilst those which are deeper and more humose are "puffy" and difficult to consolidate when ploughed from old grass. During the 1939–45 war, crops grown on such land were affected by manganese deficiency, oats in particular showing symptoms of grey speck (Gardner, 1960).

Although much of the land is only waterlogged in the wettest seasons, there are fields and parts of fields in each of the main valleys where the water-table rises regularly to near the surface and the grass is consequently of poor quality. Some of these lie too low in relation to the stream to drain satisfactorily, but others could be improved by ditching or by tile-drainage.

Some of the higher-lying soils may be acid, but the majority are well supplied with lime. The main fertilizer requirement is potash, since reserves are commonly low.

SOILS OF THE AYLESBURY VALE

Aylesbury Series

Soils of this series afford useful arable land, and are capable of growing excellent crops of cereals, roots and clover. Although their capacity to supply moisture is restricted to some extent by the proximity of limestone rock, they are normally less subject to this limitation than the brashy soils of the Sherborne (Avery, 1955) and related series on older Jurassic limestones. As a rule, the weathered subsoil is readily exploited by roots to a depth of at least 18 in., and it is only occasionally that compact limestone is near enough to the surface to cause crops and grass to suffer severely from drought. Tree roots commonly penetrate the fissured and rubbly substratum to considerably greater depths, and may be able to withdraw moisture held in the sandy beds below the limestone. Locally, however, rock bands may restrict growth to a marked degree and, as lime-induced chlorosis is also liable to occur, the soils cannot be generally recommended for fruit growing.

Before fertilizers were generally used, the soils were noted for their inherent fertility (Read, 1855), probably because they contain useful reserves of both phosphate and potash.

Halton Complex and Gubblecote Series

From a land-use point of view, the stiff calcareous soils of the Halton and Burwell series are intermediate in character between those of the Wantage series and the still heavier Wicken clays. Compared with the latter, they are richer in calcium carbonate and lower in clay, and hence can be brought more readily to a fine tilth, but as they are deeper and less well drained than the Wantage soils they tend to dry out more slowly and are more liable to poaching by stock. Whereas the Burwell soils are virtually free of stones, those of the Halton series are flinty and may have gravelly layers in the subsoil, but stones are rarely present in sufficient quantity to interfere with cultivation, and crops withstand drought well, often doing best in a dry season.

The Gubblecote soils are similar in most respects to those of the Halton series, the main differences being their somewhat coarser texture, and uniformly gravelly subsoil. Owing to the retentive nature of the upper horizons, and the presence of impervious marl or clay below the gravel, crops rarely suffer unduly from drought, and drainage by pipes and ditches is often beneficial in reducing the prevailing tendency to winter waterlogging.

Although difficult to work in wet seasons, the soils of these series are highly productive of cereals and leys when well managed; their natural nutrient status is high, so fertilizers should be used judiciously in accordance with previous cropping and the results of soil analyses. Some types of fruit, particularly plums, are grown successfully on the Burwell and Halton soils, but chlorosis due to iron or manganese deficiency is liable to occur, and in places the trees may be adversely affected by winter waterlogging of the roots. Symptoms of manganese deficiency also appear occasionally in other crops, notably oats, especially when the soil has been ploughed from old grass and is consequently high in organic matter (Gardner, 1960).

Harwell Complex

Although of high inherent fertility, the variants of the Harwell and Ardington series in this complex are generally stiffer and less well drained than in the Berkshire area where the series were first described, and are therefore less well suited to arable farming. Relatively free-working loams occur around Elles-borough and Kimble, where the substrata include layers of malmstone, but drainage is impeded to some extent by the intervening marl bands, and the presence of Gault at no great depth causes springs and sub-surface seepage. Elsewhere the soils are mainly dark grey retentive clay loams, which are friable at the surface under old grass, but become very cohesive when the organic-matter content is reduced by continued cultivation. Under good management, however, they will grow excellent crops, and are capable of supporting highly productive pastures. Owing to the slow and locally defective drainage conditions, they are less well suited to fruit growing than those on the Upper Greensand of Berkshire, where the Harwell series in particular produces good crops of apples and cherries.

Most of the soils have a near-neutral reaction, and many contain significant amounts of calcium carbonate, either in the surface or at depth, but others require liming from time to time. Owing to the presence in the parent rocks of glauconite and phosphatic deposits, the Ardington soils in particular have an unusually high inherent ability to supply the potash and phosphate require-ments of crops, so that, except where soil analyses indicate a definite deficiency of one or other of these nutrients, lower-than-average fertilizer dressings can safely be recommended. Soils of the Harwell series also have good reserves of potash, though the phosphate status may be low.

Wicken, Challow and Denchworth Series

These predominantly clay soils afford some of the heaviest land in England, and in common with all such soils the main factors limiting their utilization are seasonal wetness and the difficulty of obtaining a suitable tilth for drilling seeds at appropriate times of the year. Because of these limitations, much of the land is retained under grass, but this also requires very careful management to prevent deterioration. Without adequate drainage, lime and phosphate, the better grasses tend to be displaced by bent, tufted hair-grass and other inferior species; and damage by poaching results if stock are kept on the land in winter. Well managed permanent grassland produces a great bulk of herbage, but the grazing season is short, and pastures are rarely as drought-resistant as on medium-textured soils with favourable water relations. On slopes an appreciable propor-tion of the winter rain may run off, whilst the cracks developed in drought periods damage plant roots, and subsequent rain runs down them without relieving the moisture deficit in the top-soil.

Leys are not so easily established as on lighter soils and when young do not carry stock so well as the old pastures; but experience here and elsewhere has shown that with improved methods of establishment and management a greatly increased output per acre can be achieved by farming the land on a rotation of 3–5 years ley, followed by 2 or more cereal crops. For successful arable cropping, however, efficient artificial drainage is essential, and sufficient tractor power and appropriate implements must be available, so that cultivations can be performed rapidly and thoroughly in the short periods when soil conditions are suitable. Where satisfactory drainage can be achieved, ploughing to a depth of 12 in. or more in autumn is often advantageous in causing the soil to dry out earlier in the spring, although the benefit may be lost if the land is subsequently worked too deeply and clods brought to the surface. Spring-sown cereals do well when satisfactory seed-beds can be prepared in due time, but autumn-sown crops are less risky and are therefore preferred. Modern stiff-strawed varieties of wheat, such as Cappelle, Holdfast and Hybrid 46, are less liable to lodge after ploughed-up grass than the older varieties, and are capable of yielding 2 tons/acre or more under favourable conditions. Unfortunately, however, a succession of autumn-sown crops is liable to lead to infestation by weeds such as wild oats (*Avena fatua*) and black-grass (*Alopecurus myosuroides*), which cannot yet be controlled in a cereal crop by herbicides, so that occasional fallows may be necessary.

Presumably because of their calcareous nature and good natural structure, the Wicken soils are less prone to surface waterlogging than those of the Denchworth series, and are more easily drained and maintained in a productive condition. Experiments conducted on a Denchworth soil by Fourt (1960) confirm that pipe-drains spaced at intervals of 7 yards or less may be required to produce a marked improvement. The main reason for this is that water movement when the soils are saturated is confined almost entirely to the uppermost 12 in., with the result that the drains "attract" water only for a negligible distance on either side. They will, however, intercept water flowing down a slope; hence drain-lines making as small an angle as possible with the contour are likely to be most economical and efficient. Mole drains can be drawn at 9 ft. or less apart at very much lower cost than adequate tile-drainage, and are often equally effective, provided that the subsoil contains few gravelly or sandy pockets and that mains and out-falls are adequate. The Challow soils are normally associated with almost flat and depressed topography and consequently are difficult to drain satisfactorily; to prevent winter waterlogging, many fields require an efficient ditch on all four sides, and pipe-drainage may be essential, since gradients are often too gentle for effective mole draining.

With adequate drainage apples, particularly culinary varieties, can be grown successfully on the Wicken clays. The trees do not increase in size as rapidly as on coarser-textured soils, but eventually make large trees which crop well over a long period. Chlorosis due to iron or manganese deficiency is liable to occur, though to a lesser extent than on the Chalk Marl. Little fruit is grown on the Challow and Denchworth soils, and their drainage is generally too poor for them to be recommended for this purpose.

Typical Wicken clays are too calcareous to benefit from liming, but the Denchworth soils may have a high lime requirement, and those of the Challow complex are frequently non-calcareous at the surface. Even where the soils are not sufficiently acid to require liming for this reason, addition of calcium carbonate appears to improve their structure and working qualities, and there is also evidence (Childs, 1943) that drains in clay soils are less prone to silting where lime has been applied.

Except where thin drift gives rise to loamy surface horizons, the soils are generally good suppliers of potassium. Owing to the occurrence of phosphatic seams in the Gault, some of the Wicken clays are also high in phosphate, but on most of the soils phosphate is the main fertilizer required, and is particularly valuable in the improvement of grassland. The thick dark-coloured A horizons formed under well managed grass are rich in nitrogen, much of which may become available to subsequent crops when the land is ploughed, so that lower-than-average dressings of nitrogenous fertilizers will commonly be sufficient. To a considerable extent, however, the ability of the soils to supply nitrogen to plants from accumulated reserves is dependent on favourable structure and water relations, and is greatly restricted where waterlogging occurs so that in wet seasons autumn-sown crops are liable to exhibit nitrogen-deficiency symptoms in the spring.

Bierton Complex

These mainly medium-textured soils are more friable, and afford a more favourable medium for root development, than those of the adjacent clay-lands, and some are sufficiently deep and well drained for any crop to thrive. In the commoner variants, percolation is impeded at moderate depths by the underlying Kimmeridge Clay, giving rise to a fluctuating water-table which may rise to the surface in winter. Provided that surface waterlogging is prevented, the presence of a permanently moist substratum is conducive to the maintenance of high-quality pastures, and with adequate under-drainage most crops can be grown successfully.

Most of the soils are calcareous, but the less well drained variants are sometimes acid and may be expected to benefit from liming. As on the Upper Greensand, glauconite and phosphatic nodules in the parent materials can afford useful reserves of potash and phosphate.

Weston Turville Series and Rowsham Complex

The potentialities of these drift-derived soils are largely dependent on drainage conditions, which vary in accordance with relief, and with the thickness and permeability of the horizons overlying the clay substrata. Gravel layers, where present, are rarely of sufficient thickness to provide good natural drainage and, as the subsoils are often ill suited to mole draining, an efficient system of pipes and ditches is commonly necessary to prevent seasonal waterlogging in the root zone.

The flinty clay loams and sandy clay loams of the Weston Turville series form useful arable land when effectively drained, and very heavy crops of corn, kale and clover can be grown. Because of their relatively coarse texture, they can be tilled over longer periods than the nearby clay soils, and break down to give a finer, more crumbly seed-bed, but are more prone to run when wet. Owing to the danger of alternate winter waterlogging and summer drying out, the soils are only suited to fruit growing when adequately drained, and where gravel layers do not occur within 18 in. of the surface. In this respect they resemble soils of the Badsey and related series in the Vale of Evesham (Osmond *et al.*, 1949).

The soils included in the Rowsham complex are more variable. In small areas near Wingrave there are moderately well drained stony loams overlying gravel, but otherwise the soils are normally less gravelly and less well drained than those of the Weston Turville series, and often lie too wet in winter for successful arable cropping, even though they are easily worked when sufficiently dry.

The proximity of gravel layers to the surface may locally cause grassland to "burn" in drought periods, but the deeper variants of the Weston Turville series and certain of the Rowsham soils are capable of supporting highly productive swards. As appears from the observations of Read (1855),* the fattening pastures for which the Vale was formerly famed were mainly located on these drift-derived soils, rather than on the little-modified clays. Some of the finest pastures were on soils derived partly from Portlandian rocks, such as occur in small areas north of Bierton, whereas others were on the Weston Turville series at Broughton House, east of Aylesbury. Probably the most important factor affecting the establishment and maintenance of these high-quality pastures was the manner in which they were managed, whereby the fields were rested in winter and heavily grazed by mature stock during the flush period. However, the type of soil is undoubtedly an important pre-disposing factor, and more recent observations indicate that permanent grassland of the highest quality is generally associated with fertile loamy soils which are sufficiently permeable and well aerated to permit free growth of roots, and yet have subsoil horizons which remain moist for the greater part of the year. The profiles of such soils show little or no gleying in the upper 12 in., and humus is fairly evenly distributed to at least this depth. In the Vale, as elsewhere, however, these characteristics are partly dependent on management. Thus, where seasonal waterlogging or excessive poaching occur, or where acidity or nutrient deficiencies have been allowed to develop, poor quality swards which suffer badly from drought may be found on soils with otherwise favourable characteristics.

Both Weston Turville and Rowsham soils are liable to become moderately acid at the surface, especially under old grass, so that dressings of lime may be required at intervals. Potash deficiency is more likely to arise, especially in the coarser-textured variants, than on the clay soils. To judge from the limited data available, the phosphate status is commonly high, but varies with past manurial treatment and the source of the materials composing the drift. Average responses to nitrogenous fertilizers may be expected when crops are grown in arable rotation, and the results of a recent manurial experiment (N.A.A.S. South-eastern Region Experiments Committee, 1959) on spring wheat (Atson) at the County Farm, Stoke Mandeville, indicate that modern cereal varieties will give profitable increases in yield, even where the initial nutrient status of the

---

* "There are general features about rich grazing lands which strike the eye of the stranger. They have a luxuriant and deep-coloured herbage, and mostly a gentle undulation, are raised rather above the level meadows, and wherever they are found there is a foot or two of rich earth incumbent on the clay subsoil. In some places this rich deposit is evidently the washings from the Portland oolite which occupies the higher ground; in some places the small granulated pebbles of the Lower Greensand have been discovered, but more generally there is nothing for the geologist to show from what formations this valuable deposit is derived."

soil is high. This experiment tested the effects of broadcasting and combine-drilling 0·3 and 0·6 cwt. N per acre and of combine-drilling 0·22 and 0·45 cwt. K_2O, all plots receiving 0·3 cwt. P_2O_5 per acre drilled with the seed. An average yield of 41 cwt. per acre was obtained with no added nitrogen, and broadcasting 0·6 cwt. nitrogen on the seed-bed increased the yield to 49 cwt. No significant effect from added potash was recorded, nor was there any significant advantage in combine-drilling the nitrogen.

Ford End and Mead Series

The potentialities of these alluvial soils are limited to varying degrees by seasonal wetness, and locally by liability to flooding. Where drainage is relatively good, as on the Ford End series at Ivinghoe Aston, most arable crops can be grown successfully and the soils are distinctly easier to work than the adjoining clays. The finer-textured Mead soils along the Thistle Brook and its tributaries are generally unsuited to regular cultivation, and are mainly under grass, much of which is of low quality. Drainage of this low-lying land is rendered especially difficult by lack of fall, and is primarily dependent on regular clearance of the Thame and of the drains and ditches feeding it, but this alone will not prevent winter waterlogging unless backed by an efficient system of pipe-drains or surface grips to lead water off the fields.

Where recently ploughed from old grass, the soils have a high content of organic matter and are therefore relatively easy to work when sufficiently dry, but their "puffy" consistency makes it difficult to achieve the degree of consolidation necessary for the satisfactory establishment of small seeds. Consequently, attempts to improve the quality of the grassland by ploughing and re-seeding may be disappointing, especially in dry seasons. According to Hughes and Gwynne (1961), however, the difficulty may be overcome by using a rotary cultivator to prepare the seed-bed.

The soils are rarely acid, but are often deficient in readily available potash; and sufficient phosphate may also be lacking. Those which have been long under grass are rich in organic nitrogen, which is only slowly mineralized as long as the drainage remains poor. When such land is cultivated, there is a tendency for crops to suffer from manganese and copper deficiencies.

CHAPTER VII

Forestry

J. M. B. Brown (Forestry Commission)

With regard to forestry as a form of land use, the area may be divided into three sections, namely (1) the Vale, east of Aylesbury; (2) the eastern Chiltern district around Hemel Hempstead; (3) the western Chiltern district, centred on Hampden and Great Missenden. As noted in Chapter I, the well-watered Vale of Aylesbury was cleared for agriculture at an early date, and has remained very sparsely wooded for many centuries. Small park and covert woods, mainly of oak (*Quercus robur*), elm (*Ulmus* spp.) and other broad-leaf trees, occur here and there on the clay soils of the plain, serving to break the uniformity of the landscape but making no significant contribution to the pattern of land use. Compared with the Vale, the Chiltern Plateau has remained relatively well wooded, but woods are much less extensive in the eastern, mainly Hertfordshire, division than in the western, mainly Buckinghamshire division; and as already noted the Hertfordshire area is further distinguished by the replacement of beech (*Fagus sylvatica*) by oak as the dominant tree. The Chiltern area west of (and including) Ashridge Park, in which the woods are dominated by beech, thus provides the principal focus of interest, and may be considered as representative of the more widespread wooded region on similar terrain, which extends south-westward into Oxfordshire.

Historical Note

The modern history of the Chiltern woodlands may reasonably be said to begin about 1800. It has been shown by Mansfield (1952) that during the 17th and 18th centuries beech was normally treated as coppice, usually with standards, among which oak, and sometimes ash (*Fraxinus excelsior*), were more important than they are today. The beech coppice was exploited mainly for fuel, of which large quantities were sent to towns in the Vale and to London, while the standards provided timber for constructional work or repairs, and for various small woodworking industries, besides making some contribution, in the case of the oak, to the needs of the Navy.

In the latter part of the 18th century, changing circumstances profoundly affected the character and distribution of the woodlands, gradually moulding them into the form familiar to visitors in the first half of the present century. One of the most influential changes was the completion of the Grand Junction Canal (linking the Midlands directly with London) in 1805, ensuring cheap supplies of coal to consumers formerly largely dependent on the produce of the beech coppices of the Chilterns. Another was the considerable rise in the price of corn, due both to the rapid increase in population and to the partial blockade of Britain during the Napoleonic wars. Many beech coppice woods, now no longer profitable, were grubbed and the land used for agriculture, which contemporary improvements in farming practice were calculated to make more productive. Side by side with these changes, which resulted in a reduction of the area under forest on many estates, was the steady growth of small wood-working industries based on beech. During the 19th century the chair-making industry, centred on High Wycombe, provided a convenient market for beech timber and this helps to explain why the conversion of woodland to arable was not taken further.

The Enclosure movement of the late 18th and early 19th century was yet another decisive influence, for neither the clearance and cultivation of former coppice woods nor the systematic planting of scrub land could have been under-taken without the exclusion of grazing animals. Certain woods, for example Hillock Wood on the Hampden Estate, are known to have developed spon-taneously into beech or oak-beech high forest from commons or scrubs enclosed about this time: some trees still retain the marks of their coppice origin. Some-times enclosures depended on private arrangements between landlord and commoners, sometimes on Parliamentary Enclosure Acts. It may be surmised that much more opposition would have been encountered had not the fuel problem been solved by the coal brought by canal from the Midlands.

During the 19th century the High Wycombe furniture industry steadily expanded and the Chiltern beechwoods were increasingly managed with a view to supplying this principal market. The woods were exploited on a selection system, with no clear falls. They were worked through at intervals of 8–15 years and at each coupe the larger, together with a proportion of smaller, trees were removed. The small produce was commonly worked into chair legs, etc. on the site by itinerant turners, or "bodgers", operating their own lathes, while the larger material went to the factories. On many estates the interval between coupes was clearly prescribed in a plan of management and the exploitable forest was so divided that a block was due to be worked over, or "drawn", each year. It seems, however, that little attempt was made, by means of regular enumerations or otherwise, to control the quantity and quality of the produce so as to ensure a sustained yield. As long as there was a ready sale for small trees, and the marking was supervised by experienced agents or woodmen, the system seems to have proved satisfactory and the natural regeneration was not completely extinguished.

By the beginning of the 20th century, increasing mechanisation in the furni-ture industry began to cripple the trade of the local turners of chair legs, and so reduced the demand for small trees. At the same time the increasing use of imported timber weakened the ties between the High Wycombe chair manu-facturers and the producers of beech timber in the Chilterns. As a result, coupes became less regular, or were so arranged that only large, well-formed trees were taken, so that the stand became overstocked with small, sometimes malformed trees, increment suffered, little seed was produced by exiguous crowns and any regeneration was shaded out (Plate IX). In these circumstances some woodland owners adopted a group system of management to promote natural regeneration, or in some cases resorted to planting (Plate X).

During the war of 1939–45 exceptionally heavy demands were made on the Chiltern beechwoods, first for the production of rifle butts and later for ply-wood used in the manufacture of Mosquito aircraft. To a large extent the demands were met by heavy selection fellings: some woods were cleared entirely, in others group regeneration fellings were adopted, while in yet others the exploitation amounted in intensity to a shelterwood regeneration felling. There was thus a partial break with tradition, which was carried further when the woods were restocked, often by planting and sometimes with trees other than beech. Twenty-five years before this the difficulties attending the natural regeneration of beech had been thoroughly examined by Watt (1923), and the war emergency greatly hindered owners from conducting fellings in such a way and at such a time as to favour regeneration. Nevertheless the substantial mast in the autumn of 1944 produced good crops of seedlings in many Chiltern beechwoods, and further abundant masts in 1948 and 1950 were effective here and there, but the woods heavily opened out during the war had by then been invaded by a more or less profuse vegetation of brambles or grasses, and beech seedlings suffered from competition. Many owners were, therefore, constrained to restock woods by planting, making use of the opportunity to introduce a proportion of conifers and so to enhance the expected financial return. Planta-tions of conifers, mostly of European larch (*Larix decidua*), had been made previously on many estates (Plate XI), some on abandoned agricultural land, but only the youngest survived the war.

The woodlands of the eastern section of the sheet, in Hertfordshire, were in some degree subject to the same economic and social pressures as those in the west. As beech was less important and oak more so, they were less affected by the declining demand for fuel from beech coppices and by the improvement in the price offered for beech timber when the High Wycombe chair industry expanded in the 19th century. In the area connected with this industry there is little doubt that for a time forestry enjoyed a moderate prosperity such as was matched in few other areas of British broad-leaf forest. In Hertfordshire some hazel or hornbeam coppice with oak standards was replaced by oak high forest and some was devastated during two wars. The 1954 revision of the Census of Woodlands accordingly shows a relatively lower incidence of woodland and a higher proportion of scrub in this section.

Area, Composition and Present Condition of the Woods

Over the sheet as a whole, forest, as surveyed in the 1947 Census of Woodland (1954 revision for Hertfordshire), occupies about 11,200 acres (c. 8 per cent) or, excluding those areas classed as scrub, 9,000 acres (6·5 per cent). As noted in the introduction, the proportions are very different in the three arbitrary sections into which the sheet is divided.

Coppice and coppice-with-standards now occupy a very small proportion of the total woodland area (excluding scrub), and of the 7,430 acres of high forest, 5,750 were classed as broad-leaf, 710 as coniferous and 970 was mixed: recent planting has altered these figures somewhat in favour of the last category. Nearly all is in private ownership: Forestry Commission holdings, of which the most important is Wendover Forest, scarcely amount to 1,000 acres.

Beech is still the principal species and likely to remain so, partly because of the importance of amenity in a residential and tourist district within 40 miles of London. But the traditional methods of beech growing are being generally superseded, for both economic and silvicultural reasons.

The selection system, as practised in the 19th and the first half of the 20th century, yielded an excessive proportion of small trees and it is considered that an even-aged high forest, or a group system, might be managed more effectively to produce trees of the required dimensions. An even-aged beech forest yields very little material of value for many years; therefore an admixture of conifers, which can be profitably harvested at an intermediate stage, is becoming customary.

Moreover the selection system depended on natural regeneration, which costs very little if successful, but owners have become more and more dismayed by the frequent failure of the woods to regenerate naturally, and the widely practised initial cultivation of the ground at seed fall ("scarifying"), although showing some striking successes, has proved no panacea. Accordingly there is an increasing tendency to forgo natural regeneration and to replant the woods with beech (commonly mixed with a conifer) derived from superior stands outside the Chilterns. On the Hampden Estate several woods are being regenerated in this way, a light cover of old beeches being left to nurse the plantation and enhance the appearance of the wood during the transition period.

The High Wycombe furniture factories, offering a good price for trees of 18 in. diameter and over, are still the main market for beech timber. Recently, moreover, the Sudbrook Pulpwood Factory, Monmouthshire, utilizing hardwood thinnings, has collected produce from the Chiltern beechwoods, thereby providing an incentive to owners to thin stands at the appropriate time. The alien grey squirrel remains a scourge; unless more effective methods of repression can be devised it will greatly increase costs of production of beech timber, and may even lead to abandonment of beech (and of sycamore) in some cases. Deer (mostly fallow) are also injurious, but more restricted in occurrence.

Oaks (*Quercus robur* and *Q. petraea*) are the most important of the other broad-leaf trees and tend to replace the beech in Hertfordshire. Formerly oak was more frequent, forming a substantial proportion of the standards above the beech coppice, but as demand for the timber tended to exceed supply, oak probably became scarcer, and when woods were regenerated during the 19th century beech appeared to offer better prospects to the owners. It is thus at least partly due to historical circumstances that beech dominates the woodlands of the Buckinghamshire Chilterns: none the less, both in the slightly cooler and moister climate (at altitudes up to 800 ft.) and in the frequency of calcareous soils, the area around Hampden and Missenden differs ecologically from the eastern area around Hemel Hempstead, conditions tending to favour beech in the former and oak in the latter. There is very little current planting of oak on the Chilterns.

No other broad-leaf tree calls for much comment. Ash, though seldom planted, is a frequent tree, arising spontaneously in gaps and clearings. Sycamore (*Acer pseudoplatanus*) has been planted here and there, notably at Ashridge, and is well suited to deep base-rich soils on cool exposures but, like beech, it is very vulnerable to the grey squirrel. On the acid soils, birches (*Betula verrucosa*, *B. pubescens*) often appear spontaneously after felling.

Conifers, occupying some 700 acres, have only recently played any great part in the forest economy. In 1947 many estates had small plantations of European larch, but apart from the native yew (*Taxus baccata*), frequent on some chalk slopes, evergreens were less common. There were, however, occasional plantations of Norway spruce (*Picea abies*), Scots pine (*Pinus silvestris*), Corsican pine (*P. nigra* ssp. *laricio*) and Douglas fir (*Pseudotsuga taxifolia*), notably on the Air Ministry's Halton Wood property, subsequently acquired by the Forestry Commission as Wendover Forest. Numerous mixed plantations of beech and a conifer, usually larch, spruce, Douglas fir or Corsican pine, have been made during the past decade; pure plantations of conifers are in the main eschewed on the score of amenity.

Forestry and the Soil Series

In regard to the silvicultural significance of the soil series, there are four main aspects which merit consideration.

(1) In some measure the partition of land between forestry and other uses is dependent on soil properties.

(2) Sometimes, though less often than one might wish, the soil has influenced the choice of species and the silvicultural treatment.

(3) Physical and chemical soil properties affect the performance of the trees, the rate of growth and the general health; in mixed woods the ultimate composition may be determined by the soil.

(4) A tree cover affects the course of soil development.

(1) The evidence summarized in the historical notes makes it clear that there has been give and take between forestry and other forms of land use. The general slow reduction of the area under forest has been offset in some degree by the spontaneous invasion of bushes and, later, trees on forsaken commons, and by the planting of woods on agricultural land when corn prices were low, or when new estates were laid out. Through these vicissitudes, woodland tended to persist on the steep slopes of the escarpment and main valleys, and generally on soils which were shallow, stony, or otherwise intractable. There is accordingly a rather high proportion of forest on soils of the Icknield series and Coombe complex on the escarpment and the slopes of dry valleys. The escarpment was formerly used as sheep-walk: some has become colonized by trees, but much seems likely to persist as chalk grassland or scrub, because seed trees are few, rabbits are plentiful and the dry soil and absence of shelter provide a harsh environment for young trees (Plate VIIIb). Woods are also relatively frequent at the crest of the scarp and on ridge margins occupied by soils of the Winchester series, and on adjoining areas of the Batcombe or Berkhamsted series. These soils are normally more flinty or pebbly than those on the broader ridge-tops and are therefore less easy to work. In a few localities, however, substantial areas of relatively stone-free Batcombe soils are under forest. The distribution of the woods is thus not anomalous: in many cases the topography, or the physical properties of the soil, appear to have played an important part in determining their situation.

(2) There is less evidence of a relationship between soil variation and the choice of tree or treatment. As explained above, the former composition of the

woods was largely determined by the demand for beech and oak timber of different dimensions, the fortuitous occurrence of natural seedlings and the incidence of grazing. Active intervention by the owner was slight before the 19th century when the establishment, or maintenance, of a self-perpetuating beech forest, with or without some oak, appeared a sound investment. But the preponderance of oak on the predominantly non-calcareous and often imperfectly drained soils in the eastern part of the area can scarcely be without significance as indicating reduced competitive power of the beech. On calcareous soils, beechwoods have frequently arisen by colonization of scrub and clearly represent a natural climax, although on the driest chalk slopes exposed to the west and south beechwood may fail to maintain itself, yielding place to xerophile scrub or yew (Plate VIIIb). On non-calcareous soils, both ash and oak appear as important elements in the natural succession and are also represented in many of the mature beechwoods, ash reaching its maximum development on near-neutral soils, and disappearing on more acid soils where oak increases in frequency. Watt (1934) presents clear evidence that beech will supplant oak on well drained, acid soils in this area, providing conditions are favourable for its regeneration, but where drainage is impeded oak may represent the climax-dominant. It seems probable (Godwin, 1956) that in the Atlantic and Sub-Boreal periods the primaeval forest on the Chiltern Plateau was dominated by oak, and that the beech first gained entrance by colonizing the shallow calcareous soils of the scarp and the steeper valley sides, possibly after partial clearances had been effected by prehistoric agriculturalists. If this was the case, the comparative scarcity of beech in the semi-natural woods of Hertfordshire may result partly from the character of the soils, since thin chalky soils which could have acted as foci for beech invasion become increasingly widespread west of the Buckinghamshire border.

Because of the traditional dependence on beech and oak, there is not much experience of the performance of other trees, but the detailed information now available about the soils can be combined with experience from other parts of Southern England in prescriptions for admixture of the beech with different conifers according to site. Hitherto no conifer, apart from the Austrian pine (*Pinus nigra*) has been found wholly reliable on shallow calcareous soils of the Icknield series.

(3) In relating performance to soil the forester is very largely dependent on the statistics for beech. Records of beech growth from the area under consideration have been supplemented by those from comparable soils in other parts of the Chilterns to provide more than 40 sets of data covering all the soil mapping units occupying significant areas. As noted by Watt (1934), there is evidence of a relation between soil and the mature height of the beech, but in many instances it is obscured or over-ridden by the influence of topography, or by treatment. As to the latter factor, it should be pointed out that many stands gave evidence, in the butt ring-count, of many years of retarded early growth, suggesting inhibition under the shade of taller trees. Growth would doubtless have been better generally, and the records more fit for comparison, had all the stands been raised under some uniform system, whether by planting or by natural regeneration. The effects of elevation, aspect and exposure to wind are clearly important, as would be expected in the dissected Chiltern country.

For example, on the Winchester series stands of Quality I* (100 ft. at age 100) or II (90 ft.) occur on a sheltered slope with south-east aspect at Frithsden on the Ashridge Estate; and Quality II on the moderate north-facing slope of a wide valley near West Wycombe: whereas on the exposed brow of the escarpment facing west-north-west the Hale Wood beech was rated Quality V (60 ft.) and a stand on Crowell Hill, Oxon. scarcely better.

Quality V or IV was shown by stands on the Icknield series (steepland phase) on the main escarpment: better growth would be expected on sheltered valley sides, but the Icknield series is potentially rather unproductive on account of its shallowness and dryness, and the tendency for the trees to suffer from lime-induced chlorosis. Growth is variable on soils of the Coombe complex, ranging from Quality I or II on a sheltered north-facing valley side near Chesham, to Quality IV; whereas the Winchester soils, as already noted, show an even wider range among the 16 stands represented. Probably because of their lower base status, soils of the Batcombe series are in general less fertile, and they seldom occupy fully sheltered positions so that Quality III or IV is usual, the best growth being recorded in Penn Wood, Bucks. (82 ft. at age 90) and the worst (70 ft. at age 140) on a weakly podzolized soil with mor humus in Fugsdon Wood, near Wendover. In localities subject to soil and atmospheric drought, exemplified by the steepland phase of the Icknield series, cambial injuries to the beech, sometimes followed by death of the tree, may occur. This "beech bark disease" is often associated with cankers occupied by a fungus (*Nectria* sp.) or, at a later stage, with decay of the heartwood ("beech snap disease"), in which more than one kind of fungus is involved, but the fundamental cause appears to be physical, in this instance drought.

Examination of beech growth in relation to soil series thus reinforces the conclusion previously reached (Brown, 1953) that, near the two extremes of rendzina and podzol, the yield of beech is moderate to poor: on the intermediate brown earth and brown calcareous soils growth is generally superior, but is greatly influenced by the factors of relief and microclimate. On the whole the height growth of beech on the Chilterns compares unfavourably with that on the South Downs and the Cotswold Hills, and it has often been suggested that long continued beech selection forest has impaired the genetic quality of the stock, or impoverished the soil ("beech-sickness"), or both. These possibilities should not be discounted, but it may nevertheless be argued that the observed differences can be at least partly accounted for in terms of climate and soil. Ecologically the beech is thoroughly at home on the Chilterns, more especially on well drained soils of high base status. More exacting broad-leaved trees like ash, sycamore, or Wych elm (*Ulmus glabra*), may find a place on sheltered sites occupied by soils of the Winchester series, or Charity or Coombe complex, particularly on cool aspects. Oak, on the other hand, is well suited on less well drained soils of the Batcombe and Berkhamsted series and is peculiarly fitted to make the best of those soils (e.g. Cowcroft series) in which gleying is a prominent feature. In admixture with beech on these soils the oak reaches a height of 80–90 ft.

---

* In forestry, sites are classified in accordance with the yield of each species grown on them, a convenient index of site quality being the mean height (now more usually the mean height of the 100 largest trees per acre) at a given age. For beech in Britain, five site classes, represented by dominant heights of 100, 90, 80, 70 and 60 ft. respectively, at age 100 years, are recognized.

Among the conifers the larches, which have generally been favoured in the past, appear well suited, except on the more gleyed soils and on shallow calcareous soils of the Icknield series and Coombe complex. There are few existing stands of pine, which is suitable for planting in admixture with other trees on soils of the St. Albans and Berkhamsted series, and generally in frosty valley bottoms. The Corsican pine has shown promise on calcareous soils (Icknield and Coombe series) but is not wholly resistant to lime-induced chlorosis. Up to middle age the Norway spruce appears resistant to chlorosis, but the performance of small stands cut down during the war indicates that the yield is poor and butt-decay prevalent. On the other hand Douglas fir, scarcely planted in the Chilterns hitherto, may well have a future on soils of satisfactory drainage and moderate fertility (e.g. Winchester series and better drained examples of Batcombe and Berkhamsted soils) in situations which are not greatly exposed. The Western hemlock (*Tsuga heterophylla*) and the Western red cedar (*Thuja plicata*), both trees with ornamental as well as timber value, have been planted here and there under existing light cover.

Information about the growth of conifers in the Chilterns is too scanty to form the basis of any reliable forecast of probable yields on the various soil series: in addition the height growth often appears to have been accelerated by the side shelter afforded by surrounding older beech and might therefore not be an accurate index. It may be suggested that the performance of the beech provides a good rough guide to the relative potentialities of the different soil series for the growth of most of the trees suited climatically.

(4) A full discussion of the influence of forest on the soil does not come within the scope of this chapter, but the subject is too important to be ignored. Forests influence the soil generally by protecting the surface from erosion by wind or water, by modifying the climate near the ground, and in more specific ways that depend on the composition and density of the stand and on the type of litter it produces. The effect of beech forest in particular on the evolution of different types of soil has been discussed recently by Brown (1953) and by Bonneau and Duchaufour (1960). As Avery (1958) has shown, in the environment of the Chiltern beechwoods the slow decomposition of the litter on base-deficient soils (e.g. Batcombe and Berkhamsted series), or on acid soils with impeded drainage (e.g. Cowcroft series), affects the character of the humus layers and may lead to podzolization: but the phenomenon is in some degree dependent on the density of the canopy and the climate beneath the stand, as well as on the original character of the soil. Formerly the regular cutting of the coppice and the admixture of oak and ash, with sparser crowns and leaves less resistant to decomposition, may have tempered this tendency to "degradation" of the soil by the beech.

References

ARNOLD, P. W. (1958). *Potassium up-take by cation-exchange resins from soils and minerals.* Nature, Lond. **182**, 1594–5.

———————— (1960). *Potassium-supplying power of some British soils.* Nature, Lond. **187**, 436–7.

ARKELL, W. J. (1947). *The Geology of Oxford.* Oxford (Clarendon Press).

AVERY, B. W. (1955). *The Soils of the Glastonbury District of Somerset.* Mem. Soil Surv. London (H.M.S.O.).

———————— (1956). *A classification of British soils.* Rapp. 6th int. Congr. Soil Sci. E, 279–85.

———————— (1958). *A sequence of beechwood soils on the Chiltern Hills, England.* J. Soil Sci. **9**, 210–24.

AVERY, B. W., STEPHEN, I., BROWN, G. and YAALON, D. H. (1959). *The origin and development of Brown Earths on Clay-with-flints and Coombe Deposits.* J. Soil Sci. **10**, 177–95.

BARROW, G. (1919). *Some future work for the Geologists' Association.* Proc. Geol. Ass. Lond. **30**, 36–48.

BASCOMB, C. L. (1961). *A calcimeter for routine use on soil samples.* Chem. & Ind. No. 45, 1826–7.

BERESFORD, M. W. (1953). *Glebe terriers and open-field Buckinghamshire*, 2. Records of Bucks. **16**, 5–28.

BILHAM, E. G. (1938). *The Climate of the British Isles.* London (Macmillan).

BISHOP, W. W. (1958). *The Pleistocene geology and geomorphology of three gaps in the Midland Jurassic escarpment.* Phil. Trans. roy. Soc. Lond. B.**241**, 255–306.

BLOOMFIELD, C. (1951). *Experiments on the mechanism of gley formation.* J. Soil Sci. **2**, 196–221.

BONNEAU, M. and DUCHAUFOUR, Ph. (1960). *Les sols de la hetraie en Europe occidentale.* Bull. Inst. Agron. de Gembloux. **1**, 59–74.

BOUYOUCOS, G. J. (1951). *A recalibration of the Bouyoucos hydrometer method for the mechanical analysis of soils.* Agron. J. **43**, 434.

BREMNER, J. M. (1959). *Determination of fixed ammonium in soil.* J. agric. Sci. **53**, 147–60.

BROWN, G. (1954). *Soil morphology and mineralogy. A qualitative study of some gleyed soils from North-west England.* J. Soil Sci. **5**, 145–55.

BROWN, G. and FARROW, R. (1960). Priv. comm.

BROWN, J. M. B. (1953). *Studies on British Beechwoods.* Forestry Commission Bull. **20**. London (H.M.S.O.).

BUNTING, A. H. and ELSTON, J. (1962). Priv. comm.

CHILDS, E. C. (1943). *Studies in mole-draining. Interim report on an experimental drainage field.* J. agric. Sci. **33**, 136–46.

CLARKE, G. R. (1957). *The Study of the Soil in the Field.* 4th edition. Oxford (Clarendon Press).

COOK, R. S. and GILL, A. H. (1956). *Milk-selling farms of Buckinghamshire.* Misc. Publ. No. 9. Univ. of Reading Dept. of Agricultural Economics.

COOKE, G. W. (1959). *Fertilizers, crop production and soil fertility.* J. Farmer's Club. Pt. 5, 50–69.

COPPOCK, J. T. (1954). *Land-use changes in the Chilterns, 1931–1951.* Inst. British Geographers. Publ. No. 20, 113–39.

——————— (1957). *The changing arable in the Chilterns, 1875–1951.* Geography. **42**, 217–29.

——————— (1960). *Crop and livestock changes in the Chilterns, 1931–51.* Inst. British Geographers. Publ. No. 28, 179–98.

CRONEY, D. and COLEMAN, J. D. (1954). *Soil structure in relation to soil suction (pF).* J. Soil Sci. **5**, 78–94.

DARBY, H. C. and CAMPBELL, E. M. J. (Eds.). (1962). *The Domesday Geography of South-east England.* Cambridge (University Press).

DARWIN, C. (1881). *The Formation of Vegetable Mould through the Action of Worms, with Observations on their Habits.* London (Murray).

DAVIES, A. M. and BAINES, A. H. J. (1953). *A preliminary study of the sarsen and pudding-stone blocks of the Chilterns.* Proc. Geol. Ass. Lond. **64**, 1–9.

DAVIES, W. M. (1895). *On the origin of certain English rivers.* Geogr. J. **5**, 128–46.

DEB, B. C. (1950). *The estimation of free iron oxides in soils and clays and their removal.* J. Soil Sci. **1**, 212–20.

DECKERS, J. and VANSTALLEN, R. (1955). *Contribution a l'étude de la saturation en bases des sols bruns de l'Ardenne et de la Famenne.* Agricultura. **3**, 311–40.

DIMBLEBY, G. W. and GILL, J. M. (1955). *The occurrence of podzols under deciduous woodland in the New Forest.* Forestry. **28**, 95–106.

DINES, H. G., EDWARDS, W., HOLLINGWORTH, S. E., BUCHAN, S. and WELCH, F. B. A. (1940). *The mapping of Head deposits.* Geol. Mag. **77**, 198–226.

DUCHAUFOUR, Ph. (1960). *Précis de Pédologie.* Paris (Masson).

ELLIS, W. (1733). (2nd Edition, 1745). *Chiltern and Vale Farming explained.* London.

EVANS, P. and OAKLEY, K. P. (1952). *Field meeting in the Central Chilterns.* Proc. Geol. Ass. Lond. **63**, 59–62.

FOURT, D. F. (1961). *The drainage of a heavy clay site.* Rept. on Forest Research for the year ended March 1960, 137–51. London (H.M.S.O.).

GARDNER, H. W. (1958). *Variety and fertilizer trials with spring barley conducted for the Herts. Institute of Agriculture* (Unpublished MS.).

——————— (1959). *Manuring barley on Chalk.* Agriculture, Lond. **56**, 396–7.

——————— (1960). Priv. comm.

GARDNER, H. W. and GARNER, H. V. (1953). *The use of Lime in British Agriculture.* London (Farmer and Stockbreeder Publications).

GEIGER, R. (1950). *Climate near the Ground.* Harvard.

GILBERT, C. J. (1920). *On the occurrence of extensive deposits of high-level sands and gravels resting upon the Chalk at Little Heath, near Berkhamsted.* Quart. J. geol. Soc. Lond. **75**, 32–43.

————— (1924). *An address on local geology.* Trans. Herts. Nat. Hist. Soc. **18**, 88–92.

GODWIN, H. (1956). *The History of the British Flora.* Cambridge (University Press).

GREEN, F. H. W. (1940). *The Land of Britain: Hampshire.* London (Geographical Publications).

GREAVES, C. *et al.* (1876). *Discussion on rainfall, evaporation and percolation.* Proc Inst. Civil Engrs. Lond. **45**, 89.

HAWKE, E. L. (1944). *Thermal characteristics of a Hertfordshire frost-hollow.* Quart. J. R. met. Soc. **70**, 23–48.

HEAD, J. F. (1955). *Early Man in South Buckinghamshire.* Bristol (Wright).

HEY, R. W. and PERRIN, R. M. S. (1960). *The Geology and Soils of Cambridgeshire.* Cambridge Natural History Society.

HULL, E. and WHITAKER, W. (1861). *The Geology of parts of Oxfordshire and Berkshire.* Mem. Geol. Surv. U.K. London (H.M.S.O.).

HUGHES, G. P. and GWYNNE, G. W. (1961). *Improvement of pasture in east and south-east England.* Agriculture. Lond. **68**, 6–9.

KAY, F. F. (1934). *A Soil Survey of the Eastern Portion of the Vale of the White Horse.* Univ. Reading Bull. 48.

————— (1939). *A Soil Survey of the Strawberry District of South Hampshire.* Univ. Reading Bull. 52.

KERR, M. H. (1955). *On the occurrence of silcretes in southern England.* Proc. Leeds. phil. lit. Soc. **6**, 328–37.

KITSON, R. E. and MELLON, M. G. (1944). *Colorimetric determination of phosphorus as molybdovanado-phosphoric acid.* Industr. Engng. Chem. (Anal.). **16**, 379–83.

KONTA, J. (1955). *Montmorillonite and cristobalite in the clay of Kuzmice (East Slovakia).* Universitas Carolina Pragensis, Geologica. **1**, 165–76 (Czech with English summary).

KUBIENA, W. L. (1953). *The Soils of Europe.* London (Murby).

LOCKET, G. H. (1946). *A preliminary investigation of the availability to plants of the water in Chalk.* J. Ecol. **33**, 222–9.

LOVEDAY, J. (1962). *Plateau deposits of the southern Chiltern Hills.* Proc. Geol. Ass. Lond. **73**, 83–102.

LOW, A. J. and ARMITAGE, E. R. (1959). *Irrigation of grassland.* J. agric. Sci. **52**, 256–62.

LUCAS, J. (Transl.). (1892). *Kalm's Account of his visit to England on his way to America in 1748.* London (Macmillan).

MACKNEY, D. (1961). *A podzol development sequence in oakwoods and heath in Central England.* J. Soil. Sci **12**, 23–40.

MADOS, O. (1943). *Eine schnellmethode zur serienweisen Bestimmung der adsorptionsungesattigtheit von Boden.* Bodenk. u. PflErnahr. **32**, 351–8.

MANSFIELD, A. (1952). *Historical geography of the woodlands of the southern Chilterns.* M.Sc. Thesis. Lond. Univ.

McCONNELL, P. (1902). *Elements of Agricultural Geology.* London.

N.A.A.S. (SOUTH-EASTERN REGION EXPERIMENTS COMMITTEE). (1959). *Report on soil chemistry experiments* (unpublished).

NICHOLSON, H. H. (1935). *The drainage properties of heavy soils.* Trans. 3rd int. Congr. Soil Sci. **1**, 385–8.

OAKLEY, K. P. (1936). *Field meeting at Cheddington, Ivinghoe and Gubblecote.* Proc. Geol. Ass. Lond. **47**, 38–41.

———————— (1947). *Early man in Hertfordshire.* Trans. Herts. Nat. Hist. Soc. **22**, 247–56.

OLLIER, C. D. and THOMASSON, A. J. (1957). *Asymmetrical valleys of the Chiltern Hills.* Geogr. J. **123**, 71–80.

OSMOND, D. A., SWARBRICK, T., THOMPSON, C. R. and WALLACE, T. (1949). *A Survey of the Soils and Fruit in the Vale of Evesham.* Min. Agric. Bull. No. 116. London (H.M.S.O.).

PARKES, J. (1845). (i) *On the influence of water on the temperature of soils.* (ii) *On the quantity of rain-water and its discharge by drains.* J. R. agric. Soc. **5**, 119–58.

PENMAN, H. L. (1950). *Evaporation over the British Isles.* Quart. J. R. met. Soc. **76**, 372–83.

———————— (1962). *Woburn irrigation 1951–59. I. Purpose, design and weather. II. Results for grass. III. Results for rotation crops.* J. agric. Sci. **58**, 343–79.

PERRIN, R. M. S. (1956). *The nature of "Chalk Heath" soils.* Nature, Lond. **178**, 31–2.

———————— (1957). *The clay mineralogy of some tills in the Cambridge district.* Clay Min. Bull. **3**, 193–205.

PRESTWICH, J. (1854). *On the structure of the strata between the London Clay and the Chalk in the London and Hampshire Tertiary systems.* Quart. J. geol. Soc. Lond. **10**, 90.

PRIEST, ST. J. (1810). *General View of the Agriculture of Buckinghamshire.* London.

READ, C. S. (1855). *Report on the farming of Buckinghamshire.* J. R. agric. Soc. **16,** 269–322.

RICH, C. I. and THOMAS, G. W. (1960). *The clay fraction of soils.* Adv. Agron. **12**, 1–34.

ROBINSON, K. L. (1948). *The Soils of Dorset.* In GOOD, R. L. *A Geographical Handbook of the Dorset Flora.* Dorset Nat. Hist. and Archaeol. Soc.

RUSSELL, E. J. and KEEN, B. A. (1921). *The effect of chalk on the cultivation of heavy land.* J. Min. Agr. **28**, 419–22.

RUSSELL, E. W. (1961). *Soil Conditions and Plant Growth.* London (Longman).

SAWHNEY, B. L. (1958). *Aluminium interlayers in soil clay minerals, montmorillonite and vermiculite.* Nature, Lond. **182**, 1595-6.

SHERLOCK, R. L. and NOBLE, A. H. (1912). *On the glacial origin of the Clay-with-flints of Buckinghamshire and on a former course of the Thames.* Quart. J. geol. Soc. Lond. **68**, 199–212.

SHERLOCK, R. L. (1922). *The Geology of the Country around Aylesbury and Hemel Hempstead.* Mem. Geol. Surv. U.K. London (H.M.S.O.).

——————— (1924). *On the superficial deposits of south Herts. and south Bucks.* Proc. Geol. Ass. Lond. **35**, 19–28.

SMITH, W. G. (1916). *Notes on the Paleolithic floor near Caddington.* Archeologia. **57**, 53–6.

SOIL SURVEY OF GREAT BRITAIN (1951). *Soil Survey Report No. 3.* London (H.M.S.O.)

SOIL SURVEY STAFF (1951). *Soil Survey Manual.* U.S.D.A. Handbook No. 18. Washington (Government Printer).

SPARKS, B. W. and LEWIS, W. V. (1957). *Escarpment dry-valleys near Pegsdon, Herts.* Proc. Geol. Ass. Lond. **35**, 19–28.

TAMURA, T. (1958). *Identification of clay minerals from acid soils.* J. Soil Sci. **9**, 141-7.

TANSLEY, A. G. (1949). *The British Islands and their Vegetation.* Cambridge (University Press).

TATE, W. E. (1946). *A Hand-list of Buckinghamshire Enclosure Acts and Awards.* Aylesbury (Bucks C.C.).

——————— (1947). *A Hand-list of Hertfordshire Enclosure Acts and Awards.* Trans. East Herts. archaeol. Soc. **12**, 18–31.

TAYLOR, E. G. R. (1936). *A Historical Geography of England before 1900* (H. C. Darby ed.). Cambridge (University Press).

TEMPLE, M. S. (1929). *Survey of the Soils of Buckinghamshire.* Univ. Reading Bull. 38.

TINSLEY, J. (1950). *The determination of organic carbon in soils by dichromate mixtures.* Trans. 4th int. Congr. Soil Sci. **1**, 161–4.

UNIVERSITY OF CAMBRIDGE (Department of Agriculture). (1931). *An Economic Survey of Hertfordshire Agriculture.* Farm Economics Branch Report No. 18.

WATT, A. S. (1923). *On the ecology of British beechwoods, with special reference to their regeneration.* J. Ecol. **11**, 1–48.

——————— (1934). *The vegetation of the Chiltern Hills, with special reference to the beechwoods and their seral relationships.* J. Ecol. **22**, 230–70; 445–507.

WEST, R. G. (1958). *The Pleistocene epoch in East Anglia.* J. Glaciol. **3**, 211–16.

WHITAKER, W. (1889). *Geology of London.* **1**. Mem. Geol. Surv. U.K. London (H.M.S.O.).

WIDDOWSON, F. V., PENNY, A., WILLIAMS, R. J. B. and COOKE, G. W. (1959). *Comparisons between combine-drilling and broadcasting muriate of potash for spring barley.* J. agric. Sci. **53**, 11–16.

WILLIAMS, R. J. B. and COOKE, G. W. (1961). *Some effects of farmyard manure and of grass residues on soil structure.* Soil Sci. **92**, 30–39.

WOOLDRIDGE, S. W. and LINTON, D. L. (1955). *Structure, Surface and Drainage in South-east England.* London (Philip).

WOOLDRIDGE, S. W. (1957). *Some aspects of the physiography of the Thames Valley in relation to the Ice Age and Early Man.* Proc. prehist. Soc. **23**, 1–19.

YOUNG, A. (1813). *General View of the Agriculture of Hertfordshire.* London.

ZEUNER, F. E. (1959). *The Pleistocene Period.* London (Hutchinson).

Appendix

METHODS AND TERMS USED IN PROFILE DESCRIPTIONS

Depth and Clarity of Horizons

The depths of horizon boundaries are measured in inches from the surface of the mineral soil, and where they fluctuate widely the range of variation is noted. Horizon boundaries may be described as *smooth*, if nearly plane; *undulating*, if pockets projecting upwards or downwards are wider than their depth; or *irregular*, if pockets are deeper than their width.

The clarity with which the boundaries are defined is described as *sharp*, if the transition zone is less than 1 in. wide; *clear*, if the transition zone is 1–2½ in. wide; or *merging*, if there is a gradual transition through more than 2½ in.

Colour

In order to describe soil colours as objectively as possible, use is made of the Munsell Soil Colour Charts designed for this purpose. According to the Munsell system of notation each colour may be considered as a resultant of three variables, Hue, Value and Chroma,* designated in that order. Thus the Hue 10 YR, the Value 5 and the Chroma 6 are combined to give the notation 10 YR 5/6, and colours with closely related Munsell notations are grouped under standard names: the colour name "yellowish brown", for example, covers the notations 10 YR 5/4, 10 YR 5/6 and 10 YR 5/8.

In recording soil colours in the field, the basic colour of a horizon is normally taken as that of a freshly broken surface in the moist condition, and when the colour changes markedly on drying the colour of the air-dry soil may also be noted. Many soil horizons, particularly those which are incompletely weathered or subjected to seasonal waterlogging, have variegated colours, often forming a pattern related to structural faces and root channels. In describing such mottled horizons, the kind, contrast and distribution of the colours present are noted by standard terms.

Texture and Stoniness

The term texture is commonly applied by agriculturalists to a complex of physical soil characteristics, including mechanical composition, structure, consistency and porosity, which influence ease of working, permeability and water-holding capacity. In Soil Science "texture" refers specifically to the particle-size distribution of the inorganic soil material which passes a 2 mm. sieve, as obtained by standard methods of mechanical analysis.

To determine texture in the field, a small amount of moistened soil is worked between finger and thumb until natural aggregates have been destroyed and a condition of maximum plasticity is attained. The soil is then assigned to a textural

---

* The Hue notation of a soil colour indicates its relation to the spectral colours yellow and red; the Value notation indicates its lightness or brilliance; the Chroma notation indicates its strength, or departure from a neutral (black, grey or white) of the same Value.

class according to the estimated proportions of sand (2·0–0·05 mm.), silt (0·05–0·002 mm.) and clay (<0·002 mm.) particle-size grades as described in Chapter II (p. 44). In assessing the texture of surface horizons, allowance has to be made for the influence of organic matter, significant amounts of which tend to make both sandy and clayey soils feel more silty.

In describing the stoniness of soil horizons, the following broad classes are recognized:

few or occasional stones— <15 per cent by volume

stony — 15–50 per cent by volume

very stony — >50 per cent by volume

Structure

Soil structure refers to the arrangement of primary soil particles into compound units or aggregates separated by voids or surfaces of weakness. The natural development of structure is influenced by the texture and physico-chemical constitution of the soil material; by biological agencies, particularly soil fauna; and by seasonal wetting, drying and freezing. The structure of the surface soil is greatly affected by land use, and especially by cultivation, which normally results in the disruption of natural soil aggregates or *peds*, accompanied by the fabrication of more or less transient, artificial structural units (*clods*) that slake with repeated wetting and drying. In loamy and clayey soils the structure of surface and sub-surface horizons largely determines their aeration and permeability and hence is of prime significance to crop growth.

Field descriptions of soil structure note (*a*) the shape and arrangement, (*b*) the average size, and (*c*) the distinctness and durability of the structural units. Terms used to describe the shape and size are as follows:

1. Units with the vertical axis distinctly longer than the horizontal one are subdivided into:

   (*a*) *Prismatic*, with flat or pointed tops.

   (*b*) *Columnar*, with rounded tops.

   and described according to their average width as fine (<2 cm.), medium (2–5 cm.) or coarse (>5 cm.).

2. Units with the horizontal axis longer than the vertical are described as *platy* or *laminated*.

3. Units with axes roughly equal are subdivided into:

   (*a*) *Blocky*, either angular or sub-angular, with distinct edges and smooth faces which fit closely together; further described according to average size as fine (<1 cm.), medium (1–2 cm.) or coarse (>2 cm.).

   (*b*) *Granular:* small (<1 cm.), rough-surfaced, sub-rounded or irregular aggregates without distinct edges or faces; the term *crumb* is reserved for soft porous granular aggregates resembling bread-crumbs.

Many soil horizons have compound structure consisting either of peds of different shapes and sizes, or of smaller peds held together as larger peds. Thus, many surface horizons contain both sub-angular blocky and granular peds (the latter often as worm casts or residues of them); and fine-textured subsoil horizons frequently consist of large prisms, which break when disturbed into distinct angular blocky peds.

The grade or degree of structure, representing the difference between cohesion within structural units and adhesion between them, varies with moisture content, generally becoming more pronounced as the soil dries out. It is estimated in the field by noting the distinctness of the structural units and the extent to which they are broken or destroyed when the soil mass is displaced or gently crushed. The following terms are used:

0. *Structureless:* no orderly lines of weakness nor observable aggregation in either the moist or dry condition; *massive*, if coherent; *single-grain*, if incoherent.

1. *Weak:* poorly formed, indistinct units which break easily on displacement, yielding much unaggregated or fragmental material.

2. *Moderate:* well-formed, distinct units that are moderately resistant to disruption on disturbance.

3. *Strong:* well-formed units, distinct in undisturbed moist soil, which adhere only weakly to one another, and can be separated without disruption when the soil is disturbed.

Consistence

Soil consistence comprises those attributes of soil material, commonly described by such terms as "heavy" and "light", that are expressed by the degree and kind of cohesion and adhesion or by the resistance to deformation or rupture. Consistence is closely related to both texture and structure, but whereas structure results from variations in the forces of attraction within a soil mass, consistence results from the strength and nature of the forces themselves.

As consistence varies with moisture conditions it is necessary to have a set of terms for each significant moisture state: thus a ped or clod may be hard when dry, friable when moist,* and plastic when wet;† and the range of moisture content in which it is friable is an important characteristic affecting the workability of the soil. Terms used to describe consistence are:

Loose: non-coherent when moist or dry.

Friable: when moist, crushes under gentle pressure, but coheres when pressed together.

Firm: when moist, crushes under moderate pressure, but resistance is distinctly noticeable; *very firm* soil materials are difficult to crush between finger and thumb.

Soft: weakly coherent and fragile when dry; breaks to powder or individual grains under slight pressure.

Hard: when dry, moderately resistant to pressure; can be broken in the hands, but barely breakable between finger and thumb; *very hard* soil materials can be broken in the hands only with difficulty.

Indurated: brittle and hard at all moisture contents.

Compact: denotes a combination of firm consistence and close packing or arrangement of particles.

Plastic: when wet, retains an impressed shape and can be moulded into a wire or thin rod without disruption; *very plastic* soil materials require much pressure for deformation, and are normally fine-textured.

---

* Referring specifically to a moisture content roughly mid-way between air-dry and field capacity.

† Referring specifically to a moisture content at or slightly above field capacity.

INDEX

Wt. P13906   K4   2/64   Mcr.(5484)

S.O. Code No. 88–5151–6*